Software Engineering Standards:

- ANSI/IEEE Std 729-1983
  Glossary of Software Engineering Terminology

- ANSI/IEEE Std 730-1984
  Software Quality Assurance Plans

- ANSI/IEEE Std 828-1983
  Software Configuration Management Plans

- ANSI/IEEE Std 829-1983
  Software Test Documentation

- ANSI/IEEE Std 830-1984
  Software Requirements Specifications

- ANSI/IEEE Std 983-1986
  Software Quality Assurance Planning

- IEEE Std 990-1986
  Ada* As a Program Design Language

- ANSI/IEEE Std 1002-1987
  Taxonomy for Software Engineering Standards

- ANSI/IEEE Std 1008-1987
  Software Unit Testing

- ANSI/IEEE Std 1012-1986
  Software Verification and Validation Plans

- IEEE Std 1016-1987
  Software Design Descriptions

Published by
The Institute of Electrical and Electronics Engineers, Inc

Distributed in cooperation with
Wiley-Interscience, a division of John Wiley & Sons, Inc

*Ada is a registered trademark of the US Government (Ada Joint Program Office).

Second Printing

October 1987

Library of Congress Catalog Number 87-080801

ISBN: 471-63457-3

© Copyright 1987 by

The Institute of Electrical and Electronics Engineers, Inc
345 East 47th Street, New York, NY 10017, USA

May 20, 1987

SH11098

Software Engineering Standards:

- ANSI/IEEE Std 729-1983
  Glossary of Software Engineering Terminology

  729

- ANSI/IEEE Std 730-1984
  Software Quality Assurance Plans

  730

- ANSI/IEEE Std 828-1983
  Software Configuration Management Plans

  828

- ANSI/IEEE Std 829-1983
  Software Test Documentation

  829

- ANSI/IEEE Std 830-1984
  Software Requirements Specifications

  830

- ANSI/IEEE Std 983-1986
  Software Quality Assurance Planning

  983

- IEEE Std 990-1986
  Ada As a Program Design Language

  990

- ANSI/IEEE Std 1002-1987
  Taxonomy for Software Engineering Standards

  1002

- ANSI/IEEE Std 1008-1987
  Software Unit Testing

  1008

- ANSI/IEEE Std 1012-1986
  Software Verification and Validation Plans

  1012

- IEEE Std 1016-1987
  Software Design Descriptions

  1016

Software Engineering Standards

Introduction by
John W. Horch

For the last nearly 100 years, the Institute of Electrical and Electronics Engineers (IEEE) has been involved in the generation and promulgation of standards. IEEE standards represent the formalization of current norms of professional practice, through the process of obtaining the consensus of concerned, practicing professionals in the given field. Today, the IEEE Computer Society is the fastest growing area of IEEE standardization efforts.

Software engineering has emerged as a specific engineering field in recent years, and those involved have increasingly recognized the need for standards. As a result, the Computer Society of the IEEE formed a subcommittee to codify these norms of professional software engineering practice into standards by means of the consensus process. This book presents the accumulated results of these efforts and provides, in a single volume, the first eleven standards developed for software engineering using the consensus process.

(1) ANSI/IEEE Std 729-1983, IEEE Standard Glossary of Software Engineering Terminology
(2) ANSI/IEEE Std 730-1984, IEEE Standard for Software Quality Assurance Plans
(3) ANSI/IEEE Std 828-1983, IEEE Standard for Software Configuration Management Plans
(4) ANSI/IEEE Std 829-1983, IEEE Standard for Software Test Documentation
(5) ANSI/IEEE Std 830-1984, IEEE Guide to Software Requirements Specifications
(6) ANSI/IEEE Std 983-1986, IEEE Guide for Software Quality Assurance Planning
(7) IEEE Std 990-1986, IEEE Recommended Practice for Ada* As a Program Design Language
(8) IEEE Std 1002-1987, IEEE Standard Taxonomy for Software Engineering Standards
(9) ANSI/IEEE Std 1008-1987, IEEE Standard for Software Unit Testing
(10) ANSI/IEEE Std 1012-1986, IEEE Standard for Software Verification and Validation Plans
(11) IEEE Std 1016-1987, IEEE Recommended Practice for Software Design Descriptions

Standards have been written as reference documents and, therefore, text of a tutorial nature has been omitted. Background material and the rationale for making certain choices are provided in the Guides and Recommended Practices, as they provide alternative approaches or selectable options in their areas. This accurately reflects the current consensus that documentation of software requirements is a fast-moving field, and that knowledgeable tradeoffs are required.

Each IEEE software engineering standard is prepared with two goals in mind:

(1) The standard must fit with all other IEEE software engineering standards; that is, it must be compatible with and not contradict any of the other existing standards.

(2) The standard must be capable of being used without other IEEE standards. Since all IEEE standards are "voluntary use" in nature, the compliance with one software engineering standard does not require or imply compliance with any other.

Historical Perspective

For an overall viewpoint, the creation of software engineering standards has been an evolutionary process. The early standards provided a common vocabulary (ANSI/IEEE Std 729-1983) and an initial framework of relationship (ANSI/IEEE Std 730-1984) for the subsequent standardization efforts. More recently, a Taxonomy of Software Engineering Standards (IEEE Std 1002-1987) was developed to effectively map standards needs to availability and application.

*Ada is a registered trademark of the US Government (Ada Joint Program Office).

Additional standards efforts are underway to build on this foundation. The first effort is to continue the definition and expansion of the requirements contained in ANSI/IEEE Std 730-1984 and the framework presented in IEEE Std 1002-1987. A second is to move from Standards and Recommended Practices to Guides; this provides additional tutorial material for guidance in further implementations. The third goes from a product standard (for example, a document) to a process standard (for example, testing). The last is the expansion of the terminology, both to include additional terms themselves and to define associated metrics (for example, productivity metrics).

Throughout all of this work there have been several themes, the first of which has been consensus. As reflected in the balloting statistics shown in Table I, these standards have been averaging a ballot return of over 85%. And over 90% of the returned ballots have been approvals.

Table I
Software Engineering Standards Production Statistics

Standard	Members of Balloting Group	Returns	Approve	Disapprove	Abstain
729-1983	147	138/93.9%*	128/99.2%**	1/0.8%**	9/6.5%*
730-1980 (trial-use)	104	82/78.8%	64/88.8%	8/11.1%	10/12.2%
730-1981 (full-use)	120	102/85.0%	86/100%	—	16/15.7%
730-1984	181	154/85.1%	144/99.3%	1/0.7%	9/5.8%
828-1983	114	105/92.1%	99/99.0%	1/1.0%	5/4.8%
829-1983	102	96/94.1%	83/100%	—	13/13.5%
830-1984	102	90/88.2%	82/98.8%	1/1.2%	7/7.8%
983-1985	124	103/83.1%	94/97.9%	2/2.1%	7/6.8%
990-1986	261	235/90%	204/94.9%	11/5.1%	20/7.7%
1002-1987	208	175/84.1%	155/96.3%	6/3.7%	14/6.7%
1008-1987	113	99/87.6%	83/98.8%	1/1.2%	15/15.2%
1012-1986	227	189/83.3%	168/98.8%	2/1.2%	19/10.1%
1016-1987	231	178/77.1%	154/99.4%	1/0.6%	23/12.9%

*Percent of balloting group.
**Percent of those balloting "Approve" or "Disapprove."

The second theme has been timeliness. The best standards in the world will not help if they are not provided in a timely manner. As depicted in Table II, the time from project approval to approval of the resulting standard is slightly over three years. This reflects the efforts to attain consensus of concerned, practicing professionals in the field.

Table II
Software Engineering Standards Production Statistics

Standard	Date Project Approved	Date Standard Approved	Elapsed Time
729-1983	Mar 1978	Sept 1982	4½ years
730-1980 (trial-use)	Dec 1977	Dec 1979	2 years
730-1981 (full-use)	Dec 1977	Sept 1981	3¾ years
730-1984	Sept 1982	Jun 1984	1¾ years
828-1983	Mar 1980	Jun 1983	3¼ years
829-1983	Mar 1980	Dec 1982	2¾ years
830-1984	Mar 1980	Dec 1983	3½ years
983-1986	Dec 1982	Sept 1985	2¾ years
990-1986	Dec 1982	Dec 1986	4 years
1002-1987	Mar 1983	Dec 1986	3¾ years
1008-1987	Jun 1983	Mar 1986	2¾ years
1012-1986	Sept 1983	Sept 1986	3 years
1016-1987	Sept 1983	Mar 1987	3½ years

Synopses of the Standards

The main motivation behind the creation of these IEEE Standards has been to provide recommendations reflecting the state-of-the-art in the application of engineering principles to the development and maintenance of software. For those that are new to software engineering, these standards are an invaluable source of carefully considered advice, brewed in the cauldron of a consensus process of professional discussion and debate. For those that are on the leading edge of the field, these standards serve as a baseline against which advances can be communicated and evaluated.

The following are synopses of each of the standards included in this volume:

ANSI/IEEE Std 729. ANSI/IEEE Std 729 establishes definitions for most of the software engineering terms in general usage. It contains definitions for more than 500 terms and therefore establishes the basic vocabulary of software engineering. Building on a foundation of American National Standard Institute (ANSI) and International Organization for Standardization (ISO) terms, it promotes clarity and consistency in the vocabulary of software engineering and associated fields.

ANSI/IEEE Std 730. This Standard has as its basic rationale legal liability. It is directed toward the development and maintenance of critical software, that is, where failure could impact safety or cause large financial or social losses. The orientation is toward delineating all of the planned and systematic actions on a particular project that would provide adequate confidence that the software product conforms to established technical requirements.

The Standard establishes a required format and a set of minimum contents for Software Quality Assurance Plans. The description of each of the required elements is sparse and thus provides a template for development of further standards, each expanding on a specific section of this document.

ANSI/IEEE Std 828. This Standard is similar in format to ANSI/IEEE Std 730, but deals with the more limited subject of Software Configuration Management. The Standard identifies requirements for configuration identification, configuration control, configuration status accounting and reporting, and configuration audits and reviews. The implementation of these requirements provides a means by which the evolution of the software product items are recorded, communicated, and controlled. This provides assurance of the integrity and continuity of the software product items as they evolve through the Software Development and Maintenance Life Cycle.

ANSI/IEEE Std 829. This Standard defines the content and format of eight documents that cover the entire testing process.

The test plan prescribes the scope, approach, resources, and schedule of the testing activities. It identifies the items to be tested, the features to be tested, the testing tasks to be performed, the personnel responsible for each task, and the risks associated with the plan.

Test specification is covered by three document types, while test reporting is covered by four document types.

The Standard shows the relationships of these documents to one another as they are developed, and to the test process they document.

ANSI/IEEE Std 830. This Guide describes alternate approaches to good practice in the specification of software requirements. To enable the reader to make knowledgeable choices, extensive tutorial material is provided. This covers the attributes of a good software requirements specification itself, as well as specification methodologies and associated formats.

ANSI/IEEE Std 983. This Guide is intended to explain and clarify the contents of each section of a Software Quality Assurance Plan. It is directed at the requirements in ANSI/IEEE Std 730-1984.

IEEE Std 990. This Recommended Practice provides recommendations reflecting the state-of-the-art and alternate approaches to good practice for characteristics of Program Design Languages (PDLs) based on the syntax and semantics of the Ada Programming Language. In this document, these are referred to as Ada PDLs.

IEEE Std 1002. This Standard describes the form and content of a software engineering standards taxonomy. Applicability is not restricted by software application, size, complexity, criticality, or hardware environment. This taxonomy applies to standards (from the related disciplines of engineering management, systems engineering, computer hardware engineering, computer science, and information science) with which a software engineer would be reasonably acquainted. It is application independent. For example, an accounting test standard would be placed under test standards, but the qualifier, accounting, has no significance. The Standard explains the various types of software engineering standards, their functional and external relationships, and the role of various functions participating in the software life cycle. The taxonomy may be used as a method for planning the development or evaluation of standards for an organization. It could also serve as a basis for classifying a set of standards or for organizing a standards manual.

IEEE Std 1008. Software unit testing is a process that includes the performance of test planning, the development of a test set, and the measurement of a test unit against its requirements. Measuring entails the use of sample data to exercise the unit and the comparison of the unit's actual behavior with its required behavior as specified in the unit's requirements documentation.

This Standard defines an integrated approach to systematic and documented unit testing. The approach uses unit design and unit implementation information, in addition to unit requirements, to determine the completeness of the testing. The Standard describes a testing process composed of a hierarchy of phases, activities, and tasks. Further, it defines a minimum set of tasks for each activity, although additional tasks may be added to any activity.

ANSI/IEEE Std 1012. This Standard has a threefold purpose:

(1) To provide, for both critical and noncritical software, uniform and minimum requirements for the format and content of Software Verification and Validation Plans (SVVPs).

(2) To define, for critical software, specific minimum verification and validation (V&V) tasks and their required inputs and outputs that shall be included in SVVPs.

(3) To suggest optional V&V tasks to be used to tailor SVVPs as appropriate for the particular V&V effort.

IEEE Std 1016. A software design description is a representation of a software system. It is used as a medium for communicating software design information. This Recommended Practice describes that documentation of software designs. It specifies the necessary information content and the recommended organization for a software design description.

Summary

The evolution of software engineering as a recognized scientific discipline has been rapid, and not always without conflict. The work represented in this volume is an outgrowth of that evolution and represents, in many cases, the resolution of some of the evolutionary conflicts. By seeking the consensus of the concerned, practicing professionals in the field, the best, most up-to-date statements of the current norms of professional practices are developed.

Additional software engineering standards are in process, and the eleven IEEE standards contained herein will themselves be revisited, no less often than every five years, to ensure their continued applicability. In this way, through timely, consensus-based standards, the IEEE will continue to foster and support the evolution of the software engineering discipline.

An American National Standard

IEEE Standard Glossary of Software Engineering Terminology

Sponsor

Software Engineering Technical Committee
of the
IEEE Computer Society

Approved September 23, 1982

IEEE Standards Board

Approved August 9, 1983

American National Standards Institute

Foreword

(This Foreword is not a part of ANSI/IEEE Std 729-1983, IEEE Standard Glossary of Software Engineering Terminology.)

Software engineering is an emerging field. New terms are continually being generated, and new meanings are being adopted for existing terms. The Glossary of Software Engineering Terminology was undertaken to document this vocabulary. Its purpose is to identify terms currently used in software engineering and to present the current meanings of these terms. It is intended to serve as a useful reference for software engineers and for those in related fields and to promote clarity and consistency in the vocabulary of software engineering. It is recognized that software engineering is a dynamic area; thus the standard will be subject to appropriate change as becomes necessary.

This glossary was prepared by the Terminology Task Group of the Software Engineering Standards subcommittee of the Software Engineering Technical Committee of the IEEE Computer Society.

Comments are welcome and should be directed to:

The Secretary
IEEE Standards Board
345 East 47th Street
New York, NY 10017

At the time this standard was approved, the Terminology Task Group had the following members:

Shirley A. Gloss-Soler, *Chairperson*

Steering Committee:

Russell J. Abbott	Glenn C. Hughes, II	Jane W. Radatz
Joan P. Bateman	John M. Ives	Marilyn J. Stewart
Stephen R. Beason	John J. McKissick, Jr	Alan N. Sukert
Milton E. Boyd, Jr	Albrecht J. Neumann	Donald A. Woodmancy
Kurt F. Fischer	John N. Postak	David Yablon

Other members:

Duane C. Abbey	Raymond Houghton	William E. Russell
Allen Troy Acree, Jr	William B. Humphrey	David J. Schultz
Lynn Beckwith	F.T. James	Lee Shaw
Peter C. Belford	Tom Kallai	Stanley Siegel
Edward H. Bersoff	Edwin Kammerer	Gene Sievert
Grady Booch	Kathleen A. Kenney	Ronald C. Sivertson
John B. Bowen	Brij M. Khandelwal	John Smart
Martha A. Branstad	Ronald Klobert	Mark K. Smith
John R. Brown	K. Peter Koschewa	I. Richard Smook
Fletcher J. Buckley	O.J. Krten	Joseph Spellman
E. Jane Cameron	James C. Landerkin	James D. Stringer
Joseph Cavano	John B. Lane	E. Burton Swanson
James V. Cellini, Jr	Myron Lipow	Douglas B. Tabor
Karl E. Christen	Benn Manny	Barbara J. Taute
Tom Clark	Harvey Marks	Linda T. Taylor
Michele J. DiFranza	Neldon Marshall	Alex Terentiev
Paul Doelger	James A. McCall	Richard H. Thayer
Edward H. Ely	Siba Mohanty	Rinaldo A. Vaccaro
B. Dale Farrar	Dennis B. Mulcare	Don F. Utter
Carolyn Gannon	John Nissen	Keith Waters
David Gelperin	John O'Rourke	Andrew H. Weigel
R.R. Gordon	R. Poston	Herb Weiner
Robert M. Gross	Stephen Pozgaj	Peter J. Weyman
David A. Gustafson	J.A. (Jock) Rader	Terry Wolf
Virl Haas	Geraldine (Burke) Rajcula	Yvonne Wong
George B. Hawthorne	Jean C. Rault	Ralph Worrest
Herbert Hecht	R. Ravichandran	Martin Young
Robert E. Hite	Donald J. Reifer	Peter F. Zoll
Daniel E. Hocking	Debra J. Richardson	Jean Cochrane Zolnowski

At the time it approved this glossary, the Software Engineering Standards Subcommittee had the following membership:

Fletcher J. Buckley, *Chairperson*

Russell J. Abbott	Andre Fortier	William M. Lively	R. Waldo Roth
Peter G. Anderson	Heinz H. Frey	Alan Cheuk-Wai Ma	Clarence W. Rutter, III
William L. Anderson	Morris Frimer	G. H. MacEwen	Burnett H. Sams
Joan P. Bateman	M. Galinier	Andy K. Mahindru	Norman F. Schneidewind
Leo Beltracchi	G. W. Gates	Ben Manny	Harvey E. Shock, Jr
Moredechai Ben-Menachem	David Gelperin	Philip C. Marriott	Roger W. Scholten
Richard L. Bernstein	Edward L. Gibbs	W. R. Mattersdorff	Leonard W. Seagren
Edward H. Bersoff	Shirley A. Gloss-Soler	Lawrence J. Mazlack	I. Lee Shaw
Barry W. Boehm	Amrit L. Goel	James A. McCall	Stanley Siegel
John B. Bowen	Jack A. Goetz	John McIntosh	Roy L. Skelton
Martha A. Branstad	John J. Greene	John McKissick, Jr	Orval N. Skousen
A. Winsor Brown, Jr	Robert M. Gross	Bertrand Meyer	Marian P. Smith
Fletcher J. Buckley	H. Mark Grove	Edward F. Miller, Jr	I. Richard Smook
Brian H. Burger	Russell T. Gustin	Siba N. Mohanty	Harry M. Sneed
James V. Cellini, Jr	Paul E. Haddon	M. F. Moon	Al R. Sorkowitz
John Center	Thomas L. Hannan	Gene T. Morun	D. Steinberg
Won L. Chung	George B. Hawthorne	David G. Mullens	Edward A. Straker
Antonio M. Cicu	Joel J. Hebert	Walter G. Murch	Alan N. Sukert
Bruce M. Clay	Herbert Hecht	John D. Musa	Douglas B. Tabor
Marlene Conklin	Leslie R. Heselton, III	Myron L. Nack	Barbara J. Taute
Guy L. Copeland	Charles P. Hollocker	Saied Najafi	Daniel Thalmann
Jack Cowan	Grace M. Hopper	Geraldine Neidhart	Rush Thompson
Stewart G. Crawford	Sam Horvitz	John O. Neilson	George D. Tice, Jr
George Darling	Glenn C. Hughes, II	Albrecht J. Neumann	Terrence L. Tillmanns
James R. Dildine	Donald J. Humcke	Leon Osterweil	George W. Trever
James V. Dinkey	Shuenn-Chang Hwang	Donald J. Ostrom	William S. Turner, III
Walter Du Blanica	Jim H. Ingram	Thomas Pittman	R.L. Van Tilburg
Lorraine Duvall	John M. Ives	John N. Postak	Robert D. Vavra
Robert E. Dwyer	Dwayne L. Knirk	Robert M. Poston	Udo Voges
Mary L. Eads	George Konomos	Patricia B. Powell	Dale R. Webdale
John D. Earls	Richard W. Kubica	Jane W. Radatz	Andrew H. Weigel
Leo G. Egan, Jr	Thomas M. Kurihara	Steven R. Rakitin	Peter J. Weyman
Richard E. Fairley	Dominic V. LaRosa	Jean C. Rault	Farrell L. White
Chungpeng Fan	Gregory N. Larsen	T.L. Regulinski	Paul A. Willis
Dennis W. Fife	Arvid G. Larson	Hans Reiche	Saul A. Zaveler
Kurt F. Fischer	Albert M. Lerner	Donald J. Reifer	Jean C. Zolnowski
Joel J. Forman	Paul J. Levine, Jr	R. San Roman	

Special representatives to the Software Engineering Subcommittee were as follows:

American Society for Quality Control: **A. Ferlan**
Wayne Kost

ANSI Z1:   J. Milandin

EDP Auditors Association: Roy Pritchett

The Group wishes to acknowledge the close coordination and assistance of the American National Standard Committee X3K5 Subcommittee.

The following organizations supported the development of this standard:

When the IEEE Standards Board approved this standard on September 23, 1982, it had the following membership:

An American National Standard

IEEE Standard Glossary of Software Engineering Terminology

1. Scope

This glossary defines terms in general use in the software engineering field.

A term was excluded from the glossary if it was considered to be:

(1) Parochial to one particular group or organization.

(2) A company proprietary term.

(3) A standard term in some other well defined discipline, although terms used in software engineering were repeated in this glossary to avoid conflicts.

(4) A multi-word term whose meaning could be inferred from definitions of the component terms.

(5) A term whose meaning for software engineering could be directly inferred from its standard English meaning.

2. Glossary Structure

The structure of the glossary is as follows.

(1) Entries in the glossary are arranged alphabetically.

(2) If a term has more than one definition, the definitions are listed with numerical prefixes.

(3) Where necessary, examples have been added to clarify the definitions.

(4) The following crossreferences have been used to show a term's relationship to other terms in the glossary.

(a) *Compare with* refers to a complementary term.

(b) *Contrast with* refers to a term with an opposite or substantially different meaning.

(c) *Synonymous with* refers to a synonymous term.

(d) *See* refers the reader to a preferred or highly related term.

(e) *See also* refers to a related term.

(f) Words which appear in bold face type within a definition are defined elsewhere in the glossary. When a phrase is in bold face type, the glossary may define either the entire phrase or its component words.

3. Sources

In order to avoid conflict with accepted standards, American National Standards Institute (ANSI) and International Organization for Standardization (ISO) definitions that have relevance to software engineering are included. In those cases where the ANSI or ISO definitions do not fully reflect current software engineering usage, additional definition(s) are provided.

Sources are identified as follows.

(1) Definitions extracted from the ANSI Technical Report, American National Dictionary for Information Processing, X3/TR-1-77, September 1977, are identified by (ANSI) following the definition.

(2) Definitions developed by Technical Committee 97, (Information Systems), Subcommittee 1, (Vocabulary) of The International Organization for Standardization are identified by (ISO) following the definition.

(3) Definitions appearing in other standards are identified by that standard number following the definition. See Appendix A for complete identification of these references.

4. Terms

abort. To terminate a **process** prior to completion.

absolute machine code. Machine language code that must be loaded into fixed storage locations at each use and may not be relocated. Contrast with **relocatable machine code.**

abstract machine. (1) A representation of the characteristics of a **process** or machine.
(2) A **module** that processes inputs as though it were a machine.

abstraction. (1) A view of a problem that extracts the essential information relevant to a par-ticular purpose and ignores the remainder of the informa-ion.
(2) The process of forming an abstraction.

acceptance criteria. The criteria a **software product** must meet to successfully complete a **test phase** or meet **delivery requirements.**

acceptance testing. Formal testing conducted to determine whether or not a **system** satisfies its **acceptance criteria** and to enable the customer to determine whether or not to accept the system. See also **qualification testing, system testing.**

accessibility. The extent to which **software** facilitates selective use or **maintenance** of its **components.**

access-control mechanism. Hardware or **software** features, operating **procedures,** or management procedures designed to permit authorized access and prevent unauthorized access to a **computer system.**

accuracy. (1) A quality of that which is free of **error.** (ISO)
(2) A qualitative assessment of freedom from **error,** a high assessment corresponding to a small error. (ISO)
(3) A quantitative measure of the magnitude of **error,** preferably expressed as a function of the relative error, a high value of this measure corresponding to a small error. (ISO)
(4) A quantitative assessment of freedom from **error.**
Contrast with **precision.**

actual parameter. An argument or expression used within a call to a **subprogram** to specify **data** or **program** elements to be transmitted to the subprogram. Contrast with **formal parameter.**

adaptability. The ease with which **software** allows differing **system** constraints and user needs to be satisfied.

adaptive maintenance. Maintenance performed to make a **software product** usable in a changed environment.

address. (1) A character or group of characters that identifies a register, a particular part of storage, or some other **data** source or destination. (ISO)
(2) To refer to a device or an item of **data.** (ISO)

address space. The range of **addresses** available to a **computer program.**

algorithm. (1) A finite set of well-defined rules for the solution of a problem in a finite number of steps; for example, a complete specification of a sequence of arithmetic operations for evaluating sin x to a given **precision.** (ISO)
(2) A finite set of well-defined rules that gives a sequence of operations for performing a specific task.

algorithm analysis. The examination of an **algorithm** to determine its **correctness** with respect to its intended use, to determine its operational characteristics, or to understand it more fully in order to modify, simplify, or improve it.

alias. (1) An additional name for an item.
(2) An alternate **label.** For example, a label and one or more aliases may be used to refer to the same **data** element or point in a **computer program.** (ANSI)

analysis phase. See **requirements phase.**

analytical model. A representation of a **process** or phenomenon by a set of solvable equations. Contrast with **simulation.**

application-oriented language. (1) A computer-oriented language with facilities or notations applicable primarily to a single application area; for example, a language for statistical analysis or machine design.

(2) A problem-oriented language whose statements contain or resemble the terminology of the occupation or profession of the user. (ANSI)

application software. Software specifically produced for the functional use of a **computer system;** for example, software for navigation, gun fire control, payroll, general ledger. Contrast with **system software.**

architecture. See **program architecture, system architecture.**

architectural design. (1) The **process** of defining a collection of **hardware** and **software components** and their **interfaces** to establish a framework for the development of a **computer system.**

(2) The result of the architectural design process.

artificial language. See **formal language.**

assemble. To translate a **program** expressed in an **assembly language** into a **machine language** and perhaps to link **subroutines.** Assembling is usually accomplished by substituting machine language operation codes for assembly language operation codes and by substituting absolute addresses, immediate addresses, relocatable addresses, or virtual addresses for symbolic addresses. Contrast with **compile, interpret.**

assembler. A **computer program** used to **assemble.** (ISO) Contrast with **compiler, interpreter.** Synonymous with assembly **program.**

assembly language. (1) A computer-oriented language whose **instructions** are usually in one-to-one correspondence with **computer** instructions and that may provide facilities such as the use of **macroinstructions.** (ISO) Contrast with **machine language, higher order language.** See also **assemble, assembler.**

(2) A machine-specific language whose **instructions** are usually in one-to-one correspondence with **computer** instructions.

assertion. A logical expression specifying a **program** state that must exist or a set of conditions that program **variables** must satisfy at a particular point during program **execution;** for example, *A is positive and A is greater than B.* See also **input assertion, output assertion.**

assignment statement. An **instruction** used to express a sequence of operations, or used to assign **operands** to specified **variables,** or symbols, or both. (ANSI)

audit. (1) An independent review for the purpose of assessing compliance with **software requirements, specifications, baselines,** standards, **procedures,** instructions, codes, and contractual and licensing requirements. See also **code audit.**

(2) An activity to determine through investigation the adequacy of, and adherence to, established **procedures, instructions, specifications,** codes, and standards or other applicable contractual and licensing requirements, and the effectiveness of **implementation.** (ANSI N45.2.10-1973)

automated design tool. A **software tool** that aids in the synthesis, analysis, modeling, or **documentation** of a software **design.** Examples include **simulators,** analytic aids, design representation processors, and documentation generators.

automated test case generator. See **automated test generator.**

automated test data generator. See **automated test generator.**

automated test generator. A **software tool** that accepts as input a **computer program** and test criteria, generates test input **data** that meet these criteria, and, sometimes, determines the expected results.

automated verification system. A **software tool** that accepts as input a **computer program** and a representation of its **specification,** and produces, possibly with human help, a **correctness proof** or disproof of the **program.** See also **automated verification tools.**

automated verification tools. A class of **software tools** used to evaluate products of the **software development process.** These **tools** aid in the **verification** of such characteristics as **cor-**

rectness, completeness, consistency, traceability, **testability,** and adherence to standards. Examples include **design analyzers, automated verification systems, static analyzers, dynamic analyzers,** and **standards enforcers.**

availability. (1) The probability that **software** will be able to perform its designated **system function** when required for use.

(2) The ratio of **system** up-time to total operating time.

(3) The ability of an item to perform its designated **function** when required for use. (ANSI/ASQC A3-1978)

availability model. A **model** used for predicting, estimating, or assessing **availability.**

back-up. Provisions made for the recovery of **data files** or **software,** for restart of processing, or for use of alternative **computer** equipment after a **system failure** or a disaster.

backup programmer. The assistant leader of a **chief programmer team;** a senior-level programmer whose responsibilities include contributing significant portions of the **software** being developed by the team, aiding the **chief programmer** in reviewing the work of the other team members, substituting for the chief programmer when necessary, and having an overall technical understanding of the software being developed.

baseline. (1) A **specification** or product that has been formally reviewed and agreed upon, that thereafter serves as the basis for further development, and that can be changed only through formal **change control procedures.**

(2) A **configuration identification document** or a set of such documents formally designated and fixed at a specific time during a **configuration item's** life cycle. Baselines, plus approved changes from those baselines, constitute the current configuration identification. For **configuration management** there are three baselines, as follows:

(a) Functional baseline. The initial approved functional configuration.

(b) Allocated baseline. The initial approved allocated configuration.

(c) Product baseline. The initial approved or conditionally approved product configuration identification. (DoD-STD 480A)

begin-end block. A sequence of **design** or programming statements bracketed by *begin* and *end* delimiters and characterized by a single entrance and single exit.

binding. The assigning of a value or referent to an **identifier;** for example, the assigning of a value to a **parameter** or the assigning of an absolute address, virtual address, or device identifier to a symbolic address or **label** in a **computer program.** See also **dynamic binding, static binding.**

bit. A contraction of the term *binary digit*; a unit of information represented by either a zero or a one.

block. (1) A **string** of **records,** a string of **words,** or a character string, formed for technical or logic reasons to be treated as an entity. (ISO)

(2) A collection of contiguous **records** recorded as a unit. Blocks are separated by interblock gaps and each block may contain one or more records. (ANSI)

(3) A group of **bits** or **N-ary** digits, transmitted as a unit. An encoding procedure is generally applied to the group of bits or N-ary digits for error-control purposes. (ANSI)

(4) A set of things, such as **words,** characters, or digits, handled as a unit. (ANSI)

(5) See **program block.**

block diagram. A diagram of a **system,** a **computer,** or a device in which the principal parts are represented by suitably annotated geometrical figures to show both the basic **functions** of the parts and their functional relationships. (ISO) Contrast with **flowchart.**

block-structured language. A **design** or programming language in which sequences of statements are demarcated, usually with *begin* and *end* delimiters. See also **program block.**

bootstrap. (1) A short **computer program** that is permanently resident or easily loaded into a **computer,** whose **execution** brings another, larger **program,** such as an **operating system** or its **loader,** into memory.

(2) A set of **instructions** that causes additional instructions to be loaded until the complete **computer program** is in storage. (ISO)

(3) A technique or device designed to bring itself into a desired state by means of its own action; for

example, a machine **routine** whose first few **instructions** are sufficient to bring the rest of itself into the **computer** from an input device. (ANSI)

(4) That part of a **computer program** used to establish another version of the computer program. (ANSI)

(5) To use a bootstrap. (ISO)

bootstrap loader. An input **routine** in which preset **computer** operations are used to load a **bootstrap.** (ISO)

bottom-up. Pertaining to an approach that starts with the lowest level **software components** of a **hierarchy** and proceeds through progressively higher levels to the top level component; for example, **bottom-up design,** bottom-up programming, bottom-up **testing.** Contrast with **top-down.**

bottom-up design. The **design** of a **system** starting with the most basic or primitive **components** and proceeding to higher level components that use the lower level ones. Contrast with **top-down design.**

bug. See **fault.**

bug seeding. See **fault seeding.**

build. An operational version of a **software product** incorporating a specified subset of the capabilities that the final product will include.

building block. An individual unit or **module** that is utilized by higher-level **programs** or modules.

byte. (1) A binary character **string** operated upon as a unit and usually shorter than a **computer word** (ISO).

(2) A group of adjacent binary digits operated on as a unit and usually shorter than a computer word (frequently connotes a group of eight **bits**). (ANSI/IEEE Std 488-1978)

case. A multi-branch conditional statement that allows for selective **execution** of bounded groups of **program** statements depending upon the value of a control expression. See also **control structure.**

certification. (1) A written guarantee that a **system** or **computer program** complies with its specified **requirements.**

(2) A written authorization that states that a **computer system** is secure and is permitted to operate in a defined environment with or producing sensitive information.

(3) The formal demonstration of **system** acceptability to obtain authorization for its **operational** use.

(4) The process of confirming that a **system, software subsystem,** or **computer program** is capable of satisfying its specified **requirements** in an operational environment. Certification usually takes place in the field under actual conditions, and is utilized to evaluate not only the software itself, but also the **specifications** to which the software was constructed. Certification extends the process of **verification** and **validation** to an actual or simulated operational environment.

(5) The procedure and action by a duly authorized body of determining, verifying, and attesting in writing to the qualifications of personnel, **processes, procedures,** or items in accordance with applicable **requirements.** (ANSI/ASQC A3-1978)

chained list. A **list** in which the items may be dispersed but in which each item contains an **identifier** for locating the next item. (ISO) Synonymous with **linked list.**

change control. The process by which a change is proposed, evaluated, approved or rejected, scheduled, and tracked.

chief programmer. The leader of a **chief programmer team;** a senior-level programmer whose responsibilities include producing key portions of the **software** assigned to the team, coordinating the activities of the team, reviewing the work of the other team members, and having an overall technical understanding of the software being developed.

chief programmer team. A **software** development group that consists of a **chief programmer,** a **backup programmer,** a **secretary/librarian,** and additional programmers and specialists as needed, and that employs support **procedures** designed to enhance group communication and to make optimum use of each member's skills.

code. (1) A set of unambiguous rules specifying the manner in which **data** may be represented in a discrete form. (ISO)

(2) To represent **data** or a **computer program** in a symbolic form that can be accepted by a processor. (ISO)

(3) To write a **routine**. (ANSI)

(4) Loosely, one or more **computer programs,** or part of a computer program.

(5) An encryption of **data** for **security** purposes.

code audit. An independent review of source **code** by a person, team, or **tool** to verify compliance with **software design documentation** and programming standards. **Correctness** and **efficiency** may also be evaluated. See also **audit, static analysis, inspection, walk-through.**

code generator. A **program** or program **function,** often part of a **compiler,** that transforms a **computer program** from some intermediate level of representation (often the output of a parser) into a lower level representation such as assembly **code** or machine code.

code inspection. See **inspection.**

code walk-through. See **walk-through.**

cohesion. The degree to which the tasks performed by a single **program module** are functionally related. Contrast with **coupling.**

command language. A set of procedural **operators** with a related **syntax,** used to indicate the **functions** to be performed by an **operating system.** Synonymous with control language. (ISO)

comment. (1) Information embedded within a **computer program, command language,** or set of **data** that is intended to provide clarification to human readers and that does not effect machine interpretation.

(2) A description, reference, or explanation added to or interspersed among the statements of the **source language,** that has no effect in the **target language.** (ISO)

comparator. A **software tool** used to compare two **computer programs, files,** or sets of **data** to identify commonalities or differences. Typical objects of comparison are similar versions of source **code,** object code, **data base** files, or test results.

compatibility. The ability of two or more **systems** to exchange information. Compare with **interoperability.**

compile. To translate a **higher order language program** into its **relocatable** or **absolute machine code** equivalent. Contrast with **assemble, interpret.**

compiler. A **computer program** used to **compile.** (ISO) Contrast with **assembler, interpreter.**

compiler generator. A **translator** or an **interpreter** that is used to construct **compilers.** (ISO) Synonymous with **metacompiler.**

compiler compiler. See **compiler generator.**

complexity. The degree of complication of a **system** or system **component,** determined by such factors as the number and intricacy of **interfaces,** the number and intricacy of conditional branches, the degree of **nesting,** the types of **data structures,** and other system characteristics.

component. A basic part of a **system** or **program.**

computer. (1) A **functional unit** that can perform substantial computation, including numerous arithmetic operations or logic operations, without intervention by a human operator during a run. (ISO).

(2) A functional programmable unit that consists of one or more associated processing units and peripheral equipment, that is controlled by internally stored **programs,** and that can perform substantial computation, including numerous arithmetic operations or logic operations, without human intervention.

computer data. Data available for communication between or within **computer** equipment. Such data can be external (in computer-readable form) or resident within the computer equipment and can be in the form of analog or digital signals.

computer network. A complex consisting of two or more interconnected **computers.** (ANSI)

computer program. A sequence of **instructions** suitable for processing by a **computer**. Processing may include the use of an **assembler**, a **compiler**, an **interpreter**, or a **translator** to prepare the **program** for **execution** as well as to execute it. (ISO) See also **program.**

computer program abstract. A brief description of a **computer program**, providing sufficient information for potential users to determine the appropriateness of the computer program to their needs and resources.

computer program annotation. See **comment.**

computer program certification. See **certification.**

computer program configuration identification. See **configuration identification.**

computer program development plan. See **software development plan.**

computer program validation. See **validation.**

computer program verification. See **verification.**

computer system. A **functional unit**, consisting of one or more **computers** and associated **software**, that uses common storage for all or part of a **program** and also for all or part of the **data** necessary for the **execution** of the program; **executes** user-written or user-designated programs; performs user-designated data manipulation, including arithmetic operations and logic operations; and that can execute programs that modify themselves during their execution. A computer system may be a standalone unit or may consist of several interconnected units. Synonymous with ADP system, computing system. (ISO)

concurrent processes. Processes that may execute in parallel on multiple processors or asynchronously on a single processor. Concurrent processes may interact with each other, and one process may suspend **execution** pending receipt of information from another process or the occurrence of an external event. Contrast with **sequential processes.**

conditional control structure. A programming **control structure** that allows alternative **flow of control** in a **program** depending upon the fulfillment of specified conditions; for example, **case**, if...then... else...

configuration. (1) The arrangement of a **computer system** or **network** as defined by the nature, number, and the chief characteristics of its **functional units.** More specifically, the term configuration may refer to a **hardware** configuration or a **software** configuration. (ISO)

(2) The **requirements, design,** and **implementation** that define a particular version of a **system** or system **component.**

(3) The functional and/or physical characteristics of **hardware/software** as set forth in technical **documentation** and achieved in a product. (DoD-STD 480A)

configuration audit. The process of verifying that all required **configuration items** have been produced, that the current version agrees with specified **requirements,** that the technical **documentation** completely and accurately describes the configuration items, and that all change requests have been resolved.

configuration control. (1) The process of evaluating, approving or disapproving, and coordinating changes to **configuration items** after formal establishment of their **configuration identification.**

(2) The systematic evaluation, coordination, approval or disapproval, and **implementation** of all approved changes in the **configuration** of a **configuration item** after formal establishment of its **configuration identification.** (DoD-STD 480A)

configuration control board. The authority responsible for evaluating and approving or disapproving proposed engineering changes, and ensuring **implementation** of the approved changes.

configuration identification. (1) The process of designating the **configuration items** in a **system** and recording their characteristics.

(2) The approved **documentation** that defines a **configuration item.**

(3) The current approved or conditionally approved technical **documentation** for a **configuration item** as set forth in **specifications**, drawings and associated lists, and **documents** referenced therein. (DoD-STD 480A)

configuration item. (1) A collection of **hardware** or **software** elements treated as a unit for the purpose of **configuration management.**

(2) An aggregation of **hardware/software,** or any of its discrete portions, that satisfies an end use **function** and is designated for **configuration management.** Configuration items may vary widely in **complexity,** size, and type from an aircraft, electronic or ship **system** to a test meter or round of ammunition. During development and initial production, Configuration items are only those specification items that are referenced directly in a contract (or an equivalent in-house agreement). During the operation and maintenance period, any reparable item designated for separate procurement is a configuration item. (DoD-STD 480A)

configuration management. (1) The process of identifying and defining the **configuration items** in a **system,** controlling the release and change of these items throughout the system life cycle, recording and reporting the status of configuration items and change requests, and verifying the completeness and **correctness** of configuration items. See also **change control, configuration identification, configuration control, configuration status accounting, configuration audit.**

(2) A discipline applying technical and administrative direction and surveillance to (a) identify and document the functional and physical characteristics of a **configuration item,** (b) control changes to those characteristics, and (c) record and report change processing and **implementation** status. (DoD-STD 480A)

configuration status accounting. The recording and reporting of the information that is needed to manage a **configuration** effectively, including a listing of the approved **configuration identification,** the status of proposed changes to the configuration, and the **implementation** status of approved changes. (DoD-Std 480A)

confinement. (1) Prevention of unauthorized alteration, use, destruction, or release of **data** during authorized access. See also **integrity.**

(2) Restriction on **programs** and **processes** so that they do not access or have influence on **data,** programs, or processes other than that allowed by specific authorization.

connection. (1) A reference in one part of a **program** to the **identifier** of another part (that is, something found elsewhere). See also **interface.**

(2) An association established between **functional units** for conveying information. (ISO)

control data. Data that selects an operating mode or submode in a **program,** directs the sequential flow, or otherwise directly influences the operation of **software.**

control statement. A **programming language** statement that affects the order in which operations are performed.

control structure. A construct that determines the **flow of control** through a **computer program.** See also **conditional control structure.**

conversational. Pertaining to an **interactive** system that provides for interaction between a user and a **system** similar to a human dialog.

conversion. Modification of existing **software** to enable it to operate with similar functional capability in a different environment; for example, converting a **program** from FORTRAN to Ada, converting a program that runs on one **computer** to run on another computer.

coroutines. Two or more **modules** that can call each other, but that are not in a superior to subordinate relationship.

corrective maintenance. Maintenance performed specifically to overcome existing **faults.** (ISO) See also **software maintenance.**

correctness. (1) The extent to which **software** is free from **design** defects and from coding defects; that is, **fault** free.

(2) The extent to which **software** meets its specified **requirements.**

(3) The extent to which **software** meets user expectations.

correctness proof. See **proof of correctness.**

coupling. A measure of the interdependence among **modules** in a **computer program.** Contrast with **cohesion.**

critical piece first. Pertaining to an approach to **software** development that focuses on implementing the most critical aspects of a software **system** first. The critical piece may be defined in terms of services provided, degree of risk, difficulty, or some other criterion.

critical section. A **segment** of **code** to be **executed** mutually exclusively with some other segment of code that is also called a critical section. Segments of code are required to be executed mutually exclusively if they make competing uses of a **computer** resource or **data** item.

criticality. A classification of a **software error** or **fault** based upon an evaluation of the degree of impact of that error or fault on the development or operation of a **system** (often used to determine whether or when a fault will be corrected).

cross-assembler. An **assembler** that executes on one **computer** but generates object **code** for a different computer.

cross-compiler. A **compiler** that executes on one **computer** but generates assembly **code** or object code for a different computer.

data. A representation of facts, concepts, or **instructions** in a formalized manner suitable for communication, interpretation, or processing by human or automatic means. (ISO) See also **computer data, control data, error data, reliability data, software experience data.**

data abstraction. The result of extracting and retaining only the essential characteristic properties of **data** by defining specific **data types** and their associated functional characteristics, thus separating and hiding the representation details. See also **information hiding.**

data base. (1) A set of **data,** part or the whole of another set of data, and consisting of at least one **file** that is sufficient for a given purpose or for a given data processing **system.** (ISO)

(2) A collection of **data** fundamental to a **system.** (ANSI)

(3) A collection of **data** fundamental to an enterprise. (ANSI)

data dictionary. (1) A collection of the names of all **data** items used in a **software system,** together with relevant properties of those items; for example, length of data item, representation, etc.

(2) A set of definitions of **data** flows, data elements, **files, data bases,** and **processes** referred to in a leveled **data flow diagram** set.

data flow chart. See **data flow diagram.**

data flow diagram. A graphic representation of a **system,** showing **data** sources, data sinks, storage, and **processes** performed on data as **nodes,** and logical flow of data as links between the nodes. Synonymous with **data flow graph, data flow chart.**

data flow graph. See **data flow diagram.**

data structure. A formalized representation of the ordering and accessibility relationships among **data** items without regard to their actual storage configuration.

data type. A class of **data** characterized by the members of the class and the operations that can be applied to them; for example, integer, real, logical.

debugging. The process of locating, analyzing, and correcting suspected **faults.** Compare with **testing.**

debugging model. See **error model.**

decision table. (1) A **table** of all contingencies that are to be considered in the description of a problem together with the actions to be taken for each set of contingencies. (ISO)

(2) A presentation in either matrix or tabular form of a set of conditions and their corresponding actions. (ANSI)

defect. See **fault.**

definition phase. See **requirements phase.**

delivery. (1) The point in the **software development cycle** at which a product is released to its intended user for **operational** use.

(2) The point in the **software development cycle** at which a product is accepted by its intended user.

design. (1) The process of defining the **software architecture, components, modules, interfaces,** test approach, and **data** for a software **system** to satisfy specified **requirements.**

(2) The result of the design process.

design analysis. (1) The evaluation of a **design** to determine **correctness** with respect to stated **requirements,** conformance to design standards, **system efficiency,** and other criteria.

(2) The evaluation of alternative **design** approaches. See also **preliminary design.**

design analyzer. An **automated design tool** that accepts information about a **program's design** and produces such outputs as **module hierarchy** diagrams, graphical representations of control and **data structure,** and **lists** of accessed **data blocks.**

design inspection. See **inspection.**

design language. A language with special constructs and, sometimes, **verification** protocols used to develop, analyze, and **document** a **design.**

design methodology. A systematic approach to creating a **design,** consisting of the ordered application of a specific collection of **tools,** techniques, and guidelines.

design phase. The period of time in the **software life cycle** during which the **designs** for **architecture,** software **components, interfaces,** and **data** are created, documented, and verified to satisfy **requirements.**

design requirement. Any **requirement** that impacts or constrains the **design** of a **software system** or software system **component;** for example, **functional requirements, physical requirements, performance requirements,** software development standards, **software quality assur-**ance standards. See also **requirements specification.**

design review. (1) A formal meeting at which the preliminary or **detailed design** of a **system** is presented to the user, customer, or other interested parties for comment and approval.

(2) The formal review of an existing or proposed **design** for the purpose of detection and remedy of design deficiencies that could affect fitness-for-use and environmental aspects of the product, process or service, and/or for identification of potential improvements of **performance,** safety and economic aspects. (ANSI/ASQC A3-1978)

design specification. A **specification** that documents the **design** of a **system** or system **component; for example, a software configuration item.** Typical contents include **system** or component **algorithms,** control logic, **data structures, data** set-use information, input/output formats, and **interface** descriptions. See also **requirements specification.**

design verification. See **verification.**

design walk-through. See **walk-through.**

desk checking. The manual **simulation** of **program execution** to detect **faults** through step-by-step examination of the source **code** for **errors** in logic or **syntax.** See also **static analysis.**

detailed design. (1) The process of refining and expanding the **preliminary design** to contain more detailed descriptions of the processing logic, **data structures,** and **data** definitions, to the extent that the **design** is sufficiently complete to be **implemented.**

(2) The result of the detailed design process.

development cycle. See **software development cycle.**

development life cycle. See **software development cycle.**

development methodology. A systematic approach to the creation of **software** that defines development phases and specifies the activities, products, **verification procedures,** and completion criteria for each phase.

development specification. Synonymous with **requirements specification.** (DOD usage).

diagnostic. (1) A message generated by a **computer program** indicating possible **faults** in another **system component**; for example, a **syntax** fault flagged by a **compiler.**

(2) Pertaining to the detection and isolation of **faults** or **failures.**

digraph. See **directed graph.**

directed graph. A **graph** whose edges are unidirectional.

document. (1) A **data** medium and the data recorded on it, that generally has permanence and that can be read by man or machine. (ISO) Often used to describe human readable items only, for example, technical documents, **design** documents, version description documents.

(2) To create a document.

documentation. (1) A collection of **documents** on a given subject. (ISO) See also **user documentation, software documentation, system documentation.**

(2) The management of **documents** which may include the actions of identifying, acquiring, processing, storing, and disseminating them. (ISO)

(3) The process of generating a **document.**

(4) Any written or pictorial information describing, defining, specifying, reporting or certifying activities, **requirements, procedures,** or results. (ANSI N45.2.10-1973)

documentation level. See **level of documentation.**

driver. A **program** that exercises a **system** or system **component** by simulating the activity of a higher level component. See also **test driver.**

dual coding. A development technique in which two functionally identical versions of a **program** are developed from the same **specification** by different programmers or different programming teams. The resulting source **code** may be in the same or different languages. The purpose of dual coding is to provide for **error** detection, increase **reliability,** provide additional **documentation,** or reduce the probability of systematic programming errors or **compiler** errors influencing the end result.

dummy parameter. See **formal parameter.**

dump. (1) **Data** that have been dumped. (ISO)

(2) To write the contents of a storage, or of part of a storage, usually from an internal storage to an external medium, for a specific purpose such as to allow other use of the storage, as a safeguard against **faults** or **errors,** or in connection with **debugging.** (ISO)

dynamic allocation. The allocation of addressable storage and other resources to a **program** while the program is executing.

dynamic analysis. The process of evaluating a **program** based on **execution** of the program. Contrast with **static analysis.**

dynamic analyzer. A **software tool** that aids in the evaluation of a **computer program** by monitoring **execution** of the **program.** Examples include **instrumentation tools, software monitors,** and **tracers.** Contrast with **static analyzer.**

dynamic binding. Binding performed during **execution** of a **program.** Contrast with **static binding.**

dynamic restructuring. (1) The process of changing **software components** or structure while a **system** is running.

(2) The process of restructuring a **data base** or **data structure** during **program execution.**

editor. A **computer program** that permits selective revision of **computer**-stored **data.**

efficiency. The extent to which **software** performs its intended **functions** with a minimum consumption of computing resources.

egoless programming. An approach to **software** development based upon the concept of team responsibility for **program** development. Its purpose is to prevent the programmer from identifying so closely with his or her output that objective evaluation is impaired.

embedded computer system. A **computer system** that is integral to a larger system whose primary purpose is not computational; for example, a computer system in a weapon, aircraft, command and control, or rapid transit system.

embedded software. Software for an **embedded computer system.**

emulation. The imitation of all or part of one **computer system** by another, primarily by **hardware,** so that the imitating computer system accepts the same **data,** executes the same **programs,** and achieves the same results as the imitated system. (ISO)

emulator. Hardware, software, or **firmware** that performs **emulation.**

encapsulation. The technique of isolating a **system function** within a **module** and providing a precise **specification** for the module. See also **information hiding.**

error. (1) A discrepancy between a computed, observed, or measured value or condition and the true, specified, or theoretically correct value or condition. (ANSI)
(2) Human action that results in **software** containing a **fault.** Examples include omission or misinterpretation of user **requirements** in a software **specification,** incorrect translation or omission of a requirement in the **design specification.** This is not a preferred usage.
See also **failure, fault.**

error analysis. (1) The process of investigating an observed **software fault** with the purpose of tracing the fault to its source.
(2) The process of investigating an observed **software fault** to identify such information as the cause of the fault, the phase of the development process during which the fault was introduced, methods by which the fault could have been prevented or detected earlier, and the method by which the fault was detected.
(3) The process of investigating **software errors, failures,** and **faults** to determine quantitative rates and trends.

error category. One of a set of classes into which an **error, fault,** or **failure** might fall. Categories may be defined for the cause, **criticality,** effect, life cycle phase when introduced or detected, or other characteristics of the error, fault, or failure.

error data. A term commonly (but not precisely) used to denote information describing **software** problems, **faults, failures,** and changes, their characteristics, and the conditions under which they are encountered or corrected.

error model. A mathematical **model** used to predict or estimate the number of remaining **faults, reliability,** required test time, or similar characteristics of a **software system.** See also **error prediction.**

error prediction. A quantitative statement about the expected number or nature of **software** problems, **faults,** or **failures** in a software **system.** See also **error model.**

error prediction model. See **error model.**

error recovery. See **failure recovery.**

error seeding. See **fault seeding.**

exception. An event that causes suspension of normal **program execution.**

execution. The process of carrying out an **instruction** or the instructions of a **computer program** by a computer. (ISO)

execution time. (1) The amount of actual or central processor time used in executing a **program.**
(2) The period of time during which a **program** is executing.
See also **run time.**

execution time theory. A theory that uses cumulative **execution time** as the basis for estimating **software reliability.**

executive program. See **supervisory program.**

exit. (1) Any **instruction** in a **computer program,** in a **routine,** or in a **subroutine,** after the

execution of which control is no longer exercised by that computer program, that routine, or that subroutine. (ISO)

(2) The point beyond which control is no longer exercised by a **routine**.

failure. (1) The termination of the ability of a **functional unit** to perform its required **function**. (ISO)

(2) The inability of a **system** or system **component** to perform a required **function** within specified limits. A failure may be produced when a **fault** is encountered.

(3) A departure of **program** operation from program **requirements**.

failure category. See **error category**.

failure data. See **error data**.

failure rate. (1) The ratio of the number of **failures** to a given unit of measure; for example, failures per unit of time, failures per number of transactions, failures per number of **computer** runs.

(2) In **reliability** modeling, the ratio of the number of **failures** of a given category or severity to a given period of time; for example, failures per second of **execution time**, failures per month. Synonymous with **failure ratio**.

failure ratio. See **failure rate**.

failure recovery. The return of a **system** to a reliable operating state after **failure**.

fault. (1) An accidental condition that causes a **functional unit** to fail to perform its required **function**. (ISO)

(2) A manifestation of an **error(2)** in **software**. A fault, if encountered, may cause a **failure**. Synonymous with **bug**.

fault category. See **error category**.

fault insertion. See **fault seeding**.

fault seeding. The process of intentionally adding a known number of **faults** to those already in a **computer program** for the purpose of estimating the number of **indigenous faults** in the **program**. Synonymous with **bug seeding**.

fault tolerance. The built-in capability of a **system** to provide continued correct **execution** in the presence of a limited number of **hardware** or **software faults**.

file. A set of related **records** treated as a unit. (ISO) See also **logical file**.

finite state machine. A computational **model** consisting of a finite number of states, and transitions between these states.

firmware. (1) **Computer programs** and **data** loaded in a class of memory that cannot be dynamically modified by the **computer** during processing. See also **microcode, microprogram**.

(2) **Hardware** that contains a **computer program** and **data** that cannot be changed in its user environment. The computer programs and data contained in firmware are classified as **software**; the circuitry containing the computer program and data is classified as **hardware**.

(3) **Program instructions** stored in a read-only storage.

(4) An assembly composed of a **hardware** unit and a **computer program** integrated to form a functional entity whose **configuration** cannot be altered during normal operation. The computer program is stored in the hardware unit as an integrated circuit with a fixed logic configuration that will satisfy a specific application or operational **requirement**.

flag. (1) An indicator that signals the occurrence of an **error**, state, or other specified condition.

(2) Any of various types of indicators used for identification; for example, a **word** mark. (ANSI)

(3) A character that signals the occurrence of some condition, such as the end of a **word**. (ANSI)

(4) To indicate an **error**, state, or other specified condition in a **program**.

flow of control. The sequence of operations performed in the **execution** of an **algorithm**.

flowchart. A graphical representation of the definition, analysis, or solution of a problem in which symbols are used to represent operations, **data**, flow, and equipment. Contrast with **block diagram**. (ISO)

formal language. A language whose rules are explicitly established prior to its use. Synonymous with **artificial language.** Examples include **programming languages,** such as FORTRAN and Ada, and mathematical or logical languages, such as predicate calculus. Contrast with **natural language.**

formal parameter. A **variable** used in a **subprogram** to represent **data** or **program** elements to be transmitted to the subprogram by a calling **routine.** Synonymous with **dummy parameter.** Contrast with **actual parameter.**

formal specification. (1) A **specification** written and approved in accordance with established standards.

(2) In **proof of correctness,** a description in a **formal language** of the externally visible behavior of a **system** or system **component.**

formal testing. The process of conducting **testing** activities and reporting results in accordance with an approved **test plan.**

function. (1) A specific purpose of an entity or its characteristic action. (ANSI)

(2) A **subprogram** that is invoked during the evaluation of an expression in which its name appears and that returns a value to the point of invocation. Contrast with **subroutine.**

functional decomposition. A method of designing a **system** by breaking it down into its **components** in such a way that the components correspond directly to system **functions** and subfunctions. See also **hierarchical decomposition.**

functional design. The **specification** of the working relationships among the parts of a **data processing system.** (ISO) See also **preliminary design.**

functional requirement. A **requirement** that specifies a **function** that a **system** or system **component** must be capable of performing.

functional specification. A **specification** that defines the **functions** that a **system** or system **component** must perform. See also **performance specification.**

functional unit. An entity of **hardware, software,** or both capable of accomplishing a specified purpose. (ISO)

graph. A **model** consisting of a finite set of **nodes** having connections called edges or arcs.

hardware. Physical equipment used in **data** processing, as opposed to **computer programs, procedures,** rules, and associated **documentation.** Contrast with **software.** (ISO)

hierarchical decomposition. A method of designing a **system** by breaking it down into its **components** through a series of **top-down** refinements. See also **functional decomposition, modular decomposition, stepwise refinement.**

hierarchy. A structure whose **components** are ranked into **levels** of subordination according to a specific set of rules.

high level language. Synonymous with **higher order language.**

higher order language. A programming **language** that usually includes features such as nested expressions, user defined **data types,** and **parameter** passing not normally found in lower order languages, that does not reflect the structure of any one given **computer** or class of computers, and that can be used to write machine independent **source programs.** A single, higher-order, language statement may represent multiple machine operations. Contrast with **machine language, assembly language.**

host machine. (1) The **computer** on which a **program** or **file** is installed.

(2) A **computer** used to develop **software** intended for another computer. Contrast with **target machine.**

(3) A **computer** used to **emulate** another computer. Contrast with **target machine.**

(4) In a **computer network,** a **computer** that provides processing capabilities to users of the **network.**

identifier. (1) A symbol used to name, indicate, or locate. Identifiers may be associated with such things as **data structures, data** items, or **program** locations.

(2) A character or group of characters used to identify or name an item of **data** and possibly to indicate certain properties of that data. (ISO)

imperfect debugging. In **reliability** modeling, the assumption that attempts to correct or remove a detected **fault** are not always successful.

implementation. (1) A realization of an **abstraction** in more concrete terms; in particular, in terms of **hardware, software,** or both.

(2) A machine executable form of a **program,** or a form of a program that can be translated automatically to machine executable form.

(3) The process of translating a **design** into **code** and **debugging** the code.

implementation phase. The period of time in the **software life cycle** during which a **software product** is created from **design documentation** and debugged. See also **installation and checkout phase, test phase.**

implementation requirement. Any **requirement** that impacts or constrains the **implementation** of a **software design;** for example, design descriptions, software development standards, **programming language** requirements, software **quality assurance** standards.

independent verification and validation.

(1) **Verification** and **validation** of a **software product** by an organization that is both technically and managerially separate from the organization responsible for developing the product.

(2) **Verification** and **validation** of a **software product** by individuals or groups other than those who performed the original **design,** but who may be from the same organization. (10 CFR 50). The degree of independence must be a function of the importance of the **software.**

indigenous fault. A **fault** existing in a **computer program** that has not been inserted as part of a **fault seeding** process.

inductive assertion method. A **proof of correctness** technique in which **assertions** are written describing **program** inputs, outputs, and intermediate conditions, a set of theorems is developed relating satisfaction of the **input assertions** to satisfaction of the **output assertions,** and the theorems are proved to be true.

information hiding. The technique of **encapsulating software design** decisions in **modules** in such a way that the module's **interfaces** reveal as little as possible about the module's inner workings; thus, each module is a "black box" to the other modules in the **system.** The discipline of information hiding forbids the use of information about a module that is not in the module's **interface specification.** See also **encapsulation.**

input assertion. A logical expression specifying one or more conditions that **program** inputs must satisfy in order to be valid.

inspection. (1) A formal evaluation technique in which **software requirements, design,** or **code** are examined in detail by a person or group other than the author to detect **faults,** violations of development standards, and other problems. Contrast with **walk-through.** See also **code audit.**

(2) A phase of quality control that by means of examination, observation or measurement determines the conformance of materials, supplies, components, parts, appurtenances, **systems, processes** or structures to predetermined **quality requirements.** (ANSI N45.2.10-1973)

installation and checkout phase. The period of time in the **software life cycle** during which a **software product** is integrated into its **operational** environment and tested in this environment to ensure that it performs as required.

instruction. (1) A **program** statement that causes a **computer** to perform a particular operation or set of operations.

(2) In a **programming language,** a meaningful expression that specifies one operation and identifies its **operands,** if any. (ISO)

instruction set. The set of **instructions** of a **computer,** of a **programming language,** or of the programming languages in a programming **system.** (ISO)

instruction set architecture. An **abstract machine** characterized by an **instruction set.**

instruction trace. See **trace.**

instrumentation. See **program instrumentation.**

instrumentation tool. A **software tool** that generates and inserts counters or other probes at strategic points in another **program** to provide statistics about program **execution,** such as how thoroughly the program's **code** is exercised.

integration. The process of combining **software** elements, **hardware** elements, or both into an overall **system.**

integration testing. An orderly progression of **testing** in which **software** elements, **hardware** elements, or both are combined and tested until the entire **system** has been integrated. See also **system testing.**

integrity. The extent to which unauthorized access to or **modification** of **software** or **data** can be controlled in a **computer system.** See also **security.**

interactive. Pertaining to a **system** in which each user entry causes a response from the system. See also **conversational.**

interface. (1) A shared boundary. An interface might be a **hardware component** to link two devices or it might be a portion of storage or registers accessed by two or more **computer programs.** (ANSI)
(2) To interact or communicate with another **system component.**

interface requirement. A **requirement** that specifies a **hardware, software,** or **data base** element with which a **system** or system **component** must **interface,** or that sets forth constraints on formats, timing, or other factors caused by such an interface.

interface specification. A **specification** that sets forth the **interface requirements** for a **system** or system **component.**

interface testing. **Testing** conducted to ensure that **program** or system **components** pass information or control correctly to one another.

interoperability. The ability of two or more **systems** to exchange information and to mutually use the information that has been exchanged. Compare with **compatibility.**

interpret. To translate and to execute each **source language** statement of a **computer program** before translating and executing the next statement. (ISO) Contrast with **assemble, compile.**

interpreter. (1) **Software, hardware,** or **firmware** used to **interpret computer programs.** Contrast with **compiler, assembler.**
(2) A **computer program** used to **interpret.** (ISO)

interrupt. A suspension of a **process** such as the **execution** of a **computer program,** caused by an event external to that process, and performed in such a way that the process can be resumed. Synonymous with interruption. (ISO)

iteration. (1) The process of repeatedly executing a given sequence of **programming language** statements until a given condition is met or while a given condition is true.
(2) A single execution of a **loop.**

kernel. (1) A nucleus or core, as in the kernel of an **operating system.**
(2) An **encapsulation** of an elementary **function.** Kernels can be combined to form some or all of an **operating system** or set of **firmware.**
(3) A **model** used in **computer** selection studies to evaluate computer **performance.**

key. One or more characters, within a set of **data,** that contains information about the set, including its identification. (ISO)

label. (1) One or more characters, within or attached to a set of **data,** that contain information about the set, including its identification. (ISO)
(2) In **computer** programming, an **identifier** of an **instruction.** (ISO)
(3) An identification **record** for a tape or disk **file.**

language processor. (1) A **computer program** that performs such **functions** as translating, interpreting, and other tasks required for processing a specified **programming language;** for example, a FORTRAN processor, a COBOL processor. (ISO)
(2) A **software tool** that performs such **functions** as translating, **interpreting,** and other

tasks required for processing a specific language, such as a **requirements specification language,** a **design language,** or a **programming language.**

level. (1) The degree of subordination of an item in a hierarchical arrangement. (ISO)

(2) A rank within a **hierarchy.** An item is of the lowest level if it has no subordinates and of the highest level if it has no superiors.

level of documentation. A description of required **documentation** indicating its scope, content, format, and **quality.** Selection of the level may be based on project cost, intended usage, extent of effort, or other factors.

librarian. See **software librarian.**

library. See **software library, system library.**

life cycle. See **software life cycle.**

linkage editor. A **computer program** used to create one **load module** from one or more independently translated object modules or load modules by resolving cross-references among the object modules, and possibly by relocating elements. (ANSI) Note that not all object modules require linking prior to execution.

linked list. See **chained list.**

list. (1) An ordered set of items of **data.** (ISO)

(2) To print or otherwise display items of **data** that meet specified criteria. (ANSI)

(3) See **chained list.**

list processing. A method of processing **data** in the form of **lists.** Usually, **chained lists** are used so that the logical order of items can be changed without altering their physical locations. (ISO)

listing. (1) A **computer** output in the form of a human-readable **list.**

(2) A human-readable, textual **computer** output.

load map. A **computer** generated **list** that identifies the location or size of all or selected parts of a memory-resident **computer program** or of memory-resident **data.**

load module. A **program** unit that is suitable for loading into main storage for **execution;** it is usually the output of a **linkage editor.** (ISO)

loader. (1) A **routine** that reads an **object program** into main storage prior to its **execution.**

(2) A **routine,** commonly a **computer program,** that reads **data** into main storage. (ANSI)

logical file. A **file** independent of its physical environment. Portions of the same logical file may be located in different physical files, or several logical files or parts of logical files may be located in one physical file.

logical record. A **record** independent of its physical environment. Portions of the same logical record may be located in different physical records, or several logical records or parts of logical records may be located in one physical record. (ANSI)

loop. A set of **instructions** that may be executed repeatedly while a certain condition prevails. (ISO) See also **iteration.**

machine language. A representation of **instructions** and **data** that is directly executable by a **computer.** Contrast with **assembly language, higher order language.**

macro. (1) A predefined sequence of **instructions** that is inserted into a **program** during assembly or compilation at each place that its corresponding **macroinstruction** appears in the program.

(2) Synonymous with **macroinstruction.**

macroinstruction. An **instruction** in a **source language** that is to be replaced by a defined sequence of instructions in the same source language. The macroinstruction may also specify values for **parameters** in the instructions that are to replace it. (ISO)

macroprocessor. The portion of some **assemblers** and **compilers** that allows a programmer to define and use **macros.**

maintainability. (1) The ease with which **software** can be maintained.

(2) The ease with which **maintenance** of a **functional unit** can be performed in accordance with prescribed **requirements.** (ISO)

(3) Ability of an item under stated conditions of use to be retained in, or restored to, within a given period of time, a specified state in which it can perform its required **functions** when **maintenance** is performed under stated conditions and while using prescribed **procedures** and resources. (ANSI/ASQC A3-1978).

maintenance. See **software maintenance.**

maintenance phase. See **operation and maintenance phase.**

maintenance plan. A **document** that identifies the management and technical approach that will be used to maintain **software products.** Typically included are topics such as **tools,** resources, facilities, and schedules.

map program. A **compiler** or **assembler** feature that generates a **load map.**

master library. A **software library** containing formally released versions of **software** and **documentation.** Contrast with **production library.**

metacompiler. See **compiler generator.**

metalanguage. A language used to specify a language or languages.

microcode. (1) A symbolic representation of a **microprogram.**
(2) The internal representation of a **microprogram** in its storage medium. See also **firmware.**

microprogram. A sequence of elementary **instructions** that corresponds to a **computer** operation, that is maintained in special storage, and whose **execution** is initiated by the introduction of a computer instruction into an instruction register of a computer. (ISO) Microprograms are often used in place of hard-wired logic. See also **firmware.**

milestone. A scheduled event for which some project member or manager is held accountable and that is used to measure progress; for example, a formal review, issuance of a **specification,** product **delivery.**

mnemonic symbol. A symbol chosen to assist the human memory; for example, an abbreviation such as *"mpy"* for *"multiply"*. (ISO)

model. A representation of a real world **process,** device, or concept. See also **analytical model, availability model, debugging model, error model, reliability model, simulation, statistical test model.**

modification. (1) A change made to **software.**
(2) The process of changing **software.**

modular decomposition. A method of designing a **system** by breaking it down into **modules.** See also **hierarchical decomposition.**

modular programming. A technique for developing a **system** or **program** as a collection of **modules.**

modularity. The extent to which **software** is composed of discrete **components** such that a change to one component has minimal impact on other components.

module. (1) A **program** unit that is discrete and identifiable with respect to compiling, combining with other units, and loading; for example, the input to, or output from, an **assembler, compiler, linkage editor,** or executive **routine.** (ANSI)
(2) A logically separable part of a **program.**

module strength. See **cohesion.**

multilevel security. A mode of operation permitting **data** at various **security levels** to be concurrently stored and processed in a **computer system,** when at least some users have neither the clearance nor the need-to-know for all data contained in the system.

multiprogramming. (1) A mode of operation that provides for the interleaved **execution** of two or more **computer programs** by a single processor. (ISO)
(2) Pertaining to the concurrent **execution** of two or more **computer programs** by a computer. (ANSI)
(3) The concurrent **execution** of two or more **functions** as though each function operates alone.

mutation. See **program mutation.**

N-ary. (1) Characterized by a selection, choice, or condition that has n possible different values or states. (ISO)

(2) Of a fixed radix numeration system, having a radix of n. (ISO)

natural language. A language whose rules are based on current usage without being explicitly prescribed. (ISO) Examples include English, Chinese, French, and Swahili. Contrast with **formal language.**

nest. (1) To incorporate a structure or structures of some kind into a structure of the same kind. For example, to nest one **loop** (the nested loop) within another loop (the nesting loop); to nest one **subroutine** (the nested subroutine) within another subroutine (the nesting subroutine). (ISO)

(2) To place **subroutines** or **data** in other subroutines or data at a different hierarchical **level** so that subroutines can be executed as recursive subroutines or so that the data can be accessed recursively.

network. (1) An interconnected or interrelated group of **nodes.**

(2) In connection with a disciplinary or problem oriented qualifier, the combination of material, **documentation,** and human resources that are united by design to achieve certain objectives; for example, a social science network, a science information network.

node. (1) An end point of any branch of a **network** or **graph,** or a junction common to two or more branches.

(2) In a tree structure, a point at which subordinate items of **data** originate. (ANSI)

(3) In a **network,** a point where one or more **functional units** interconnect transmission lines. (ISO)

(4) The representation of a state or an event by means of a point on a diagram. (ANSI)

object program. A fully **compiled** or **assembled program** that is ready to be loaded into the **computer.** (ISO) Contrast with **source program.**

operand. (1) An entity on which an operation is performed. (ISO)

(2) That which is operated upon. An operand is usually identified by an **address** part of an **instruction.** (ANSI)
See also **operator.**

operating system. Software that controls the **execution** of **programs.** An operating system may provide services such as resource allocation scheduling, input/output control, and **data** management. Although operating systems are predominantly software, partial or complete **hardware implementations** are possible. (ISO) An operating system provides support in a single spot rather than forcing each program to be concerned with controlling hardware. See also **system software.**

operation and maintenance phase. The period of time in the **software life cycle** during which a **software product** is employed in its **operational** environment, monitored for satisfactory **performance,** and modified as necessary to correct problems or to respond to changing **requirements.**

operational. Pertaining to the status given a **software product** once it has entered the **operation and maintenance phase.**

operational reliability. The **reliability** of a **system** or **software subsystem** in its actual use environment. Operational reliability may differ considerably from reliability in the specified or test environment.

operational testing. Testing performed by the end user on **software** in its normal operating environment. (DoD usage)

operator. (1) In symbol manipulation, a symbol that represents the action to be performed in an operation. (ISO) Examples of operators are +,-,*,/.

(2) In the description of a **process,** that which indicates the action to be performed on **operands.** (ANSI)

(3) A person who operates a machine. (ANSI)
See also **operand.**

output assertion. A logical expression specifying one or more conditions that **program** outputs must satisfy in order for the program to be correct.

overlay. (1) In a **computer program,** a **segment** that is not permanently maintained in internal storage. (ISO)

(2) The technique of repeatedly using the same areas of internal storage during different stages of a **program.** (ANSI)

(3) In the **execution** of a **computer program,** to load a **segment** of the computer program in a storage area hitherto occupied by parts of the computer program that are not currently needed. (ISO)

parameter. (1) A **variable** that is given a constant value for a specified application and that may denote the application. (ISO)

(2) A **variable** that is used to pass values between **program routines.** See also **actual parameter, formal parameter.**

parse. To determine the syntactic structure of an **artificial** or **natural language** unit by decomposing the unit into more elementary subunits and establishing the relationships among the subunits; for example, **blocks,** statements, and expressions may be decomposed into statements, expressions, and **operators** and **operands.**

partial correctness. In **proof of correctness,** a designation indicating that a **program's output assertions** follow logically from its **input assertions** and processing steps. Contrast with **total correctness.**

patch. (1) A **modification** to an **object program** made by replacing a portion of existing machine **code** with modified machine code.

(2) To modify an **object program** without recompiling the **source program.**

path analysis. Program analysis performed to identify all possible paths through a program, to detect incomplete paths, or to discover portions of the program that are not on any path.

path condition. A set of conditions that must be met in order for a particular **program** path to be executed.

path expression. A logical expression indicating the input conditions that must be met in order for a particular **program** path to be executed.

perfective maintenance **Maintenance** performed to improve **performance, maintainability,** or other **software** attributes. See also **adaptive maintenance, corrective maintenance.**

performance. (1) The ability of a **computer system** or **subsystem** to perform its **functions.**

(2) A measure of the ability of a **computer system** or **subsystem** to perform its **functions;** for example, response time, **throughput,** number of transactions. See also **performance requirement.**

performance evaluation. The technical assessment of a **system** or system **component** to determine how effectively operating objectives have been achieved.

performance requirement. A **requirement** that specifies a **performance** characteristic that a **system** or system **component** must possess; for example, speed, **accuracy,** frequency.

performance specification. (1) A **specification** that sets forth the **performance requirements** for a **system** or system **component.**

(2) Synonymous with **requirements specification.** (U.S. Navy usage)
See also **functional specification.**

Petri net. An abstract, formal **model** of information flow, showing static and dynamic properties of a **system.** A Petri net is usually represented as a **graph** having two types of **nodes** (called places and transitions) connected by arcs, and markings (called tokens) indicating dynamic properties. See also **state diagram.**

physical requirement. A **requirement** that specifies a physical characteristic that a **system** or system **component** must possess; for example, material, shape, size, weight.

pointer. (1) An **identifier** that indicates the location of an item of **data.** (ANSI)

(2) A **data** item whose value is the location of another data item.

portability. The ease with which **software** can be transferred from one **computer system** or environment to another.

precision. (1) A measure of the ability to distinguish between nearly equal values; for example, four-place numerals are less precise than six-place numerals; nevertheless, a properly computed four-place numeral may be more accurate than an improperly computed six-place numeral. (ISO)

(2) The degree of discrimination with which a quantity is stated; for example, a three-digit numeral discriminates among 1000 possibilities. (ISO)
Contrast with **accuracy.**

precompiler. A **computer program** that preprocesses source **code,** part of which may be unacceptable to a **compiler,** to generate equivalent code acceptable to the compiler; for example, a **preprocessor** which converts structured FORTRAN to ANSI-standard FORTRAN.

preliminary design. (1) The process of analyzing **design** alternatives and defining the **software architecture.** Preliminary design typically includes definition and structuring of **computer program components** and **data,** definition of the **interfaces,** and preparation of timing and sizing estimates.
(2) The result of the preliminary design process. See also **design analysis, functional design.**

preprocessor. A **computer program** that effects some preliminary computation or organization. (ISO) See also **precompiler.**

privileged instruction. An **instruction** that may be used only by a **supervisory program.** (ISO)

procedure. (1) A portion of a **computer program** which is named and which performs a specific task. Compare with **subroutine, subprogram, function, module.**
(2) The course of action taken for the solution of a problem. (ISO)
(3) The description of the course of action taken for the solution of a problem. (ANSI)
(4) A set of manual steps to be followed to accomplish a task each time the task is to be done.

process. (1) In a **computer system,** a unique, finite course of events defined by its purpose or by its effect, achieved under given conditions. (ISO)
(2) To perform operations on **data** in process. (ISO)

product certification. See **certification.**

product specification. Synonymous with **design specification.** (DoD usage)

production library. A software **library** containing **software** approved for current **operational** use.

program. (1) A **computer program.**
(2) A schedule or plan that specifies actions to be taken.
(3) To **design,** write, and test **computer programs.** (ISO)

program architecture. The structure and relationships among the **components** of a **computer program.** The program architecture may also include the program's **interface** with its operational environment.

program block. In problem-oriented languages, a **computer program** subdivision that serves to group related statements, delimit **routines,** specify storage allocation, delineate the applicability of **labels,** or **segment** paths of the computer program for other purposes. (ANSI)

program correctness. See **correctness.**

program design language. See **design language.**

program extension. An **enhancement** made to existing **software** to increase the scope of its capabilities.

program instrumentation. (1) Probes, such as **instructions** or **assertions,** inserted into a **computer program** to facilitate **execution** monitoring, **proof of correctness,** resource monitoring, or other activities.
(2) The process of preparing and inserting probes into a **computer program.**

program library. An organized collection of **computer programs.** (ISO) See also **software library, system library.**

program mutation. (1) A **program** version purposely altered from the intended version to evaluate the ability of program **test cases** to detect the alteration. Synonymous with program mutant.
(2) The process of creating program mutations in order to evaluate the adequacy of **program test data.**

program protection. The application of internal or external controls to preclude any unauthorized access or **modification** to a **computer program.**

program specification. (1) Any **specification** for a **computer program.** See **design specification, functional specification, performance specification, requirements specification.**
 (2) Synonymous with **design specification.**

program support library. See **software development library.**

program synthesis. The use of **software tools** to aid in the transformation of a **program specification** into a **program** that realizes that **specification.**

program validation. Synonymous with **computer program validation.** See **validation.**

programming language. An **artificial language** designed to generate or express **programs.** (ISO)

programming support environment. An integrated collection of **tools** accessed via a single **command language** to provide programming support capabilities throughout the **software life cycle.** The environment typically includes tools for designing, editing, compiling, loading, **testing, configuration management,** and project management.

project file. See **project notebook.**

project notebook. A central repository of written material such as memos, plans, technical reports, etc., pertaining to a project. Synonymous with **project file.** See also **software development notebook.**

project plan. A management **document** describing the approach that will be taken for a project. The plan typically describes the work to be done, the resources required, the methods to be used, the **configuration management** and **quality assurance** procedures to be followed, the schedules to be met, the project organization, etc.

prompt. (1) A message informing a user that a **system** is ready for the next command, message, or other user action.

(2) To inform a user that a **system** is ready for the next command, element, or other input.

proof of correctness. (1) A formal technique used to prove mathematically that a **program** satisfies its **specifications.** See also **partial correctness, total correctness.**
 (2) A **program** proof that results from applying this technique.

protection. An arrangement for restricting access to or use of all, or part, of a **computer system.** (ISO)

protocol. (1) A set of conventions or rules that govern the interactions of **processes** or applications within a **computer system** or **network.**
 (2) A set of rules that govern the operation of **functional units** to achieve communication. (ISO)

pseudo code. A combination of **programming language** and **natural language** used for **computer program design.**

pushdown storage. A storage device that handles **data** in such a way that the next item to be retrieved is the most recently stored item still in the storage device; i.e., last-in-first-out (LIFO). (ISO) See also **stack.**

qualification testing. **Formal testing,** usually conducted by the developer for the customer, to demonstrate that the **software** meets its specified **requirements.** See also **acceptance testing, system testing.**

quality. (1) The totality of features and characteristics of a product or service that bears on its ability to satisfy given needs. (ANSI/ASQC A3-1978)
 (2) See **software quality.**

quality assurance. A planned and systematic pattern of all actions necessary to provide adequate confidence that the item or product conforms to established technical **requirements.** (ANSI/IEEE Std 730-1981)

quality metric. A quantitative measure of the degree to which **software** possesses a given attribute that affects its **quality.**

queue. A **list** that is accessed in a first-in, first-out manner. Contrast with **stack.**

real time. (1) Pertaining to the processing of **data** by a **computer** in connection with another **process** outside the computer according to time requirements imposed by the outside process. This term is also used to describe **systems** operating in **conversational** mode, and processes that can be influenced by human intervention while they are in progress. (ISO)

(2) Pertaining to the actual time during which a physical **process** transpires; for example, the performance of a computation during the actual time that the related physical process transpires, in order that results of the computation can be used in guiding the physical process. (ANSI)

record. A collection of related **data** or **words** treated as a unit. (ISO) See also **logical record.**

recursive routine. A **routine** that may be used as a **subroutine** of itself, calling itself directly or being called by another subroutine, one that it itself has called. The use of a recursive routine usually requires the keeping of records of the status of its unfinished uses in, for example, a pushdown **list.**

redundancy. The inclusion of duplicate or alternate **system** elements to improve **operational reliability** by ensuring continued operation in the event that a primary element fails.

regression testing. Selective retesting to detect **faults** introduced during **modification** of a **system** or system **component,** to verify that modifications have not caused unintended adverse effects, or to verify that a modified system or system component still meets its specified **requirements.**

reliability. (1) The ability of an item to perform a required **function** under stated conditions for a stated period of time. (ANSI/ASQC A3-1978)

(2) See **software reliability**.

reliability, numerical. The probability that an item will perform a required **function** under stated conditions for a stated period of time. (ANSI/ASQC A3-1978)

reliability assessment. The process of determining the achieved level of **reliability** of an existing **system** or system **component.**

reliability data. Information necessary to assess the **reliability** of **software** at selected points in the **software life cycle.** Examples include **error data** and time data for **reliability models, program** attributes such as **complexity,** and programming characteristics such as development techniques employed and programmer experience.

reliability evaluation. See **reliability assessment.**

reliability growth. The improvement in **software reliability** that results from correcting **faults** in the **software.**

reliability model. A **model** used for predicting, estimating, or assessing **reliability.** See also **reliability assessment.**

relocatable machine code. Machine language code that requires relative **addresses** to be translated into absolute addresses prior to **computer execution.** Contrast with **absolute machine code.**

rendezvous. The interaction that occurs between two parallel tasks when one task has called an entry of the other task, and a corresponding accept statement is being executed by the other task on behalf of the calling task.

repeatability. See **test repeatability.**

requirement. (1) A condition or capability needed by a user to solve a problem or achieve an objective.

(2) A condition or capability that must be met or possessed by a **system** or system **component** to satisfy a contract, standard, **specification,** or other formally imposed **document.** The set of all requirements forms the basis for subsequent development of the system or system component. See also **requirements analysis, requirements phase, requirements specification.**

requirements analysis. (1) The process of studying user needs to arrive at a definition of **system** or **software requirements.**

(2) The **verification** of **system** or **software requirements.**

requirements inspection. See **inspection.**

requirements phase. The period of time in the **software life cycle** during which the **requirements** for a **software product,** such as the functional and **performance** capabilities, are defined and documented.

requirements specification. A **specification** that sets forth the **requirements** for a **system** or system **component;** for example, a **software configuration item.** Typically included are **functional requirements, performance requirements, interface requirements, design requirements,** and development standards.

requirements specification language. A formal **language** with special constructs and **verification** protocols used to specify, verify, and **document requirements.**

requirements verification. See **verification.**

retirement phase. The period of time in the **software life cycle** during which support for a **software product** is terminated.

reusability. The extent to which a **module** can be used in multiple applications.

review. See **design review.**

robustness. The extent to which **software** can continue to operate correctly despite the introduction of invalid inputs.

root compiler. A **compiler** whose output is a machine independent, intermediate-level representation of a **program.** A root compiler, when combined with a machine-dependent **code generator,** comprises a full compiler.

routine. (1) A **computer program segment** that performs a specific task. See also **function, procedure, subroutine, subprogram.**

(2) A **program,** or a sequence of **instructions** called by a program, that may have some general or frequent use. (ISO)

run time. (1) A measure of the time expended to execute a **program.** While run time ordinarily reflects the expended central processor time, run time may also include peripheral processing and peripheral accessing time; for example, a run time of 5 hours.

(2) The instant at which a **program** begins to execute.
See also **execution time.**

secretary/librarian. The **software librarian** on a **chief programmer team.**

security. The **protection** of **computer hardware** and **software** from accidental or malicious access, use, **modification,** destruction, or disclosure. Security also pertains to personnel, **data,** communications, and the physical protection of computer installations.

security kernel. A small, self-contained collection of key **security**-related statements that works as a privileged part of an **operating system.** All criteria specified by the **kernel** must be met for a **program** or **data** to be accessed.

seeding. See **fault seeding.**

segment. (1) A self-contained portion of a **computer program** that may be executed without the entire **computer program** necessarily being maintained in internal storage at any one time. (ISO) See also **component, module, subprogram.**

(2) The sequence of **computer program** statements between two consecutive branch points. See also **path analysis.**

(3) To divide a **computer program** into segments. (ISO)

semantics. (1) The relationships of characters or groups of characters to their meanings, independent of the manner of their interpretation and use. (ISO)

(2) The relationships between symbols and their meanings. (ANSI)

(3) The discipline of expressing the meanings of **computer** language constructs in **metalanguages**.
See also **syntax**.

semaphore. A shared **variable** used to synchronize **concurrent processes** by indicating whether an action has been completed or an event has occurred.

sequential processes. Processes that execute in such a manner that one must finish before the next begins. Contrast with **concurrent processes**.

severity. See **criticality**.

side-effect. Processing or activities performed, or results obtained, secondary to the primary **function** of a **program**, **subprogram**, or operation.

simulation. The representation of selected characteristics of the behavior of one physical or abstract **system** by another system. In a digital **computer system**, simulation is done by **software**; for example, (a) the representation of physical phenomena by means of operations performed by a computer system, (b) the representation of operations of a computer system by those of another computer system. (ISO) Contrast with **analytical model**.

simulator. A device, **data** processing **system**, or **computer program** that represents certain features of the behavior of a physical or abstract system. (ANSI)

sizing. The process of estimating the amount of **computer** storage or the number of source lines that will be required for a **system** or system **component**.

software. (1) **Computer programs, procedures,** rules, and possibly associated **documentation** and **data** pertaining to the operation of a **computer system**. See also **application software, system software**.
(2) **Programs, procedures,** rules, and any associated **documentation** pertaining to the operation of a **computer system**. (ISO)
Contrast with **hardware**.

software configuration management. See **configuration management**.

software data base. A centralized **file** of **data** definitions and present values for data common to, and located internal to, an **operational software system**.

software development cycle. (1) The period of time that begins with the decision to develop a **software product** and ends when the product is delivered. This cycle typically includes a **requirements phase, design phase, implementation phase, test phase,** and sometimes, **installation** and **checkout phase**. Contrast with **software life cycle**.
(2) The period of time that begins with the decision to develop a **software product** and ends when the product is no longer being enhanced by the developer.
(3) Sometimes used as a synonym for **software life cycle**.

software development library. A **software library** containing **computer** readable and human readable information relevant to a **software** development effort.

software development notebook. A collection of material pertinent to the development of a given **software module**. Contents typically include the **requirements, design,** technical reports, **code listings, test plans,** test results, problem reports, schedules, notes, etc., for the module. See also **project notebook**.

software development plan. A **project plan** for the development of a **software product**. Synonymous with **computer program development plan**.

software development process. The process by which user needs are translated into **software requirements**, software requirements are transformed into **design,** the design is implemented in **code,** and the code is tested, documented, and certified for **operational** use.

software documentation. Technical **data** or information, including **computer listings** and printouts, in human-readable form, that describe or specify the **design** or details, explain the capabilities, or provide operating instructions for using the **software** to obtain desired results from a software system. See also **documentation, system documentation, user documentation**.

software engineering. The systematic approach to the development, operation, **maintenance,** and retirement of **software.**

software experience data. Data relating to the development or use of **software** that could be useful in developing **models, reliability** predictions, or other quantitative descriptions of software.

software librarian. The person responsible for establishing, controlling, and maintaining a **software library.**

software library. A controlled collection of **software** and related **documentation** designed to aid in software development, use, or **maintenance.** Types include **software development library, master library, production library, program library,** and **software repository.** See also **system library.**

software life cycle. The period of time that starts when a **software product** is conceived and ends when the product is no longer available for use. The software life cycle typically includes a **requirements phase, design phase, implementation phase, test phase, installation and checkout phase, operation and maintenance phase,** and sometimes, **retirement phase.** Contrast with **software development cycle.**

software maintenance. (1) **Modification** of a **software product** after **delivery** to correct **faults.**

(2) **Modification** of a **software product** after **delivery** to correct **faults,** to improve **performance** or other attributes, or to adapt the product to a changed environment. See also **adaptive maintenance, corrective maintenance, perfective maintenance.**

software monitor. A **software tool** that executes concurrently with another **computer program** and that provides detailed information about the **execution** of the other **program.**

software product. A **software** entity designated for **delivery** to a user.

software quality. (1) The totality of features and characteristics of a **software product** that bear on its ability to satisfy given needs; for example, conform to **specifications.**

(2) The degree to which **software** possesses a desired combination of attributes.

(3) The degree to which a customer or user perceives that **software** meets his or her composite expectations.

(4) The composite characteristics of **software** that determine the degree to which the software in use will meet the expectations of the customer.

software quality assurance. See **quality assurance.**

software reliability. (1) The probability that **software** will not cause the **failure** of a **system** for a specified time under specified conditions. The probability is a function of the inputs to and use of the system as well as a function of the existence of **faults** in the software. The inputs to the system determine whether existing faults, if any, are encountered.

(2) The ability of a **program** to perform a required **function** under stated conditions for a stated period of time.

software repository. A **software library** providing permanent, archival storage for **software** and related **documentation**.

software sneak analysis. A technique applied to **software** to identify latent (sneak) logic control paths or conditions that could inhibit a desired operation or cause an unwanted operation to occur.

software tool. A **computer program** used to help develop, test, analyze, or maintain another computer program or its **documentation;** for example, **automated design tool, compiler,** test **tool, maintenance tool.**

source language. (1) A language used to write **source programs.**

(2) A language from which statements are translated. (ISO) Contrast with **target language.**

source program. (1) A **computer program** that must be **compiled, assembled,** or **interpreted** before being executed by a **computer.**

(2) A **computer program** expressed in a **source language.** Contrast with **object program.** (ISO)

specification. (1) A **document** that prescribes, in a complete, precise, verifiable manner, the **requirements, design,** behavior, or other characteristics of a **system** or system **component.** See also **design specification, formal specification, functional specification, interface specification, performance specification, requirements specification.**

(2) The process of developing a specification.

(3) A concise statement of a set of **requirements** to be satisfied by a product, a material or **process** indicating, whenever appropriate, the **procedure** by means of which it may be determined whether the requirements given are satisfied. (ANSI N45.2.10-1973)

specification language. A language, often a machine-processable combination of **natural** and **formal language,** used to specify the **requirements, design,** behavior, or other characteristics of a **system** or system **component.** See also **design language, requirements specification language.**

specification verification. See **verification.**

stability. (1) The ability to continue unchanged despite disturbing or disruptive events.

(2) The ability to return to an original state after disturbing or disruptive events.

stack. A **list** that is accessed in a last-in, first-out manner. Contrast with **queue.**

standards enforcer. A **software tool** that determines whether prescribed development standards have been followed. The standards may include **module** size, module structure, commenting conventions, use of certain statement forms, and **documentation** conventions.

state diagram. A **directed graph** in which **nodes** correspond to internal states of a **system,** and edges correspond to transitions; often used for describing a system in terms of state changes. See also **Petri net.**

static analysis. The process of evaluating a **program** without executing the program. See also **desk checking, code audit, inspection, static analyzer, walk-through.** Contrast with **dynamic analysis.**

static analyzer. A **software tool** that aids in the evaluation of a **computer program** without executing the **program.** Examples include **syntax** checkers, **compilers,** cross-reference generators, **standards enforcers,** and flowcharters. Contrast with **dynamic analyzer.**

static binding. **Binding** performed prior to **execution** of a **program** and not subject to change during execution. Contrast with **dynamic binding.**

statistical test model. A **model** that relates **program faults** to the input **data** set (or sets) which cause them to be encountered. The model also gives the probability that these faults will cause the program to fail.

stepwise refinement. A **system development methodology** in which **data** definitions and processing steps are defined broadly at first and then with increasing detail. See also **hierarchical decomposition, top-down, bottom-up.**

string. A linear sequence of entities such as characters or physical elements. (ISO)

strong typing. A **programming language** feature that requires the **data type** of each **data** object to be declared, and that precludes the application of **operators** to inappropriate data objects and, thereby, prevents the interaction of data objects of incompatible **types.**

structured design. A disciplined approach to **software design** that adheres to a specified set of rules based on principles such as **top-down design, stepwise refinement,** and **data** flow analysis.

structured program. A **program** constructed of a basic set of **control structures,** each one having one entry point and one exit. The set of control structures typically includes: sequence of two or more **instructions,** conditional selection of one of two or more instructions or sequences of instructions, and repetition of an instruction or a sequence of instructions.

structured programming. (1) A well-defined **software** development technique that incorporates **top-down design** and **implementation** and strict use of **structured program** control constructs.

(2) Loosely, any technique for organizing and coding **programs** that reduces **complexity**, improves clarity, and facilitates **debugging** and **modification.**

structured programming language. A **programming language** that provides the **structured program** constructs and that facilitates the development of structured programs.

stub. (1) A dummy **program module** used during the development and **testing** of a higher-level module.

(2) A **program** statement substituting for the body of a program unit and indicating that the unit is or will be defined elsewhere.

subprogram. A **program** unit that may be invoked by one or more other program units. Examples are **procedure, function, subroutine.**

subroutine. (1) A sequenced set of statements that may be used in one or more **computer programs** and at one or more points in a computer program. (ISO)

(2) A **routine** that can be part of another routine. (ANSI)

(3) A **subprogram** that is invoked by a calling statement, that may or may not receive input vallues, and that returns any output values through **parameter** names, **program variables,** or mechanisms other than the subroutine name itself. Contrast with **function.** See also **procedure.**

subsystem. A group of assemblies or **components** or both combined to perform a single **function.** (ANSI N45.2.10-1973)

supervisor. See **supervisory program**

supervisory program. A **computer program,** usually part of an **operating system,** that controls the **execution** of other computer programs and regulates the flow of work in a **data** processing **system.** Synonymous with **executive program, supervisor.** (ISO)

symbolic execution. A **verification** technique in which **program execution** is simulated using symbols rather than actual values for input **data,** and program outputs are expressed as logical or mathematical expressions involving these symbols.

syntax. (1) The relationship among characters or groups of characters, independent of their meanings or the manner of their interpretation and use. (ISO)

(2) The structure of expressions in a language. (ANSI)

(3) The rules governing the structure of a language. (ANSI)
See also **semantics.**

system. (1) A collection of people, machines, and methods organized to accomplish a set of specific **functions.**

(2) An integrated whole that is composed of diverse, interacting, specialized structures and subfunctions.

(3) A group or **subsystem** united by some interaction or interdependence, performing many duties but functioning as a single unit. (ANSI N45.2.10-1973)

system architecture. The structure and relationship among the **components** of a **system.** The system architecture may also include the system's **interface** with its operational environment.

system design. (1) The process of defining the **hardware** and **software** architectures, **components, modules, interfaces,** and **data** for a **system** to satisfy specified system **requirements.**

(2) The result of the system design process.

system documentation. **Documentation** conveying the **requirements, design** philosophy, design details, capabilities, limitations, and other characteristics of a **system.** Contrast with **user documentation.**

system library. A controlled collection of **system**-resident **software** that can be accessed for use or incorporated into other **programs** by reference, for example, a group of **routines** that a **linkage editor** can incorporate into a program as required. See also **software library.**

system reliability. The probability that a **system,** including all **hardware** and **software subsys**-

tems, will perform a required task or mission for a specified time in a specified environment. See also **operational reliability, software reliability.**

system software. Software designed for a specific **computer system** or family of computer systems to facilitate the operation and **maintenance** of the computer system and associated **programs,** for example, **operating systems, compilers,** utilities. Contrast with **application software.**

system testing. The process of **testing** an integrated **hardware** and **software system** to verify that the system meets its specified **requirements.** See also **acceptance testing, qualification testing.**

system validation. See **validation.**

system verification. See **verification.**

table. (1) An array of **data,** each item of which may be unambiguously identified by means of one or more arguments. (ISO)
(2) A collection of **data** in which each item is uniquely identified by a **label,** by its position relative to the other items, or by some other means. (ANSI)

target language. A language into which source statements are translated. (ANSI) Contrast with **source language.**

target machine. (1) The **computer** on which a **program** is intended to operate.
(2) The **computer** being emulated by another computer.
Contrast with **host machine.**

termination proof. In **proof of correctness,** the demonstration that a **program** will terminate under all specified input conditions.

test bed. (1) A test environment containing the **hardware, instrumentation tools, simulators,** and other support **software** necessary for **testing** a **system** or system **component.**
(2) The repertoire of **test cases** necessary for **testing** a **system** or system **component.**

test case. A specific set of **test data** and associated **procedures** developed for a particular objective,

such as to exercise a particular **program** path or to verify compliance with a specific **requirement.** See also **testing.**

test case generator. See **automated test generator.**

test data. Data developed to test a **system** or system **component.** See also **test case.**

test data generator. See **automated test generator.**

test driver. A **driver** that invokes the item under test and that may provide test inputs and report test results.

test log. A chronological record of all relevant details of a **testing** activity.

test phase. The period of time in the **software life cycle** during which the **components** of a **software product** are evaluated and integrated, and the software product is evaluated to determine whether or not **requirements** have been satisfied.

test plan. A **document** prescribing the approach to be taken for intended **testing** activities. The plan typically identifies the items to be tested, the testing to be performed, test schedules, personnel requirements, reporting requirements, evaluation criteria, and any risks requiring contingency planning.

test procedure. Detailed instructions for the setup, operation, and evaluation of results for a given test. A set of associated **procedures** is often combined to form a test procedures **document.**

test repeatability. An attribute of a test indicating whether the same results are produced each time the test is conducted.

test report. A **document** describing the conduct and results of the **testing** carried out for a **system** or system **component.**

test validity. The degree to which a test accomplishes its specified goal.

testability. (1) The extent to which **software** facilitates both the establishment of test criteria and the evaluation of the software with respect to those criteria.

(2) The extent to which the definition of **requirements** facilitates analysis of the requirements to establish test criteria.

testing. The process of exercising or evaluating a **system** or system **component** by manual or automated means to verify that it satisfies specified **requirements** or to identify differences between expected and actual results. Compare with **debugging.**

throughput. A measure of the amount of work performed by a **computer system** over a period of time; for example, number of jobs per day. (ISO)

time sharing. (1) An operating technique of a **computer system** that provides for the interleaving in time of two or more **processes** in one processor. (ISO)

(2) Pertaining to the interleaved use of time on a computing **system** that enables two or more users to execute **computer programs** concurrently. (ANSI)

timing analyzer. A **software tool** that estimates or measures the **execution time** of a **computer program** or portions of a computer program either by summing the execution times of the **instructions** in each path, or by inserting probes at specific points in the **program** and measuring the execution time between probes.

tolerance. The ability of a **system** to provide continuity of operation under various abnormal conditions.

tool. (1) See **software tool.**

(2) A **hardware** device used to analyze **software** or its **performance.**

top-down. Pertaining to an approach that starts with the highest level **component** of a **hierarchy** and proceeds through progressively lower **levels;** for example, **top-down design,** top-down programming, **top-down testing.** Contrast with **bottom-up.**

top-down design. The process of designing a **system** by identifying its major **components,** decomposing them into their lower **level** components, and iterating until the desired level of detail is achieved. Contrast with **bottom-up design.**

top-down testing. The process of checking out hierarchically organized **programs,** progressively, from top to bottom, using **simulation** of lower level **components.**

total correctness. In **proof of correctness,** a designation indicating that a **program's output assertions** follow logically from its **input assertions** and processing steps, and that, in addition, the program terminates under all specified input conditions. Contrast with **partial correctness.**

trace. (1) A record of the **execution** of a **computer program;** it exhibits the sequences in which the **instructions** were executed. (ANSI)

(2) A record of all or certain classes of **instructions** or **program** events occurring during **execution** of a **computer program.**

(3) To produce a **trace.**

tracer. A **software tool** used to **trace.**

translator. A **program** that transforms a sequence of statements in one language into an equivalent sequence of statements in another language. See also **assembler, compiler, interpreter.**

tree. An abstract **hierarchical** structure consisting of **nodes** connected by branches, in which: (a) each branch connects one node to a directly subsidiary node, and (b) there is a unique node called the root that is not subsidiary to any other node, and (c) every node besides the root is directly subsidiary to exactly one other node.

type. See **data type.**

user documentation. Documentation conveying to the end user of a **system** instructions for using the system to obtain desired results; for example, a user's manual. Contrast with **system documentation.**

utility software. Computer programs or **routines** designed to perform some general support **function** required by other **application soft-**

ware, by the operating system, or by system users.

validation. The process of evaluating software at the end of the software development process to ensure compliance with software requirements. See also verification.

variable. (1) A quantity that can assume any of a given set of values. (ISO)

(2) In programming, a character or group of characters that refers to a value and, in the execution of a computer program, corresponds to an address. (ANSI)

verification. (1) The process of determining whether or not the products of a given phase of the software development cycle fulfill the requirements established during the previous phase. See also validation.

(2) Formal proof of program correctness. See proof of correctness.

(3) The act of reviewing, inspecting, testing, checking, auditing, or otherwise establishing and documenting whether or not items, processes, services, or documents conform to specified requirements. (ANSI/ASQC A3-1978).

verification system. See automated verification system.

virtual machine. A functional simulation of a computer and its associated devices.

virtual memory. See virtual storage.

virtual storage. The storage space that may be regarded as addressable main storage by the user of a computer system in which virtual addresses are mapped into real addresses. The size of virtual storage is limited by the addressing scheme of the computer system and by the amount of auxiliary storage available and not by the actual number of main storage locations. (ISO)

walk-through. A review process in which a designer or programmer leads one or more other members of the development team through a segment of design or code that he or she has written, while the other members ask questions and make comments about technique, style, possible errors, violation of development standards, and other problems. Contrast with inspection.

word. (1) An ordered set of bits or characters that is the normal unit in which information may be stored, transmitted, or operated upon within a given computer.

(2) A character string or bit string considered as an entity. (ANSI)

5. Software Life Cycle

The software life cycle consists of a set of discrete activities occurring in a given order during the development and use of software and software systems. The time periods during which these activities occur are referred to as phases. At the current time a consensus has not developed as to which phases comprise the software life cycle. The following diagram (Figure 1) provides an example illustration of the relationship among the life cycle phases. Each of the phases shown in the figure is defined in the glossary.

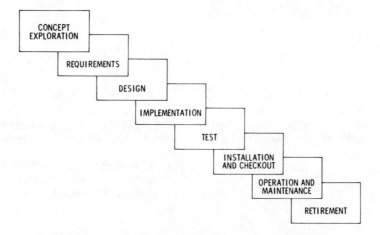

Figure 1. An Example Software Life Cycle

Appendix 1

Reference Identification

(This Appendix is not part of IEEE Std 729-1982, IEEE Standard Glossary of Software Engineering Terminology).

The following provides complete identification of the short references provided after specific terms.

(1) ANSI/ASQC A3-1978 Quality Systems Terminology.[1]

(2) ANSI N45.2.10-1973, Quality Assurance Terms and Definitions.

(3) ANSI/IEEE Std 488-1978, IEEE Standard Digital Interface for Programmable Instrumentation.[2]

(4) ANSI/IEEE Standard 730-1981, IEEE Standard for Software Quality Assurance Plans.

(5) DoD-STD 480A, Configuration Control -Engineering Changes, Deviation and Waivers.[3]

(6) Title 10, Code of Federal Regulations, Chapter 50.

---

[1]ANSI publications are available from Sales Department, Amercian National Standard Institute, 1430 Broadway, New York, NY 10018.

[2]IEEE publications are available from the IEEE Service Center, 445 Hoes Lane, Piscataway, NJ 08854.

[3]DoD documents are available from the DoD Single Stock Point, Naval Publications and Forms Center, Philadelphia, PA 19120.

ANSI/IEEE
Std 730-1984
(Revision of ANSI/IEEE
Std 730-1981)

An American National Standard

IEEE Standard for
Software Quality Assurance Plans

730

Sponsor

**Software Engineering Technical Committee
of the
IEEE Computer Society**

Approved June 14, 1984
IEEE Standards Board

Approved December 17, 1984
American National Standards Institute

Foreword

(This Foreword is not a part of ANSI/IEEE Std 730-1984, IEEE Standard for Software Quality Assurance Plans.)

This standard assists in the preparation and content of Software Quality Assurance Plans and provides a standard against which such plans can be prepared and assessed. It is directed toward the development and maintenance of critical software, that is, where failure could impact safety or cause large financial or social losses.

There are three groups to whom this standard applies: the user, the developer, and the public.

(1) The user, who may be another element of the same organization developing the software, has a need for the product. Further, the user needs the product to meet the requirements identified in the specification. The user thus cannot afford a "hands-off" attitude toward the developer and rely solely on a test to be executed at the end of the software development time period. If the product should fail, not only does the same need still exist but also a portion of the development time has been lost. The user therefore needs to obtain a reasonable degree of confidence that the product is in the process of acquiring required attributes during software development.

(2) The developer needs an established standard against which to plan and to be measured. It is unreasonable to expect a complete reorientation from project to project. Not only is it not cost-effective, but unless there exists a stable framework on which to base changes, improvements cannot be made.

(3) The public may be affected by the users' use of the product. These users include, for example, depositors at a bank and passengers using a reservation system. Users have requirements, such as legal rights, which preclude haphazard development of software. At some later date, the user and the developer may be required to show that they acted in a reasonable and prudent professional manner to ensure that required software attributes were acquired.

This standard was prepared by the Software Engineering Standards Subcommittee of the Software Engineering Technical Committee of the IEEE Computer Society and initially approved for "trial-use" by the IEEE Standards Board in December 1979. The subsequent revision was approved by the IEEE Standards Board in September of 1981 as a "full-use" standard. At the time that it approved this revision, the subcommittee had the following membership:

F. J. Buckley, *Chairperson*

R. J. Abbott
W. R. Adrion
T. Armbruster
R. L. Aurbach
W. F. Bangs
V. R. Basili
R. W. Bass
M. Ben-Menachem
L. Beltrachi
M. A. Branstad
W. C. Brantly
W. L. Bryan
D. W. Burt
H. C. Carney
C. L. Carpenter
J. Center
R. L. Chilausky
W. L. Chung
M. A. Cohn
C. M. Cooke
G. G. Cooke
J. D. Cooper
A. J. Cote
J. W. Cowan
S. G. Crawford
J. W. Currier
M. A. Daniels
G. Darling
J. A. Darling
C. Davis

J. T. Deignan
F. A. Denbrock
P. A. Denny
M. J. Devlin
J. V. Dinkey
F. M. Discenzo
A. Dniestrowski
D. C. Doty
H. B. Doyle
W. DuBlancia
R. H. Dunn
R. E. Dwyer
M. L. Eads
J. D. Earls
L. G. Egan, Jr
D. Eller
W. J. Ellis
B. W. Englar
R. J. Felker
K. F. Fisher
J. J. Forman
J. Forster
S. J. Foster
C. R. Fredrick
M. Frimer
L. Gagner
M. Galinier
L. B. Gardner
D. Gelperin
E. W. Gibbs

J. L. Gildersleeve
S. A. Gloss-Soler
A. L. Goel
R. W. Graves
J. J. Greene
K. Greene
J. Greenhill
J. W. Grigsby
H. M. Grove
D. A. Gustafson
R. T. Gustin
V. E. Haas
T. Hannan
D. A. Heath
J. J. Herbert
G. H. Heblinger
L. S. Heselton
G. Hokel
C. J. Hornback
S. Horvitz
P. Hung
M. Jennings
L. M. Johmann
L. V. Kaleda
R. Kessler
J. J. Klock
R. W. Kubica
T. M. Kurihara
J. W. Kyle
D. V. La Rosa

R. A. C. Lane
G. N. Larson
R. C. Lewis
F. C. Lim
A. J. Lindabury
G. S. Lindsay
M. Lipow
J. Long
A. C. Ma
A. J. Maher
A. K. Mahindru
H. Malec
W. A. Mandeville
B. Manny
P. C. Marcondes
P. C. Marriott
R. J. Martin
R. F. Martini
C. F. Martiny
J. A. McCall
M. P. McDonald
J. McKissick, Jr
D. C. McMann
B. Menkus
D. F. Meronek
E. F. Miller, Jr
G. S. Morris
G. T. Morun
W. G. Murch
B. Mutafelelja

J. Nebb	J. A. Ronback	J. E. Skeen, Jr	G. D. Tice, Jr
G. R. Neidhart	S. M. Rowan	R. L. Skelton	T. L. Tillmanns
W. J. Newsom	A. Rudeseal	J. C. Slucki	E. A. Ulbrich, Jr
P. C. Olsen	F. Salvia	M. P. Smith	D. L. Ulery
D. E. Peercy	R. San-Roman	W. Smith	D. Usechak
M. T. Perkins	C. Sanchez III	H. M. Sneed	R. L. Van Tilburg
D. J. Pfeiffer	R. E. Sandborgh	R. L. Spear	U. Voges
R. M. Poston	N. F. Schneidewind	E. A. Straker	A. Weigel
P. B. Powell	H. A. Shock, Jr	W. B. Strigel	M. L. Weisbein
R. P. Pritchett	R. Scholten	D. B. Tabor	B. B. White
S. J. Raddue	R. G. Schuppert	B. J. Taute	W. M. Wong
J. R. Rault	D. J. Schultz	E. F. Testa	W. Woo
L. K. Reed	E. P. Shaughnessy	R. H. Thayer	C. Wortz
D. J. Reifer	C. L. Shermer	J. R. Thompson	V. L. Wright
G. S. Robinson	D. S. Simkins	P. U. Thompson	J. C. Zolnowski

Special representatives to the Software Engineering Standards Subcommittee were as follows:

H. R. Berlack: Electronic Industry Association
N. C. Farr: Nuclear Power Engineering Committee,
 IEEE Power Engineering Society
A. Ferlan: American Society for Quality Control
S. R. Jarocki: EDP Auditors Association
J. Milandin: ANSI Z1
W. E. Perry: Data Processing Manufacturers Association
T. L. Regulinski: IEEE Reliability Society

The working group had the following members:

F. J. Buckley, *Chairperson*
R. J. Felker, *Co-Chairperson*

M. J. Berg	R. L. Evans	R. M. Poston
D. Boehm	C. Fan	H. Reeves
R. H. Brickley	N. Farr	B. J. Taute
R. L. Chilausky	E. L. Gibbs	E. F. Testa
G. G. Cooke	J. Gilbert	J. Thomas
S. G. Crawford	C. P. Hollocker	N. Thomas
J. T. Deignan	R. A. Kessler	D. Usechak
R. Dumas	J. J. Klock	N. P. Wilburn
J. Edwards	G. Pedrocchi	M. J. Wise
R. F. Ely, Jr	R. E. Pingleton	J. C. Zolnowski

Comments on this standard are welcomed and should be addressed to:
Secretary
IEEE Standards Board
345 East 47th Street
New York, NY 10017

At the time this standard was approved on June 14, 1984, the IEEE Standards Board had the following membership:

James H. Beall, *Chairman*   **John E. May,** *Vice Chairman*

Sava I. Sherr, *Secretary*

J. J. Archambault	Jay Forster	R. F. Lawrence
John T. Boettger	Daniel L. Goldberg	Donald T. Michael*
J. V. Bonucchi	Donald N. Heirman	John P. Riganati
Rene Castenschiold	Irvin N. Howell	Frank L. Rose
Edward Chelotti	Jack Kinn	Robert W. Seelbach
Edward J. Cohen	Joseph L. Koepfinger*	Jay A. Stewart
Len S. Corey	Irving Kolodny	Clifford O. Swanson
Donald C. Fleckenstein	George Konomos	W. B. Wilkens
		Charles J. Wylie

*Member emeritus

Contents

An American National Standard
IEEE Standard for
Software Quality Assurance Plans

1. Scope

The purpose of this standard is to provide uniform, minimum acceptable requirements for preparation and content of Software Quality Assurance Plans (SQAP).

In considering adoption of this standard, regulatory bodies should be aware that specific application of this standard may already be covered by one or more IEEE or ANSI standards documents relating to quality assurance, definitions, or other matters. It is not the purpose of IEEE Std 730 to supersede, revise or amend existing standards directed to specific industries or applications.

This standard applies to the development and maintenance of critical software; for example, where failure could impact safety or cause large financial or social losses. For non-critical software, or for software already developed, a subset of the requirements of this standard may be applied.

The existence of this standard should not be construed to prohibit additional content in a Software Quality Assurance Plan. An assessment should be made for the specific software product item to assure adequacy of coverage. Where this standard is invoked for a project engaged in producing several software items, the applicability of the standard should be specified for each of the software product items encompassed by the project.

2. Definition and Acronyms

2.1 Definition. The definition listed below establishes meaning in the context of this standard. Other definitions can be found in ANSI/IEEE Std 729-1983, IEEE Standard Glossary of Software Engineering Terminology, or latest revision thereof. For the purpose of this standard, the term *Software* includes documentation and data, and execution control statements (e.g., command files, Job Control Language, etc.).

quality assurance. A planned and systematic pattern of all actions necessary to provide adequate confidence that the item or product conforms to established technical requirements.

2.2 Acronyms. The following alphabetical contractions appear within the text of this standard:

CDR critical design review
PDR preliminary design review
SDD software design description
SQA software quality assurance
SQAP software quality assurance plan
SRR software requirements review
SRS software requirements specification
SVVP software verification and validation plan
SVVR software verification and validation report

3. Software Quality Assurance Plan

The organization responsible for Software Quality Assurance shall prepare a Software Quality Assurance Plan (also referred to as the Plan) that includes the sections listed below. The sections should be ordered in the described sequence. If there is no information pertinent to a section, the following shall appear below the section heading, *This section is not applicable to this plan*, together with the appropriate reasons for the exclusion.

(1) Purpose
(2) Reference Documents
(3) Management
(4) Documentation
(5) Standards, Practices, and Conventions
(6) Reviews and Audits
(7) Software Configuration Management
(8) Problem Reporting and Corrective Action
(9) Tools, Techniques, and Methodologies
(10) Code Control
(11) Media Control
(12) Supplier Control
(13) Records Collection, Maintenance, and Retention

Additional sections may be added at the end, as required. Some of the material may appear in other documents. If so, then reference to those documents should be made in the body of the plan.

This plan shall be authenticated by the chief operating officer of each unit of the organization having responsibilities defined within this plan.

Details for each outline paragraph are described in 3.1 through 3.13 of this standard.

3.1 Purpose (Section 1 of the Plan). This section shall delineate the specific purpose and scope of the particular Software Quality Assurance Plan (SQAP). It shall list the name(s) of the software product items covered by the SQAP and the intended use of the software.

3.2 Reference Documents (Section 2 of the Plan). This section shall provide a complete list of documents referenced elsewhere in the text of the plan.

3.3 Management (Section 3 of the Plan). This section shall describe the organization, tasks, and responsibilities.

3.3.1 Organization. This paragraph shall depict the organizational structure that influences the quality of the software. This shall include a description of each major element of the organization together with the delegated responsibilities. Organizational dependence or independence of the elements responsible for SQA from those responsible for software development and use shall be clearly described or depicted.

3.3.2 Tasks. This paragraph shall describe the tasks associated with that portion of the software life cycle covered by this plan with special emphasis on software quality assurance activities. The sequence of the tasks shall be indicated.

3.3.3 Responsibilities. This paragraph shall identify the specific organizational elements responsible for each task.

3.4 Documentation (Section 4 of the Plan).
3.4.1 Purpose. This section shall:
(1) Identify the documentation governing the development, verification and validation, use, and maintenance of the software.

(2) State how the documents are to be checked for adequacy. The statement shall include identification of the review or audit by which the adequacy of each document shall be confirmed, with reference to Section 6 of the Plan.

3.4.2 Minimum Documentation Requirements. To ensure that the implementation of the software satisfies the requirements, the following documentation is required as a minimum:

3.4.2.1 *Software Requirements Specification* (SRS). The SRS shall clearly and precisely describe each of the essential requirements (functions, performances, design constraints, and attributes) of the software and the external interfaces. Each requirement shall be defined such that its achievement is capable of being objectively verified and validated by a prescribed method, for example, inspection, analysis, demonstration, or test.

3.4.2.2 *Software Design Description* (SDD). The SDD shall describe the major components of the software design including data bases and internal interfaces. An expansion of this description shall be included to describe each subcomponent of the major components.

3.4.2.3 *Software Verification and Validation Plan* (SVVP). The SVVP shall describe the methods (for example, inspection, analysis, demonstration, or test) to be used:
(1) To verify that:
(a) The requirements in the SRS are implemented in the design expressed in the SDD.
(b) The design expressed in the SDD is implemented in the code.

(2) To validate that the code, when executed, complies with the requirements expressed in the SRS.

3.4.2.4 *Software Verification and Validation Report* (SVVR). The SVVR shall describe the results of the execution of the SVVP. This shall include the results of all reviews, audits, and tests required by the SQA plan.

3.4.2.5 *User Documentation.* The User Documentation (e.g., manual, guide, etc.) shall specify and describe the required data and control inputs, input sequences, options, program limitations and other activities/items necessary for successful execution of the software. All error messages shall be identified and corrective actions described. A method of describing user-identified errors/problems to the developer/owner of the software shall be described. (Embedded software that has no direct user interaction has no need for User Documentation and is therefore exempted from this requirement.)

3.4.3 Other. Other documentation may include the following:

(1) Software Development Plan

(2) Software Configuration Management Plan

(3) Standards and Procedures Manual

3.5 Standards, Practices, and Conventions (Section 5 of the Plan).

3.5.1 Purpose. This section shall:

(1) Identify the standards, practices, and conventions to be applied.

(2) State how compliance with these items is to be monitored and assured.

3.5.2 Content. The subjects covered shall include the basic technical, design, and programming activities involved, such as documentation naming and coding, programming languages, and unit testing. As a minimum the following information shall be provided:

(1) Documentation standards

(2) Logic structure standards

(3) Coding standards

(4) Commentary standards

3.6 Review and Audits (Section 6 of the Plan).

3.6.1 Purpose. This section shall:

(1) Define the technical and managerial reviews and audits to be conducted.

(2) State how the reviews and audits are to be accomplished.

3.6.2 Minimum Requirements. As a minimum, the following reviews shall be conducted:

3.6.2.1 *Software Requirements Review* (SRR). The SRR is held to ensure the adequacy of the requirements stated in the Software Requirements Specification.

3.6.2.2 *Preliminary Design Review* (PDR). The PDR is held to evaluate the technical adequacy of the preliminary design of the software as depicted in a preliminary version of the Software Design Description.

3.6.2.3 *Critical Design Review* (CDR). The CDR is held to determine the acceptability of the detailed software designs as depicted in the Software Design Description in satisfying the requirements of the Software Requirements Specification.

3.6.2.4 *Software Verification and Validation Review.* The Software Verification and Validation Review is held to evaluate the adequacy and completeness of the verification and validation methods defined in the SVVP.

3.6.2.5 *Functional Audit.* This audit is held prior to the software delivery to verify that all requirements specified in the Software Requirements Specifications have been met.

3.6.2.6 *Physical Audit.* This audit is held to verify that the software and its documentation are internally consistent and are ready for delivery.

3.6.2.7 *In-Process Audits.* In-process audits of a sample of the design are held to verify consistency of the design, including:

(1) Code versus design documentation

(2) Interface specifications (hardware and software)

(3) Design implementations versus functional requirements

(4) Functional requirements versus test descriptions

3.6.2.8 *Managerial Reviews.* These reviews are held periodically to assess the execution of this plan. These reviews shall be held by an organizational element independent of the unit being audited, or by a qualified third party.

3.7 Software Configuration Management (Section 7 of the Plan). This section shall document the methods to be used for identifying the software product items, controlling and implementing changes, and recording and reporting change implementation status. This documentation shall either be provided explicitly in this section or by reference to an existing software configuration management plan.

3.8 Problem Reporting and Corrective Action (Section 8 of the Plan).
This section shall:

(1) Describe the practices and procedures to be followed for reporting, tracking, and resolving software problems.

(2) State the specific organizational responsibilities concerned with their implementation.

3.9 Tools, Techniques, and Methodologies (Section 9 of the Plan). This section shall identify the special software tools, techniques, and methodologies employed on the specific project that support Quality Assurance, state their purposes, and describe their use.

3.10 Code Control (Section 10 of the Plan). This section shall define the methods and facilities used to maintain and store controlled versions of identified software. This may be implemented in conjunction with a Computer Program Library.

3.11 Media Control (Section 11 of the Plan). This section shall state the methods and facilities to be used to protect computer program physical media from unauthorized access or inadvertent damage or degradation.

3.12 Supplier Control (Section 12 of the Plan). This section shall state the provisions for assuring that vendor-provided and subcontractor-developed software meets established technical requirements. As a minimum the supplier shall be required to prepare and implement a Software Quality Assurance Plan in accordance with this standard.

3.13 Records Collection, Maintenance and Retention (Section 13 of the Plan). This section shall identify the SQA documentation to be retained, shall state the methods and facilities to be used to assemble, safeguard and maintain this documentation and shall designate the retention period.

An American National Standard

IEEE Standard for
Software Configuration Management Plans

828

Sponsor

**Software Engineering Technical Committee
of the
IEEE Computer Society**

Approved June 23, 1983

IEEE Standards Board

Approved December 17, 1984

American National Standards Institute

Foreword

(This Foreword is not a part of ANSI/IEEE Std 828-1983, IEEE Standard for Software Configuration Management Plans.)

Software Configuration Management (SCM) is a formal engineering discipline which provides software developers and users with the methods and tools to identify the software developed, establish baselines, control changes to these baselines, record and track status, and audit the product. SCM is the means through which the integrity and continuity of the software product are recorded, communicated, and controlled. The application of SCM, together with Hardware Configuration Management and overall Systems Configuration Management, benefits all phases of the life cycle of a system containing software components and is a matter of good engineering practice. Without SCM, the reliability and the quality of the software cannot be assured.

This standard assists in the preparation of SCM plans for all environments; for example, large-scale ADP systems, embedded computer systems, control processors, etc, and provides a standard against which such plans can be prepared and assessed. It is directed toward the development and maintenance of all software, including critical software, that is, software whose failure could impact safety or cause large financial or social losses.

There are three groups served by this standard: the users, the developers, and the public.

(1) It aids the users in obtaining and supporting a software product consistent with the users' evolving needs. It assists the users in obtaining a reasonable degree of confidence that the product is in the process of acquiring required attributes as the software is being developed and maintained.

(2) It aids the developers by providing an established standard against which a cost-effective solution to SCM needs can be planned and measured throughout the applicable portions of the software life cycle.

(3) It aids the public by enhancing the likelihood that a software product will perform as expected. The public has legal rights which preclude haphazard control of software development and maintenance. At some later date, the users and developers may be required to show that they acted in a reasonable and prudent manner to ensure that adequate controls were applied.

This standard is consistent with ANSI/IEEE Std 730-1981, IEEE Standard for Software Quality Assurance Plans and IEEE Std 729-1983, IEEE Standard Glossary of Software Engineering Terminology. This standard may be applied in conjunction with those standards, or independently.

This standard was prepared by a working group of the Software Engineering Subcommittee of the Technical Committee on Software Engineering of the IEEE Computer Society. The working group had the following members:

R. Frederick, *Chairman*

H. R. Berlack	J. Granton	J. Postak
E. Bersoff	N. Hill	R. M. Poston
F. J. Buckley	J. H. Johnston	P. B. Powell
R. Clingan	C. Kolb	S. Siegel
D. Dorazio	T. M. Kurihara	L. Starbuck
R. Evans	W. A. Mandeville	B. Taute
A. Ets	J. Miguel	A. Terentiev
J. J. Forman	J. Neilson	N. Thomas
J. Fonj	D. Paster	R. L. Van Tilburg
N. P. Ginex	R. Phillips	J. Williamson

At the time the Software Engineering Standards Subcommittee approved the standard, it had the following members:

F. J. Buckley, *Chairman*

Special representatives to the Software Engineering Standards Subcommittee were:

At the time the IEEE Standards Board approved this standard on June 23, 1983, it had the following members:

James H. Beall, *Chairman*   **Edward Chelotti,** *Vice Chairman*

Sava I. Sherr, *Secretary*

*Member emeritus

Contents

An American National Standard
IEEE Standard for
Software Configuration Management Plans

Note

In considering adoption of this standard, regulatory bodies should be aware that specific application of this standard may already be covered by one or more IEEE or ANSI standards documents relating to quality assurance, definitions, or other matters. It is not the purpose of IEEE Std 828-1983 to supersede, revise, or amend existing standards directed to specific industries or applications.

1. Scope and References

1.1 Scope. This standard provides minimum requirements for preparation and content of Software Configuration Management (SCM) Plans. SCM Plans document the methods to be used for identifying software product items, controlling and implementing changes, and recording and reporting change implementation status.

This standard applies to the entire life cycle of critical software; for example, where failure could impact safety or cause large financial or social losses. For noncritical software, or for software already developed, a subset of the requirements may be applied.

This standard identifies those essential items that shall appear in all Software Configuration Management Plans. In addition to these items, the users of this standard are encouraged to incorporate additional items into the plan, as appropriate, to satisfy unique configuration management needs, or to modify the contents of specific sections to fully describe the scope and magnitude of the software configuration management effort. Where this standard is invoked for a project engaged in producing several software items, the applicability of the standard shall be specified for each of the software product items encompassed by the project.

Examples are incorporated into the text of this standard to enhance clarity and to promote understanding. Examples are either explicitly identified as such, or can be recognized by the use of the verb *may*. Examples shall not be construed as mandatory implementations.

NOTE: For application to nuclear power generating stations, see IEEE Std 1033-1985, IEEE Recommended Practice for Application of IEEE Std 828 to Nuclear Power Generating Stations [4].[1]

1.2 References. The standards listed here should be considered when applying this standard. The latest revisions shall apply.

[1] ANSI/IEEE Std 730-1981, IEEE Standard for Software Quality Assurance Plans.[2]

[2] IEEE Std 729-1983, IEEE Standard Glossary of Software Engineering Terminology.

[3] IEEE Std 829-1983, IEEE Standard for Software Test Documentation.

[4] IEEE Std 1033-1985, IEEE Recommended Practice for Application of IEEE Standard 828 to Nuclear Power Generating Stations.

2. Definitions and Acronyms

2.1 Definitions. The definition listed here establishes meaning in the context of this standard. Other definitions can be found in IEEE Std 729-1983 [2]. See specifically: **baseline, configuration item, configuration management, configuration control, configuration control board, configuration audit, configuration identification, configuration status accounting,** and **software library.**

interface control. The process of: (1) Identifying all functional and physical characteristics relevant to the interfacing of two or more configuration items provided by one or more organizations. (2) Ensuring that proposed changes to these characteristics are evaluated and approved prior to implementation.

2.2 Acronyms. The following acronyms are referred to within the text of this standard:

CCB   Configuration Control Board
SCM   Software Configuration Management
SCMP   Software Configuration Management Plan

---

[1] The numbers in brackets correspond to references in 1.2.

[2] ANSI standards are available from the Sales Department, American National Standards Institute, 1430 Broadway, New York, NY 10018.

3. Software Configuration Management Plans

The organization or person responsible for Software Configuration Management shall prepare a Software Configuration Management Plan (hereafter referred to as the Plan) that includes the sections and subsections listed below. The sections and subsections shall be ordered in the described sequence (if there is no information pertinent to a section or subsection, the following information shall appear below the section or subsection heading: **There is no pertinent information for this section** together with the appropriate reasons for the exclusion).

(1) Introduction
    (a) Purpose
    (b) Scope
    (c) Definitions and acronyms
    (d) References
(2) Management
    (a) Organization
    (b) SCM responsibilities
    (c) Interface control
    (d) SCMP implementation
    (e) Applicable policies, directives and procedures
(3) SCM activities
    (a) Configuration identification
    (b) Configuration control
    (c) Configuration status accounting
    (d) Audits and reviews
(4) Tools, techniques, and methodologies
(5) Supplier control
(6) Records collection and retention

Additional sections may be added at the end, as required. Some of the material may appear in other documents. If so, reference to those documents shall be made in the body of the plan.

The cover page of the plan shall identify the plan and the project to which the plan pertains. As a minimum, the plan shall be signed by the chief operating-officer of each unit having responsibilities defined within the SCMP.

Detailed requirements for each portion of the Plan are described in 3.1 through 3.6 of this standard.

3.1 Introduction (Section 1 of the Plan). This section shall provide an overview of the plan.

3.1.1 Purpose (1.1 of the Plan). This subsection shall delineate the specific purpose of the particular Software Configuration Management Plan.

3.1.2 Scope (1.2 of the Plan). This subsection shall identify the software items to be produced and used, the organizations, the activities, and the phases of the software life cycle to which the plan applies.

3.1.3 Definitions and Acronyms (1.3 of the Plan). This subsection shall define or provide a reference to the definitions of all terms and acronyms required to properly interpret the SCMP.

3.1.4 References (1.4 of the Plan). This subsection shall:

(1) Provide a complete list of all documents referenced elsewhere in the SCMP.

(2) Identify each document by title, report number, if applicable, date, and publishing organization.

(3) Specify the sources from which the referenced documents can be obtained.

3.2 Management (Section 2 of the Plan). This section shall describe the organization, and associated responsibilities.

3.2.1 Organization (2.1 of the Plan). This subsection shall describe the organizational structure that influences the configuration management of the software during the development and the operation and maintenance phases. This shall:

(1) Describe each major element of the organization together with the delegated responsibilities. Organizational dependence or independence of the elements responsible for SCM from those responsible for software development and use shall be clearly described or depicted.

(2) Include an organizational chart or list for the project which illustrates the structure for program/project/system management.

(3) Describe the organization responsible for SCM during the operation and maintenance phase.

(4) Describe the interface between the developing organization and the using organization, if any, with particular emphasis on the transfer of SCM functions in the operation and maintenance phase.

(5) Specifically cover the organizational relationships with the Configuration Control Board

in the development and the operation, and maintenance phases.

3.2.2 SCM Responsibilities (2.2 of the Plan). This subsection shall describe:

(1) The organizational responsibilities for each SCM task; for example, identification, control, status accounting, and reviews and audits.

(2) The relationships with software quality-assurance, software development, and other functional organizations required to ensure delivery of the approved final product configuration.

(3) The responsibilities of the users and developer/maintenance activity in the review, audit, and approval process during each phase of the life cycle indicated in 1.2 of the Plan.

(4) Any SCM responsibilities of the representatives from each organization participating in the product development.

(5) The overall responsibility of the Configuration Control Board.

(6) Any unusual responsibilities such as special approval requirements necessary to meet SCM requirements.

3.2.3 Interface Control (2.3 of the Plan). This subsection shall describe the methods to be utilized to:

(1) Identify interface specifications and control documents.

(2) Process changes to released interface specifications and documents.

(3) Provide follow-up on action items scheduled to be accomplished on items pertaining to SCM.

(4) Maintain status of interface specifications and control documents.

(5) Control the interface between software and the hardware on which it is running.

3.2.4 SCMP Implementation (2.4 of the Plan). This subsection shall establish the major milestones for implementation of the SCMP.

Example milestones include the establishment of:

(1) The configuration control board

(2) Each configuration baseline

(3) Schedules and procedures for SCM reviews and audits

(4) Configuration management of related software development, test, and support tools

3.2.5 Applicable Policies, Directives, and Procedures (2.5 of the Plan). This subsection shall:

(1) Identify all applicable SCM policies, directives, and procedures which are to be implemented as part of this plan. The degree of implementation of each shall be stated

(2) Describe any SCM policies, directives, and procedures that are to be written and implemented for this project

Examples of material which may be covered by policies, directives, and procedures are:

(a) Identification of levels of software in a hierarchical tree

(b) Program and module naming conventions

(c) Version level designations

(d) Software product identification methods

(e) Identification of specifications, test plans and procedures, programming manuals, and other documents

(f) Media identification and file management identification

(g) Document release process

(h) Turnover or release of software products to a library function

(i) Processing of problem reports, change requests, and change orders

(j) Structure and operation of configuration control boards

(k) Release, and acceptance of software products

(l) Operation of software library systems to include methods of preparing, storing, and updating modules

(m) Auditing of SCM activities

(n) Problem report, change request or change order documentation requirements describing purpose and impact of a configuration change, or both

(o) Level of testing required prior to entry of software into configuration management

(p) Level of quality assurance; for example, verification against development standards, required prior to entry of software into configuration management

3.3 SCM Activities (Section 3 of the Plan). This section shall describe how the following requirements for SCM shall be satisfied:

(1) Configuration identification

(2) Configuration control

(3) Configuration status accounting and reporting

(4) Configuration audits and reviews

3.3.1 Configuration Identification (3.1 of the Plan). This subsection shall:

3.3.1.1 Identify the software project baselines (that is, the initial approved configuration identifications) and correlate them to the specific life-cycle phases defined in 1.2 of the Plan. For each baseline, the following shall be described:

3.3.1.1.1 The items which form each baseline (for example, software requirements specification, deliverable software, etc).

3.3.1.1.2 The review and approval events, and the acceptance criteria associated with establishing each baseline.

3.3.1.1.3 The users' and developers' participation in establishing baselines.

The following are example baselines which may be established as indicated:

(1) *Functional Baseline.* The agreement between the developers and the users that defines all the system level functions and the system test criteria.

(2) *Allocated Baseline.* The agreement between the developers and the users that identifies all the software requirements to include design constraints and user-required standards.

(3) *Product Baseline.* The agreement between the developer and the user that defines the exact version of the software product which is to be accepted. Elements of this baseline definition might include the following:

(a) Product name and nomenclature

(b) Product identification number

(c) For each new version release, the version release number, a description of the new changes, the change release vehicle, the changes to any support software, and the changes to the associated documentation

(d) Installation instructions

(e) Known faults and failures

(f) Software media and media identification

3.3.1.2 Delineate the project titling, labeling, numbering, and cataloging procedures for all software code and documentation.

As an example, for code:

3.3.1.2.1 The compilation date may be indicated as a part of the identification for each delivered module.

3.3.1.2.2 The sequence numbering of all source lines of code in a module may be structured so that future changes to any module can be properly noted.

3.3.2 Configuration Control (3.2 of the Plan). This subsection shall:

3.3.2.1 Describe the level of authority for change approval to be used in each of the life cycle phases identified in 1.2 of the Plan.

3.3.2.2 Define the methods to be used to process change proposals to established configurations. As a part of this, this section shall:

(1) Identify the routing of change proposals during each of the software life cycle phases identified in 1.2 of the Plan. This may be provided in chart form with narrative support.

(2) Describe the methods of implementing approved change proposals (to include changes in source and object code, and documentation).

(3) Describe the procedures for software library control including those procedures which provide for:

(a) Access control

(b) Read and write protection for applicable baselines

(c) Member protection

(d) Member identification

(e) Archive maintenance

(f) Change history

(g) Disaster recovery

(4) If patches must be used to change object code, describe the methods for identification and control

3.3.2.3 For each CCB and other change management bodies:

(1) Define the role of each; for example, change review authority

(2) Specify their authority and responsibility

(3) Identify the chairperson and the membership in the organizations, if the organizations have been formed

(4) State how the chairperson and the members (and alternates) are to be appointed, if the organizations have not yet been formed

(5) State the relationships of the developers and the users to the CCB(s)

3.3.2.4 State the methods to be used for configuration control of interfaces with programs/projects beyond the scope of this SCMP. If the software changes are required to be reviewed by other boards or teams prior to or in addition to the CCB(s), this subsection shall describe these boards (or teams, or both) and their relationship to the CCB(s) and to each other.

3.3.2.5 State the control procedures for associated special software products, such as nonreleased software, off-the-shelf software, user-furnished software, and in-house support software.

3.3.3 Configuration Status Accounting (3.3 of the Plan). This subsection shall:

(1) Delineate how information on the status of configuration items is to be collected, verified, stored, processed, and reported

(2) Identify the periodic reports to be provided, and their distribution

(3) State what dynamic inquiry capabilities, if any, are to be provided

(4) Describe the means to be used to implement any special status accounting requirements specified by the user

Some examples of information normally desired is as follows:

(a) Status of specifications

(b) Status of proposed changes

(c) Reports of approved changes

(d) Status of product versions or revisions

(e) Reports of the implementation of installed updates or releases

(f) Status of user-furnished property; for example, user-furnished operating systems

3.3.4 Audits and Reviews (3.4 of the Plan). This subsection shall:

(1) Define the SCM role in audits and reviews to be performed at specified points in the software life cycle defined in 1.2 of the SCMP

(2) Identify the configuration items to be covered at each of these audits and reviews

(3) State the procedures to be used for the identification and resolution of problems occurring during these audits and reviews

3.4 Tools, Techniques, and Methodologies (Section 4 of the Plan). This section shall identify, state the purposes, and describe (within the developers' scope of proprietary rights) the use of the specific software tools, techniques, and methodologies to be employed to support SCM on the specific project. This shall include the tools, techniques, and methodologies used to:

(1) Identify software media and media documentation

(2) Bring documentation and media under SCM control and formally release it to a user

As examples, it may:

(a) Provide a description of the tools, methodologies, and techniques to be used for source and object control within the software libraries, to include a description of the Database Management System, if used

(b) State how the software library tools, methodologies, and techniques are to be used to process software products for release

(3) Document the status of changes made to software and associated documentation. It shall further define the tools, methodologies, and techniques to be used to prepare reports for various levels of management, such as the project manager, CCB, SCM, and the user.

3.5 Supplier Control (Section 5 of the Plan). This section shall state the provisions for assuring that vendor-provided and subcontractor-developed software meet established SCM requirements. As a part of this, this section shall:

(1) Indicate the proposed methods for control of subcontractors and vendors insofar as it impacts on the execution of this SCMP

(2) Explain the methods to be used:

(a) To determine the SCM capability of subcontractors and vendors

(b) To monitor their adherence to the requirements of this SCMP

As a minimum, the supplier shall be required to prepare and implement a SCM plan in accordance with this standard.

3.6 Records Collection and Retention (Section 6 of the Plan). This section shall:

(1) Identify the SCM documentation to be retained

(2) State the methods and facilities to be used to assemble, safeguard, and maintain this documentation. As part of this, identify any off-site backup facilities to be used

(3) Designate the retention period

An American National Standard

IEEE Standard for
Software Test Documentation

829

Sponsor

**Software Engineering Technical Committee
of the
IEEE Computer Society**

Approved December 3, 1982

IEEE Standards Board

Approved August 19, 1983

American National Standards Institute

Foreword

(This Foreword is not a part of ANSI/IEEE Std 829-1983, IEEE Standard for Software Test Documentation.)

Purpose

The purpose of this standard is to describe a set of basic software test documents. A standardized test document can facilitate communication by providing a common *frame of reference* (for example, a customer and a supplier have the same definition for a test plan). The content definition of a standardized test document can serve as a completeness checklist for the associated testing process. A standardized set can also provide a baseline for the evaluation of current test documentation practices. In many organizations, the use of these documents significantly increases the manageability of testing. Increased manageability results from the greatly increased visibility of each phase of the testing process.

This standard specifies the form and content of individual test documents. It does not specify the required set of test documents. It is assumed that the required set of test documents will be specified when the standard is applied. Appendix B contains an example of such a set specification.

Overview

The documents outlined in this standard cover test planning, test specification, and test reporting.

The test plan prescribes the scope, approach, resources, and schedule of the testing activities. It identifies the items to be tested, the features to be tested, the testing tasks to be performed, the personnel responsible for each task, and the risks associated with the plan.

Test specification is covered by three document types:

(1) A test-design specification refines the test approach and identifies the features to be covered by the design and its associated tests. It also identifies the test cases and test procedures, if any, required to accomplish the testing and specifies the feature pass/fail criteria.

(2) A test-case specification documents the actual values used for input along with the anticipated outputs. A test case also identifies any constraints on the test procedures resulting from use of that specific test case. Test cases are separated from test designs to allow for use in more than one design and to allow for reuse in other situations.

(3) A test procedure specification identifies all steps required to operate the system and exercise the specified test cases in order to implement the associated test design. Test procedures are separated from test-design specifications as they are intended to be followed step by step and should not have extraneous detail.

Test reporting is covered by four document types:

(1) A test item transmittal report identifies the test items being transmitted for testing in the event that separate development and test groups are involved or in the event that a formal beginning of test execution is desired.

(2) A test log is used by the test team to record what occurred during test execution.

(3) A test incident report describes any event that occurs during the test execution which requires further investigation.

(4) A test summary report summarizes the testing activities associated with one or more test-design specifications.

Figure 1 shows the relationships of these documents to one another as they are developed and to the testing process they document.

Terminology

The words *shall, must,* and the imperative form identify the mandatory material within this standard. The words *should* and *may* identify optional material.

Appendixes

The examples found in Appendix A are meant to clarify the intent of the document descriptions found in the standard. Some suggestions about implementing and using the standard are in Appendix B. Appendix C contains references to related test documentation standards. Appendix D contains references to testing-related documents of general interest which are not focused on test documentation.

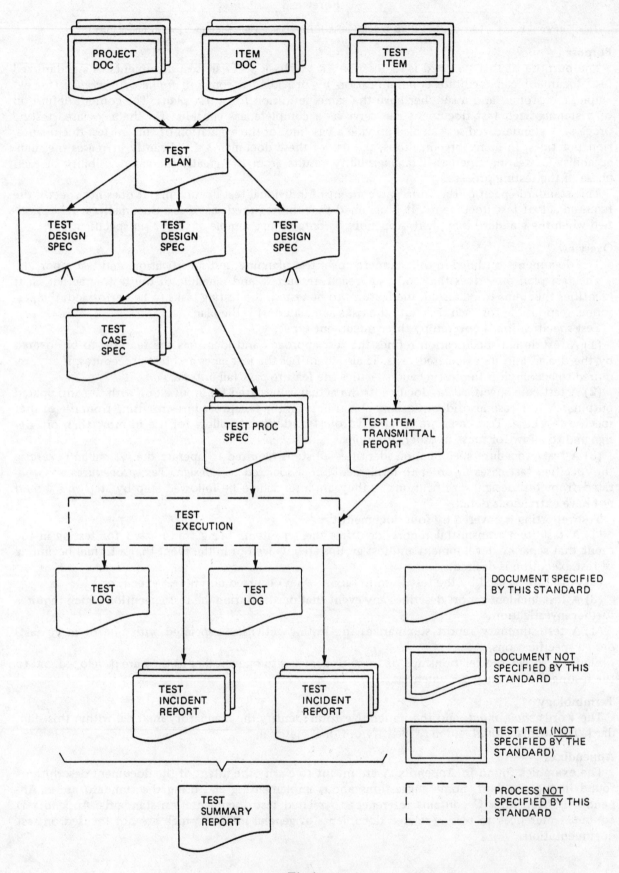

Fig 1
Relationship of Test Documents to Testing Process

Audience

The standard should be of interest to software users and software procurement personnel; to development, test, and maintenance personnel; to operations and acquisition support managers; to software quality assurance personnel and auditors; and to participants in the legal system.

History

The development of this standard began from discussions within the Software Engineering Standards Subcommittee in 1977. Some initial work was done by a group including Joan Bateman, Leonard Birns, Herb Hecht, and Bob Poston and resulted in an early draft outline. The project authorization request for this effort was approved by the IEEE Standards Board in May, 1980. Following authorization, a series of ten meetings which were held across the country from September, 1980 to May, 1982 produced the first draft submitted for balloting.

Suggestions for improvement of the standard will be welcome. They should be sent to:
Secretary
IEEE Standards Board
Institute of Electrical and Electronics Engineers
345 East 47th Street
New York, NY 10017.

At the time this standard was approved on December 3, 1982, the IEEE Standards Board had the following membership:

Irvin N. Howell, *Chairman*   **Edward Chelotti,** *Vice Chairman*

Sava I. Sherr, *Secretary*

G. Y. R. Allen	D. C. Fleckenstein	A. R. Parsons
J. J. Archambault	Jay Forster	J. P. Riganati
James H. Beall	Kurt Greene	Frank L. Rose
John T. Boettger	Joseph L. Koepfinger	Robert W. Seelbach
J. V. Bonucchi	Irving Kolodny	Jay A. Stewart
Edward J. Cohen	John E. May	Clifford O. Swanson
Len S. Corey	Donald T. Michael*	Robert E. Weiler

*Member emeritus

This standard was completed by a working group with the following members:

David Gelperin, *Chairman*

Rick Adrion	Tom Gilb	Art Pollari
Jules Aronson	Loretta Guarino	Robert Poston
Joan Bateman	John Hawthorne	Sam Redwine
Charlie Bates	Herb Hecht	Charles Schult
A. Birnbaum	Mike Hennell	David Schultz
Leonard Birns	Dan Hocking	Dennis Sharp
John Bowen	Mark Holthouse	Jerry Smith
Martha Branstad	Ray Houghton	Wayne Smith
Fletcher Buckley	Paul Howley	Joan Spalding
Douglas Burt	John Kalasky	Bob Stewart
Ian Burton	Jason Kazarian	S. L. Stewart
John Cain	Ed Kit	Sarah Swales
John Center	Denise Krauss	Barbara Taute
George Chapman	Joseph Krupinski	J. R. Taylor
Santosh Chokhani	Tom Kurihara	Rudolf Van Megen
Bruce Clay	Costa J. Labovites	David Vatsaas
D. L. Cooper	Paula Levinton	John Walter
Doc Craddock	Leo Lippman	Andrew Weigel
James Cridge	Alex Long	Jonathon Wexler
Patricia Daggett	Mable Love	Paul White
Bill Dupras	Ben Manny	Bruce Wilkins
Mary Eads	Albrecht Newmann	Harry Wilkinson
Sharon Freid	Bill Newsom	F. T. Woodall
Tom Frost	C. Donald Ostler	Fred Yonda
	Varsha Pai	

The standard was approved by the Software Engineering Standards Subcommittee of the IEEE Computer Society. At the time it approved this standard, the subcommittee had the following membership:

Fletcher J. Buckley, *Chairman*

Russell J. Abbott
A. Frank Ackerman
Leo Beltracchi
Richard L. Bernstein
Nestore G. Biasi
Dennis W. Bragg
Douglas W. Burt
Homer C. Carney
John Center
Won L. Chung
Anonio M. Cicu
Lori A. Clarke
Gilmore G. Cooke
A. J. Cote, Jr
Patricia W. Daggett
George Darling
B. Dasarathy
Noah S. Davids
James A. Dobbins
Mary L. Eads
John D. Earls
Leo G. Egan, Jr
John W. Fendrich
Dennis W. Fife
Joel J. Forman
M. Galinier
Forrest Karl Gardner
David Gelperin
Gary Gladden
Shirley A. Gloss-Soler
John J.Greene
Jack W. Grigsby
Robert M. Gross
David A. Gustafson

Russell T. Gustin
Thomas L. Hannan
Herbert Hecht
Leslie R. Heselton, III
Sam Horvitz
Paul Howley
Shuenn-Chang Hwang
Jim H. Ingram
John P. Kalasky
Laurel V. Kaleda
Thomas M. Kurihara
Domenic V. La-Rosa
Robert A. C. Lane
Gregory N. Larsen
Geoffrey R. Lewis
A. Lip Lim
G. S. Lindsay
Myron Lipow
William M. Lively
Marvin Lubofsky
Don Lundquist
Alan Cheuk-Wai Ma
Andy K. Mahindru
Philip C. Marriott
Mike McCollough
Belden Menkus
Edward F. Miller, Jr
G. Scott Morris
Gene T. Morun
Walter G. Murch
Jack Nebb
Geraldine Rajcula Neidhart
Michael A. Neighbors

Leon Osterweil
Donald J. Ostrom
William E. Perry
Donald J. Pfeiffer
Robert M. Poston
Patricia B. Powell
Farzad Raji
Jean Claude Rault
Samuel T. Redwine
T. L. Regulinski
William E. Riddle
Clarence W. Rutter, III
Norman F. Schneidewind
Antonia D. Schuman
Leonard W. Seagren
Wayne Smith
Harry M. Sneed
Lee Sprague
Edward A. Straker
Kou Chung Tai
Barbara J. Taute
George D. Tice, Jr
Terrence L. Tillmanns
William S. Turner, III
Edwin A. Ulbrich, Jr
Udo Voges
John P. Walter
Andrew H. Weigel
N. P. Wilburn
Martin Wong
David C. Wood
Ted Workman
Alfred W. Yonda
Peter F. Zoll

Special representatives to the Software Engineering Subcommittee were as follows:

William E. Perry, *DPMA*
Roy P. Pritchett, Jr, *EDP Auditors Association*
John Milandin, *ANSI Z1*

Contents

An American National Standard

IEEE Standard for Software Test Documentation

1. Scope

This standard describes a set of basic test documents which are associated with the dynamic aspects of software testing (that is, the execution of procedures and code). The standard defines the purpose, outline, and content of each basic document. While the documents described in the standard focus on dynamic testing, several of them may be applicable to other testing activities (for example, the test plan and test incident report may be used for design and code reviews).

The standard may be applied to commercial, scientific, or military software which runs on any digitial computer. Applicability is not restricted by the size, complexity, or criticality of the software. However, the standard does *not* specify any class of software to which it must be applied. The standard addresses the documentation of both initial development testing and the testing of subsequent software releases. For a particular software release, it may be applied to all phases of testing from module testing through user acceptance. However, since all of the basic test documents may not be useful in each test phase, the particular documents to be used in a phase are *not* specified. Each organization using the standard will need to specify the classes of software to which it applies and the specific documents required for a particular test phase.

The standard does *not* call for specific testing methodologies, approaches, techniques, facilities, or tools, and does *not* specify the documentation of their use. Additional test documentation may be required (for example, code inspection checklists and reports). The standard also does *not* imply or impose specific methodologies for documentation control, configuration management, or quality assurance. Additional documentation (for example, a quality assurance plan) may be needed depending on the particular methodologies used.

Within each standard document, the content of each section (that is, the text which covers the designated topics) may be tailored to the particular application and the particular testing phase. In addition to tailoring content, additional documents may be added to the basic set, additional sections may be added to any document and additional content to any section. It may be useful to organize some of the sections into subsections. Some or all of the contents of a section may be contained in another document which is then referenced. Each organization using the standard should specify additional content requirements and conventions in order to reflect their own particular methodologies, approaches, facilities, and tools for testing, documentation control, configuration management, and quality assurance.

The standard applies to documentation on electronic media as well as paper. Paper must be used for documents requiring approval signatures, unless the electronic documentation system has a secure approval annotation mechanism and that mechanism is used.

2. Definitions

This section contains key terms as they are used in the standard.

design level. The design decomposition of the software item (for example, system, subsystem, program, or module).

pass/fail criteria. Decision rules used to determine whether a software item or a software feature passes or fails a test.

software feature. A distinguishing characteristic of a software item (for example, performance, portability, or functionality).

software item. Source code, object code, job control code, control data, or a collection of these items.

test. (1) A set of one or more test cases, or

(2) A set of one or more test procedures, or

(3) A set of one or more test cases and procedures.

test case specification. A document specifying inputs, predicted results, and a set of execution conditions for a test item.

test design specification. A document specifying the details of the test approach for a software feature or combination of software features and identifying the associated tests.

test incident report. A document reporting on any event that occurs during the testing process which requires investigation.

test item. A software item which is an object of testing.

test item transmittal report. A document identifying test items. It contains current status and location information.

test log. A chronological record of relevant details about the execution of tests.

test plan. A document describing the scope, approach, resources, and schedule of intended testing activities. It identifies test items, the features to be tested, the testing tasks, who will do each task, and any risks requiring contingency planning.

test procedure specification. A document specifying a sequence of actions for the execution of a test.

test summary report. A document summarizing testing activities and results. It also contains an evaluation of the corresponding test items.

testing. The process of analyzing a software item to detect the differences between existing and required conditions (that is, bugs) and to evaluate the features of the software item.

3. Test Plan

3.1 Purpose. To prescribe the scope, approach, resources, and schedule of the testing activities. To identify the items being tested, the features to be tested, the testing tasks to be performed, the personnel responsible for each task, and the risks associated with this plan.

3.2 Outline. A test plan shall have the following structure:

1. Test-plan identifier
2. Introduction
3. Test items
4. Features to be tested
5. Features not to be tested
6. Approach
7. Item pass/fail criteria
8. Suspension criteria and resumption requirements
9. Test deliverables
10. Testing tasks
11. Environmental needs
12. Responsibilities
13. Staffing and training needs
14. Schedule
15. Risks and contingencies
16. Approvals

The sections shall be ordered in the specified sequence. Additional sections may be included immediately prior to *Approvals.* If some or all of the content of a section is in another document, then a reference to that material may be listed in place of the corresponding content. The referenced material must be attached to the test plan or available to users of the plan.

Details on the content of each section are contained in the following sections.

3.2.1 Test-Plan Identifier. Specify the unique identifier assigned to this test plan.

3.2.2 Introduction. Summarize the software items and software features to be tested. The need for each item and its history may be included.

References to the following documents, when they exist, are required in the highest-level test plan:

Project authorization

Project plan

Quality assurance plan

Configuration management plan

Relevant policies

Relevant standards

In multilevel test plans, each lower-level plan must reference the next higher-level plan.

3.2.3 Test Items. Identify the test items including their version/revision level. Also specify characteristics of their transmittal media which impact hardware requirements or indicate the need for logical or physical transformations before testing can begin (for example, programs must be transferred from tape to disk).

Supply references to the following item documentation, if it exists:

Requirements specification
Design specification
Users guide
Operations guide
Installation guide
Reference any incident reports relating to the test items.

Items which are to be specifically excluded from testing may be identified.

3.2.4 Features to be Tested. Identify all software features and combinations of software features to be tested. Identify the test-design specification associated with each feature and each combination of features.

3.2.5 Features Not to be Tested. Identify all features and significant combinations of features which will not be tested and the reasons.

3.2.6 Approach. Describe the overall approach to testing. For each major group of features or feature combinations, specify the approach which will ensure that these feature groups are adequately tested. Specify the major activities, techniques, and tools which are used to test the designated groups of features.

The approach should be described in sufficient detail to permit identification of the major testing tasks and estimation of the time required to do each one.

Specify the minimum degree of comprehensiveness desired. Identify the techniques which will be used to judge the comprehensiveness of the testing effort (for example, determining which statements have been executed at least once). Specify any additional completion criteria (for example, error frequency). The techniques to be used to trace requirements should be specified.

Identify significant constraints on testing such as test-item availability, testing-resource availability, and deadlines.

3.2.7 Item Pass/Fail Criteria. Specify the criteria to be used to determine whether each test item has passed or failed testing.

3.2.8 Suspension Criteria and Resumption Requirements. Specify the criteria used to suspend all or a portion of the testing activity on the test items associated with this plan. Specify the testing activities which must be repeated, when testing is resumed.

3.2.9 Test Deliverables. Identify the deliverable documents. The following documents should be included:

Test plan
Test design specifications
Test case specifications
Test procedure specifications
Test item transmittal reports
Test logs
Test incident reports
Test summary reports
Test input data and test output data should be identified as deliverables.

Test tools (for example, module drivers and stubs) may also be included.

3.2.10 Testing Tasks. Identify the set of tasks necessary to prepare for and perform testing. Identify all intertask dependencies and any special skills required.

3.2.11 Environmental Needs. Specify both the necessary and desired properties of the test environment. This specification should contain: the physical characteristics of the facilities including the hardware, the communications and system software, the mode of usage (for example, stand-alone), and any other software or supplies needed to support the test. Also specify the level of security which must be provided for the test facilities, system software, and proprietary components such as software, data, and hardware.

Identify special test tools needed. Identify any other testing needs (for example, publications or office space). Identify the source for all needs which are not currently available to the test group.

3.2.12 Responsibilities. Identify the groups responsible for managing, designing, preparing, executing, witnessing, checking, and resolving. In addition, identify the groups responsible for providing the test items identified in 3.2.3 and the environmental needs identified in 3.2.11.

These groups may include the developers, testers, operations staff, user representatives, technical support staff, data administration staff, and quality support staff.

3.2.13 Staffing and Training Needs. Specify test staffing needs by skill level. Identify training options for providing necessary skills.

3.2.14 Schedule. Include test milestones identified in the Software Project Schedule as well as all item transmittal events.

Define any additional test milestones needed. Estimate the time required to do each testing task. Specify the schedule for each testing task and test milestone. For each testing resource (that is, facilities, tools, and staff), specify its periods of use.

3.2.15 Risks and Contingencies. Identify the high-risk assumptions of the test plan. Specify contingency plans for each (for example, delayed delivery of test items might require increased night shift scheduling to meet the delivery date).

3.2.16 Approvals. Specify the names and titles of all persons who must approve this plan. Provide space for the signatures and dates.

4. Test-Design Specification

4.1 Purpose. To specify refinements of the test approach and to identify the features to be tested by this design and its associated tests.

4.2 Outline. A test-design specification shall have the following structure:

(1) Test-design-specification identifier
(2) Features to be tested
(3) Approach refinements
(4) Test identification
(5) Feature pass/fail criteria

The sections shall be ordered in the specified sequence. Additional sections may be included at the end. If some or all of the content of a section is in another document, then a reference to that material may be listed in place of the corresponding content. The referenced material must be attached to the test-design specification or available to users of the design specification.

Details on the content of each section are contained in the following sections.

4.2.1 Test-Design-Specification Identifier. Specify the unique identifier assigned to this test-design specification. Supply a reference to the associated test plan, if it exists.

4.2.2 Features to be Tested. Identify the test items and describe the features and combinations of features which are the object of this design specification. Other features may be exercised, but need not be identified.

For each feature or feature combination, a reference to its associated requirements in the item requirement specification or design description should be included.

4.2.3 Approach Refinements. Specify refinements to the approach described in the test plan. Include specific test techniques to be used. The method of analyzing test results should be identified (for example, comparator programs or visual inspection).

Specify the results of any analysis which provides a rationale for test-case selection. For example, one might specify conditions which permit a determination of error tolerance (for example, those conditions which distinguish valid inputs from invalid inputs).

Summarize the common attributes of any test cases. This may include input constraints that must be true for every input in the set of associated test cases, any shared environmental needs, and any shared special procedural requirements, and any shared case dependencies.

4.2.4 Test Identification. List the identifier and a brief description of each test case associated with this design. A particular test case may be identified in more than one test design specification. List the identifier and a brief description of each procedure associated with this test-design specification.

4.2.5 Feature Pass/Fail Criteria. Specify the criteria to be used to determine whether the feature or feature combination has passed or failed.

5. Test-Case Specification

5.1 Purpose. To define a test case identified by a test-design specification.

5.2 Outline. A test-case specification shall have the following structure:

(1) Test-case-specification identifier
(2) Test items
(3) Input specifications
(4) Output specifications
(5) Environmental needs
(6) Special procedural requirements
(7) Intercase dependencies

The sections shall be ordered in the specified sequence. Additional sections may be included at the end. If some or all of the content of a section is in another document, then a reference to that material may be listed in place of the corresponding content. The referenced material must be attached to the test-case specification or available to users of the case specification.

Since a test case may be referenced by several test-design specifications used by different groups over a long time period, enough specific information must be included in the test-case specification to permit reuse.

Details on the content of each section are contained in the following sections.

5.2.1 Test-Case-Specification Identifier. Specify the unique identifier assigned to this test-case specification.

5.2.2 Test Items. Identify and briefly describe the items and features to be exercised by this test case.

For each item, consider supplying references to the following item documentation.

(1) Requirements specification
(2) Design specification
(3) Users guide
(4) Operations guide
(5) Installation guide

5.2.3 Input Specifications. Specify each input required to execute the test case. Some of the inputs will be specified by value (with tolerances where appropriate), while others, such as constant tables or transaction files, will be specified by name. Identify all appropriate data bases, files, terminal messages, memory resident areas, and values passed by the operating system.

Specify all required relationships between inputs (for example, timing).

5.2.4 Output Specifications. Specify all of the outputs and features (for example, response time) required of the test items. Provide the exact value (with tolerances where appropriate) for each required output or feature.

5.2.5 Environmental Needs.

5.2.5.1 Hardware. Specify the characteristics and configurations of the hardware required to execute this test case (for example, 132 character × 24 line CRT).

5.2.5.2 Software. Specify the system and application software required to execute this test case. This may include system software such as operating systems, compilers, simulators, and test tools. In addition, the test item may interact with application software.

5.2.5.3 Other. Specify any other requirements such as unique facility needs or specially trained personnel.

5.2.6 Special Procedural Requirements. Describe any special constraints on the test procedures which execute this test case. These constraints may involve special set up, operator intervention, output determination procedures, and special wrap up.

5.2.7 Intercase Dependencies. List the identifiers of test cases which must be executed prior to this test case. Summarize the nature of the dependencies.

6. Test-Procedure Specification

6.1 Purpose. To specify the steps for executing a set of test cases or, more generally, the steps used to analyze a software item in order to evaluate a set of features.

6.2 Outline. A test-procedure specification shall have the following structure:

(1) Test-procedure-specification identifier
(2) Purpose
(3) Special requirements
(4) Procedure steps

The sections shall be ordered in the specified sequence. Additional sections, if required, may be included at the end. If some or all of the content of a section is in another document, then a reference to that material may be listed in place of the corresponding content. The referenced material must be attached to the test-procedure specification or available to users of the procedure specification.

Details on the content of each section are contained in the following sections.

6.2.1 Test-Procedure-Specification Identifier. Specify the unique identifier assigned to this test-procedure specification. Supply a reference to the associated test-design specification.

6.2.2 Purpose. Describe the purpose of this procedure. If this procedure executes any test cases, provide a reference for each of them.

In addition, provide references to relevant sections of the test item documentation (for example, references to usage procedures).

6.2.3 Special Requirements. Identify any special requirements that are necessary for the execution of this procedure. These may include prerequisite procedures, special skills requirements, and special environmental requirements.

6.2.4 Procedure Steps. Include the following steps as applicable:

6.2.4.1 Log. Describe any special methods or formats for logging the results of test execution, the incidents observed, and any other events pertinent to the test (see Test Log, Section 8 and Test Incident Report, Section 9).

6.2.4.2 Set Up. Describe the sequence of actions necessary to prepare for execution of the procedure.

6.2.4.3 Start. Describe the actions necessary to begin execution of the procedure.

6.2.4.4 Proceed. Describe any actions necessary during execution of the procedure.

6.2.4.5 Measure. Describe how the test

measurements will be made (for example, describe how remote terminal response time is to be measured using a network simulator).

6.2.4.6 Shut Down. Describe the actions necessary to suspend testing, when unscheduled events dictate.

6.2.4.7 Restart. Identify any procedural restart points and describe the actions necessary to restart the procedure at each of these points.

6.2.4.8 Stop. Describe the actions necessary to bring execution to an orderly halt.

6.2.4.9 Wrap Up. Describe the actions necessary to restore the environment.

6.2.4.10 Contingencies. Describe the actions necessary to deal with anomolous events which may occur during execution.

7. Test-Item Transmittal Report

7.1 Purpose. To identify the test items being transmitted for testing. It includes the person responsible for each item, its physical location, and its status. Any variations from the current item requirements and designs are noted in this report.

7.2 Outline. A test-item transmittal report shall have the following structure:

(1) Transmittal-report identifier
(2) Transmitted items
(3) Location
(4) Status
(5) Approvals

The sections shall be ordered in the specified sequence. Additional sections may be included just prior to *Approvals*. If some or all of the content of a section is in another document, then a reference to that material may be listed in place of the corresponding content. The referenced material must be attached to the test-item transmittal report or available to users of the transmittal report.

Details on the content of each section are contained in the following sections.

7.2.1 Transmittal-Report Identifier. Specify the unique identifier assigned to this test-item transmittal report.

7.2.2 Transmitted Items. Identify the test items being transmitted, including their version/revision level. Supply references to the item documentation and the test plan relating to the transmitted items. Indicate the people responsible for the transmitted items.

7.2.3 Location. Identify the location of the transmitted items. Identify the media that contain the items being transmitted. When appropriate, indicate how specific media are labeled or identified.

7.2.4 Status. Describe the status of the test items being transmitted. Include deviations from the item documentation, from previous transmittals of these items, and from the test plan. List the incident reports which are expected to be resolved by the transmitted items. Indicate if there are pending modifications to item documentation which may affect the items listed in this transmittal report.

7.2.5 Approvals. Specify the names and titles of all persons who must approve this transmittal. Provide space for the signatures and dates.

8. Test Log

8.1 Purpose. To provide a chronological record of relevant details about the execution of tests.

8.2 Outline. A test log shall have the following structure:

(1) Test log identifier
(2) Description
(3) Activity and event entries

The sections shall be ordered in the specified sequence. Additional sections may be included at the end. If some or all of the content of a section is in another document, then a reference to that material may be listed in place of the corresponding content. The referenced material must be attached to the test log or available to users of the log.

Details on the content of each section are contained in the following sections.

8.2.1 Test-Log Identifier. Specify the unique identifier assigned to this test log.

8.2.2 Description. Information which applies to all entries in the log except as specifically noted in a log entry should be included here. The following information should be considered.

(1) Identify the items being tested including their version/revision levels. For each of these items, supply a reference to its transmittal report, if it exists.

(2) Identify the attributes of the environments in which the testing is conducted. Include facility identification, hardware being used (for example, amount of memory being

used, CPU model number, and number and model of tape drives, and/or mass storage devices), system software used, and resources available such as the amount of memory available.

8.2.3 Activity and Event Entries. For each event, including the beginning and end of activities, record the occurrence date and time along with the identity of the author.

The following information should be considered:

8.2.3.1 Execution Description. Record the identifier of the test procedure being executed and supply a reference to its specification. Record all personnel present during the execution including testers, operators, and observers. Also indicate the function of each individual.

8.2.3.2 Procedure Results. For each execution, record the visually observable results (for example, error messages generated, aborts, and requests for operator action). Also record the location of any output (for example, reel number). Record the successful or unsuccessful execution of the test.

8.2.3.3 Environmental Information. Record any environmental conditions specific to this entry (for example, hardware substitutions).

8.2.3.4 Anomalous Events. Record what happened before and after an unexpected event occurred (for example, *A summary display was requested and the correct screen displayed, but response seemed unusually long. A repetition produced the same prolonged response*). Record circumstances surrounding the inability to begin execution of a test procedure or failure to complete a test procedure (for example, a power failure or system software problem).

8.2.3.5 Incident-Report Identifiers. Record the identifier of each test-incident report, whenever one is generated.

9. Test-Incident Report

9.1 Purpose. To document any event that occurs during the testing process which requires investigation.

9.2 Outline. A test-incident report shall have the following structure:

(1) Test-incident-report identifier
(2) Summary

(3) Incident description
(4) Impact

The sections shall be ordered in the specified sequence. Additional sections may be included at the end. If some or all of the content of a section is in another document, then a reference to that material may be listed in place of the corresponding content. The referenced material must be attached to the test-incident report or available to users of the incident report.

Details on the content of each section are contained in the following sections.

9.2.1 Test-Incident-Report Identifier. Specify the unique identifier assigned to this test incident report.

9.2.2 Summary. Summarize the incident. Identify the test items involved indicating their version/revision level. References to the appropriate test-procedure specification, test-case specification, and test log should be supplied.

9.2.3 Incident Description. Provide a description of the incident. This description should include the following items:

Inputs
Expected results
Actual results
Anomalies
Date and time
Procedure step
Environment
Attempts to repeat
Testers
Observers

Related activities and observations that may help to isolate and correct the cause of the incident should be included. For example, describe any test-case executions that might have a bearing on this particular incident and any variations from the published test procedure.

9.2.4 Impact. If known, indicate what impact this incident will have on test plans, test-design specifications, test-procedure specifications, or test-case specifications.

10. Test-Summary Report

10.1 Purpose. To summarize the results of the designated testing activities and to provide evaluations based on these results.

10.2 Outline. A test-summary report shall have the following structure:

(1) Test-summary-report identifier
(2) Summary
(3) Variances
(4) Comprehensive assessment
(5) Summary of results
(6) Evaluation
(7) Summary of activities
(8) Approvals

The sections shall be ordered in the specified sequence. Additional sections may be included just prior to *Approvals.* If some or all of the content of a section is in another document, then a reference to that material may be listed in place of the corresponding content. The referenced material must be attached to the test-summary report or available to users of the summary report.

Details on the content of each section are contained in the following sections.

10.2.1 Test-Summary-Report Identifier. Specify the unique identifier assigned to this test-summary report.

10.2.2 Summary. Summarize the evaluation of the test items. Identify the items tested, indicating their version/revision level. Indicate the environment in which the testing activities took place.

For each test item, supply references to the following documents if they exist: test plan, test-design specifications, test-procedure speci-

fications, test-item transmittal reports, test logs, and test-incident reports.

10.2.3 Variances. Report any variances of the test items from their design specifications. Indicate any variances from the test plan, test designs, or test procedures. Specify the reason for each variance.

10.2.4 Comprehensiveness Assessment. Evaluate the comprehensiveness of the testing process against the comprehensiveness criteria specified in the test plan (3.2.6) if the plan exists. Identify features or feature combinations which were not sufficiently tested and explain the reasons.

10.2.5 Summary of Results. Summarize the results of testing. Identify all resolved incidents and summarize their resolutions. Identify all unresolved incidents.

10.2.6 Evaluation. Provide an overall evaluation of each test item including its limitations. This evaluation must be based upon the test results and the item level pass/fail criteria. An estimate of failure risk may be included.

10.2.7 Summary of Activities. Summarize the major testing activities and events. Summarize resource consumption data, for example, total staffing level, total machine time, and total elapsed time used for each of the major testing activities.

10.2.8 Approvals. Specify the names and titles of all persons who must approve this report. Provide space for the signatures and dates.

Appendixes

(The following Appendixes are not a part of IEEE Std 829-1983, IEEE Standard for Software Test Documentation.)

A. Examples

The following examples are taken from commercial data processing. This should not imply any limitations on the applicability of the standard to other classes of software.

Contents

A1. Corporate Payroll-System Test Documentation

A1.1. Introduction

A1.1.1. Scope. The system test documentation example presented here is done in accordance with the IEEE Standard for Software Test Documentation. Each document is represented as it might be used for the system test of a payroll system.

The payroll system used in this example contains the following major functions:

(1) Maintain employee information
(2) Maintain payroll history information
(3) Prepare payroll checks
(4) Prepare payroll tax reports
(5) Prepare payroll history reports

A Phase 2.0 development plan exists for the payroll system which will be started at some future time. This phase covers, primarily, a personnel reporting system.

A1.1.2. Assumptions. The following assumptions were made when preparing this example:

(1) System testing activities assume that *module* and *integration* testing have been done. This implies that single program functionality has been comprehensively tested. System level testing, therefore, focuses on the testing of multiprogram functionality (for example, year-end processing) as well as external interfaces, security, recovery, and performance. In addition, operator and user procedures are tested.

(2) The payroll system will be system tested at only one site.

A1.1.3. Naming Conventions. The naming conventions which follow are used throughout the payroll-system example.

Corporate Payroll System

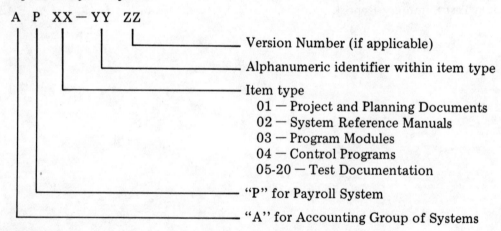

A   P   XX — YY ZZ

Version Number (if applicable)

Alphanumeric identifier within item type

Item type
  01 — Project and Planning Documents
  02 — System Reference Manuals
  03 — Program Modules
  04 — Control Programs
  05-20 — Test Documentation

"P" for Payroll System

"A" for Accounting Group of Systems

Project Planning Documents

AP01-01	Statement of Requirements
AP01-02	Preliminary Development Plan
AP01-03	Project Authorization
AP01-04	System Design Description
AP01-05	Business Plan
AP01-06	Final Development Plan
AP01-08	Quality Assurance Plan
AP01-09	Configuration Management Plan
AP01-12	Statement of Completion

System Reference Manuals

AP02-01	System Reference Manual
AP02-02	Operation Reference Manual

ANSI/IEEE
Std 829-1983

AP02-03	Module Reference Manual
AP02-04	User Transaction Reference Manual

Program Modules

AP03-	Program Modules

Control Programs

AP04-	Control Programs, Utilities, Sorts

Test Documentation

AP05-YYZZ	Test Plan
AP06-YYZZ	Test Design Specification
AP07-YYZZ	Test Case Specification
AP08-YYZZ	Test Procedure Specification
AP09-YY	Test Log
AP10-00	Test Incident Report Log*
AP11-YY	Test Incident Report
AP12-YY	Test Summary Report
AP13-YY	Test Item Transmittal Report

_____

*Note: This *test* document is not specified by this standard.

A.1.2

System Test Plan
for the
Corporate Payroll System

XYZ Corporation

AP05-0101

Prepared by
Manager, System Test Group
Manager, Corporate Payroll Department

January 21, 1982

System Test Plan
Corporate Payroll System

Contents

1. Test Plan Identifier

AP05-0103

2. Introduction

2.1 Objectives. A system test plan for the corporate payroll system should support the following objectives.

(1) To detail the activities required to prepare for and conduct the system test.

(2) To communicate to all responsible parties the tasks which they are to perform and the schedule to be followed in performing the tasks.

(3) To define the sources of the information used to prepare the plan.

(4) To define the test tools and environment needed to conduct the system test.

2.2 Background. Last year the XYZ Corporate Systems and Programming Department developed a new General Ledger System at the request of the Corporate Accounting Department. A request was made at the same time for a new corporate payroll system to be developed which would interface with the general ledger system.

The Management Systems Review Committee approved the request for the payroll system in September of 1981 and named a corporate payroll system advisory group to decide on the system requirements. The group finished a Statement of Requirements (AP01-01) and a Preliminary Development Plan (AP01-02) in December, 1981.

2.3 Scope. This test plan covers a full systems test of the corporate payroll system. This includes operator and user procedures, as well as programs and job control. In addition to comprehensively testing multiprogram functionality, external interfaces, security, recovery, and performance will also be evaluated.

2.4 References. The following documents were used as sources of information for the test plan.

Corporate Payroll System Preliminary Development Plan (AP01-02)

Corporate Payroll System Authorization (AP01-03)

Corporate Payroll System Final Development Plan (AP01-06)

Corporate Payroll System Quality Assurance Plan (AP01-08)

Corporate Payroll System Configuration Management Plan (AP01-09)

XYZ Corporate Systems Development Standards and Procedures (XYZ01-0100)

Corporate General Ledger System Design Description (AG01-04)

Corporate General Ledger System Test Plan (AG05-01)

3. Test Items

All items which make up the corporate payroll system will be tested during the system test. The versions to be tested will be placed in the appropriate libraries by the configuration administrator. The administrator will also control changes to the versions under test and notify the test group when new versions are available.

The following documents will provide the basis for defining correct operation.

Corporate Payroll System Statement of Requirements (AP01-01)

Corporate Payroll System Design Description (AP01-04)

Corporate Payroll System Reference Manual (AP02-01)

Corporate Payroll System Module Reference Manual (AP02-03)

The items to be tested are:

3.1 Program Modules. The program modules to be tested will be identified as follows:

Type	Library	Member Name
Source Code	SOURLIB1	AP0302
		AP0305

Executable Code	MACLIB1	AP0301
	SYSLIB1	AP0302
		AP0305

3.2 Job-Control Procedures. The control procedures for application programs, sorts, and utility programs will be identified as follows:

Type	Library	Member Name
Application Programs	PROCLIB1	AP0401
Sorts	PROCLIB1	AP0402
Utility Programs	PROCLIB1	AP0403

3.3 User Procedures. The online procedures specified in the Corporate Payroll Sytem User Transaction Reference Manual (AP02-04) will be tested.

3.4 Operator Procedures. The system test includes the procedures specified in the Corporate Payroll System Operation Reference Manual (AP02-02).

4. Features to be Tested

The following list describes the features that will be tested.

Test Design Specification Number	Description
AP06-01	Data base conversion
AP06-02	Complete payroll processing for salaried employees only
AP06-03	Complete payroll processing for hourly employees only
AP06-04	Complete payroll processing for all employees
AP06-05	Periodic reporting
AP06-06	General Ledger transaction building
AP06-07	Security
AP06-08	Recovery
AP06-09	Performance

5. Features not to be Tested

The following features will not be included in the system tests because they are not to be used when the system is initially installed.

Equal Employment Opportunity Commission Compliance Reports

Internal Training Schedule Reports

Salary/Performance Review Reports

The development Phase 2.0 documentation will contain a test plan for these features.

The test cases will not cover all possible combinations of options within the transaction or report being tested. Only combinations that are known to be required for current XYZ Corporate Payroll processing will be tested.

6. Approach

The test personnel will use the system documentation to prepare all test design, case, and procedure specifications. This approach will verify the accuracy and comprehensiveness of the information in the documentation in those areas covered by the tests.

Personnel from the Payroll and Corporate Accounting Departments will assist in developing the test designs and test cases. This will help ensure that the tests represent the production use of the system.

In order to ensure privacy, all test data extracted from production files will have privacy sensitive fields changed.

6.1 Conversion Testing. In addition to counting the input and output records, the validity of the converted data base will be verified in two ways. The first verification method involves the use of a *data base auditor* which must be built by the development group. When run against the converted data base, the data base auditor will check value ranges within a record and the required relationships between records.

The second verification method involves the random selection of a small subset of old records and than a direct comparison against a corresponding subset of the new records. The number of direct comparisons, c, and the number of old records, r, must be specified. A set of c random numbers will be generated from the range 1 to r. This set will be sorted and used during the conversion process to drive the selection of records for direct comparison.

NOTE: This same two-pronged verification approach should be used during the actual conversion.

6.2 Job Stream Testing. A comprehensive set of records of salaried employees, hourly employees, and a merged set of these two should be used to test payroll processing. The standard job stream testing approach should be used.

Run each of the periodic reporting job streams at least once.

6.3 Interface Testing. In order to test the interface between the payroll and general-ledger systems, the payroll system will build a comprehensive set of general-ledger transactions. These transactions will then be input to the general-ledger test system. The resulting general-ledger entries must be extracted, printed, and compared with a printout of the general-ledger transactions prepared by the payroll system.

6.4 Security Testing. Attempted access without a proper password to the online data entry and display transactions will be tested.

6.5 Recovery Testing. Recovery will be tested by halting the machine during stand alone time and then following the recovery procedures.

6.6 Performance Testing. Performance will be evaluated against the performance requirements (AP01-01) by measuring the run times of several jobs using production data volumes.

6.7 Regression. It is assumed that several iterations of the system test will be done in order to test program modifications made during the system test period. A regression test will be performed for each new version of the system to detect unexpected impact resulting from program modifications.

The regression test will be done by running all of the tests on a new version that were run on the previous version and then comparing the resulting files. The standard comparator program, UT08-0100, will be used to compare all system outputs.

6.8 Comprehensiveness. Each of the system features described in the Corporate Payroll System Reference Manual (AP02-01) will have at least one associated test-design specification. Each of the user procedures specified in the Corporate Payroll-System User Transaction Reference Manual (AP02-04) will be tested at least once. Each of the operating procedures specified in the Corporate Payroll-System Operation Reference Manual (AP02-02) also will be tested at least once. In addition, each job control procedure will be executed at least once.

A coverage matrix will be used to related test-design specifications to each of the areas described above.

6.9 Constraints. A final implementation date of August 31, 1982 has been planned for the Corporate Payroll System. It will be necessary to meet this date because the new ABC Division begins full operation on September 1, and they must have this payroll system to pay their employees.

7. Item Pass/Fail Criteria

The system must satisfy the standard requirements for system pass/fail stated in the XYZ Corporate Systems Development Standards and Procedures (XYZ01-0100).

The system must also satisfy the following requirements:

Memory requirements must not be greater than 64K of real storage

Consistency of user procedures with other accounting systems must satisfy the Payroll Supervisor

8. Suspension Criteria and Resumption Requirements

8.1 Suspension Criteria. Inability to convert the Employee Information Data Base will cause suspension of all testing activities.

8.2 Resumption Requirements. When a new version of the system is transmitted to the test group after a suspension of testing has occurred, a regression test as described in 6.7 will be run.

9. Test Deliverables

The following documents will be generated by the system test group and will be delivered to the configuration management group after test completion.

Test Documentation:
  System Test Plan
  System Test Design Specifications
  System Test Case Specifications
  System Test Procedure Specifications
  System Test Logs
  System Test Incident Report Log
  System Test Incident Reports
  System Test Summary Report

Test Data:
  (1) Copies of all data entry and inquiry screens and the reply screens are to be attached to the related test case document.
  (2) Copies of the input and output test files should be delivered to the configuration management group.
  (3) Microfiche copies of the printed output from the final execution of each test procedure are to be delivered to the configuration management group along with the test documentation.

10. Testing Tasks

See Task List, Attachment A, page 28.

11. Environmental Needs

11.1 Hardware. The testing will be done on the XYZ hardware configuration.

Since most testing must be done during prime operating hours, 3 on-line terminals must be available to the test group during this period.

11.2 Software

11.2.1 Operating System. The production operating system will be used to execute these tests.

11.2.2 Communications Software. All on-line programs will be tested under the control of the test communication software.

11.3 Security. Security will be limited to existing controls.

11.4 Tools. The following test tools are required to develop and evaluate the system tests.

(1) Test Data Generator (UT09-0200). This program will be used to generate the majority of the test data. It is located in the standard system library, SYSLIBA.

(2) Comparator Program (UT08-0100). This program will be used to compare system results during the regression tests. It is located in the standard system library, SYSLIBA.

(3) Data Base Auditor. This program audits value ranges and interrecord relationships in the data base. It must be supplied by the development group.

11.5 Publications. The following documents are required to support systems testing.
Corporate Payroll System Statement of Requirements (AP01-01)
Corporate Payroll System Design Description (AP01-04)
Corporate Payroll System Reference Manual (AP02-01)
Corporate Payroll Operation Reference Manual (AP02-02)
Corporate Payroll System Module Reference Manual (AP02-03)
Corporate Payroll System User Transaction Reference Manual (AP02-04)

12. Responsibilities

The following groups have responsibility for segments of the testing.

12.1 System Test Group. This group provides the overall management of the testing and the technical testing expertise.

12.2 Corporate Payroll Department. This group is the end user of the Corporate Payroll System and will provide assistance to the test group in the following activities:
Reviewing the test-design specifications.
Executing the on-line tests.
Checking output screens and reports.

12.3 Development Project Group. This group transmits the system to be tested and responds to the System Test Incident Reports. This group does any program debugging that is required. It also supplies the data-base auditor.

13. Staffing and Training Needs

13.1 Staffing. The following staff is needed to carry out this testing project.
    13.1.1 Test Group.

Test Manager	1
Senior Test Analyst	1
Test Analysts	2
Test Technician	1

    13.1.2 Payroll Department.

Payroll Supervisor	1

13.2 Training. The Corporate Payroll Department personnel must be trained to do the data entry transactions. The User Transaction Reference Manual (AP02-04) will be the basis of this training.

14. Schedule

See attached Task List (Attachment A).

Hardware, software, and test tools will be used for testing during the period from June 1, 1982 through August 1, 1982.

15. Risks and Contingencies

If the testing schedule is significantly impacted by system failure, the development manager has agreed to assign a full-time person to the test group to do debugging.

If one payroll supervisor is not sufficiently available for testing, then the payroll manager has agreed to identify a second supervisor.

If hardware problems impact system availability during the day, then the test group will schedule their activities during the evening.

The first production runs of the Corporate Payroll System must be checked out in detail before the payroll checks are distributed, and any checks in error must be corrected manually.

16. Approvals

Test Manager	Date
Development Project Manager	Date
Quality Assurance Manager	Date

Attachment — A. Task List

Task	Predecessor Tasks	Special Skills	Responsibility	Effort	Finish Date
(1) Prepare test plan.	Complete payroll system design description (AP01-04) and preliminary development plan (AP01-02)		Test manager Senior test analyst	4	01-21-82
(2) Prepare test-design specifications.	Task 1	Knowledge of corporate payroll procedures	Senior test analyst	9	04-01-82
(3) Prepare test-case specifcations.	Complete corresponding test designs (Task 2)		Test analyst	4	04-15-82
(4) Prepare test-procedure specifications.	Complete corresponding test cases (Task 3)		Test analyst	6	05-15-82
(5) Build the initial employee-information data base.	Task 4		Test analyst	6	06-01-82
(6) Complete test-item transmittal and transmit the corporate payroll system to the test group.	Complete integration testing		Development project manager		06-01-82
(7) Checkout all job-control procedures required to execute the system.	Task 6	Job control experience	Test technician	1	06-08-82
(8) Assemble and link the corporate payroll system.	Task 6		Test technician	1	06-08-82
(9) Execute data-entry test procedures.	Task 5 Task 8		Test analyst	1	06-22-82
(10) Execute batch test procedures.	Task 5 Task 8		Test technician	3	06-30-82
(11) Check out batch test results.	Task 10	Knowledge of payroll-report requirements	Test analyst	1	07-02-82
(12) Resolve test-incident reports.	Task 9 Task 11		—Development group manager —System test-group manager —Corporate payroll department manager	2	07-16-82
(13) Repeat tasks (6)—(12) until all test procedures have succeeded.	Task 12			2	07-30-82
(14) Write the system test summary report.	Task 13		—System test-group manager —Corporate payroll-department manager	1	08-06-82
(15) Transmit all test documentation and test data to the configuration management group.	Task 14		System test group	1	08-06-82

A1.3. Corporate Payroll
System Test-Procedure Specification

1. Test-Procedure Specification Identifier

AP08-0101 March 5, 1982

2. Purpose

This procedure describes the steps necessary to perform the test specified in the test-design specification for data-base conversion (AP06-0101). The procedure describes the execution of the test case described in System Test-Case Specification AP07-0101. (NOTE: Neither the test-design specification nor test-case specification are included in this set of system test examples). This test will exercise the Employee Information Data Base Conversion Procedures specified in the Corporate Payroll System Reference Manual (AP02-01) and the conversion program (AP03-07) described in the Corporate Payroll System Module Reference Manual (AP02-03).

3. Special Requirements

In order to execute this procedure, the "random subset" program, the old data extract program, the new data extract program, and the data base auditor specified in AP06-0101 must be available.

4. Procedure Steps

4.1 Log. Record the execution of this procedure on a standard test log (AP09-YY).

4.2 Set Up
(1) Generate a test version of the old employee data base according to the test-case specification in AP07-0101 using the test data generator (UT09-0200).
(2) Execute the random subset program requesting 50 random numbers in the range 1 to 500.
(3) Sort the random number file into an increasing sequence.
(4) Execute the old data extract program with the test version of the old employee-information data base using the sorted random number file.
(5) Print the extracted records.

4.3 Proceed. Execute the conversion program with the test version of the old data base generating the new employee information data base.

4.4 Measure
(1) Execute the data-base auditor with the new employee information data base. Report violations in test-incident reports.
(2) Execute the new data extract program with the new data base using the sorted random-number file.
(3) Print the extracted records.
(4) Compare the extracted old records with the extracted new records. Report differences in test-incident reports.

4.5 Wrap Up. Delete both extracted files and the random number file.

A1.4. Corporate Payroll
System Transmittal Report

1. Transmittal Report Identifier

AP13-03 June 24, 1982

2. Transmitted Items

A new version of the data conversion program (AP03-0702) is being transmitted.

The program is described in the Module Reference Manual (AP02-0305). The associated conversion procedures are specified in the System Reference Manual (AP02-0109). The transmitted program is associated with system test plan AP05-0103.

Communication about this program should be directed to the manager of the payroll system development project.

3. Location

The transmitted code is located as follows:

Source Code   SOURLIB1 (AP0307)
Object Code   SYSLIB1 (AP0307)

The system documentation and test plans are available in the documentation library.

4. Status

The conversion program has been fully retested at the unit and integration levels. The three incident reports (AP11-15, 16, and 17) generated by the June 10th execution of AP08-0101 are resolved by this new version.

The *invalid department code* messages (AP11-15) and the *blank home addresses* (AP11-16) resulted from insufficient logic in the conversion program. Additional logic was added. The *number of dependents* field processing problem (AP11-17) resulted from an imprecise program specification. The logic has been changed and comments have been added for clarity.

5. Approvals

_____   _____

Development Manager   Date

_____   _____

Test Manager   Date.

A1.5 Corporate Payroll-
System Test Log

1. Test Log Identifier

AP09-04 June 10, 1982

2. Description

The first version of the data conversion program (AP03-0701) is being tested. The program was transmitted (AP13-01) to the test group along with the entire payroll system.

This batch testing is being conducted using the standard corporate data-center facilities.

This log records the execution of the data conversion test procedure (AP08-0101). The tests are being submitted to background processing through a CRT by a senior test analyst.

3. Activities and Event Entries

June 10, 1982	Incidents
2:00 PM — Dick J. started testing.	
2:15 PM — Began to generate the old test data base.	
3:30 PM — Discovered a possible bug in the test data generator. Filled out an incident report and worked around the problem.	AP11-14
6:00 PM — Completed the old test data base generation. It is located on TEST1.	
6:15 PM — Dick J. stopped testing.	

June 11, 1982	Incidents
9:45 AM — Dick J. started testing.	
10:00 AM — Began to create the random number file.	
10:45 AM — Generated a sorted random number file.	
11:30 AM — Selected and printed a random subset of records from the old test data base.	
12:30 PM — Dick J. stopped testing.	
12:45 PM — Jane K. started testing.	
1:00 PM — Ran the conversion program against the old test data base. The new data base is on TEST2. The status report from the run contained 3 messages warning of invalid data in the department code field. The three records were checked and the values appeared valid. An incident report was generated.	AP11-15
3:30 PM — Ran the data-base auditor against the new data base. The auditor reported multiple instances of blank home addresses. A check found these addresses nonblank in the old data base. The incident was reported.	AP11-16
4:00 PM — Jane K. stopped testing.	

ANSI/IEEE
Std 829-1983

June 12, 1982   Incidents

     8:15 AM — Jane K. started testing.

     8:30 AM — Selected and printed the random subset of   AP11-17
                 records from the new data base. In one case,
                 the *number of dependents* field was changed
                 from three to zero (possibly because no names
                 were present). The incident was reported.

11:30 AM — The extract and random number files were
                 deleted.

11:45 AM — Jane K. stopped testing.

A1.6. Corporate Payroll
System Test Incident Report

1. Report Identifier

AP11-17 June 12, 1982

2. Summary

Changes in the *number of dependents* field were found by comparing records from the new employee data base created by the conversion program (AP03-0701) with those from the old data base. Test log AP09-04 records this incident. The incident occurred during execution of test procedure AP08-0101.

3. Incident Description

June 12, 1982   8:30 AM   Jane K.

A test version of the old employee data base was converted to its new format. The value in the *number of dependents* field was not expected to change during this process. This field value changed in the record indicated on the attached printouts.

Note that although the dependent count is three in the original record, none of the names appear. The number of names matches the count in all of the other records.

Perhaps the program is counting the names and forcing consistency.

4. Impact

Testing activity is suspended until this incident is resolved.

A2. Normalize Numeric Expression
Module-Test Documentation

The following example describes the testing of a module which reformats a numeric expression entered on a CRT. The module removes all commas, the sign, and the decimal point. It also checks the validity of the input expression.

A2.1 Introduction

General Requirements. To provide user-friendly entry of numeric data on a CRT, a system permits the keying of numeric expressions containing optional non-numeric symbols such as commas, a decimal point, and a leading sign. Any of the following examples would be valid entries:

+0
1234.
-.012
12,345.6

To facilitate editing of such input, a routine is required to normalize the numeric expression to a decimal point aligned value and to describe it. An expression is described by various characteristics such as:

Includes sign
Includes commas
Includes decimal point
Number of fractional digits and
Number of integer digits

A return code should identify the specific nature of any edit error.
The routine will be accessed by COBOL programs.

Functional Design.
Input: A character string of length 25 called NUMERIC-EXPRESSION contains a numeric expression. The expression must contain at least 1 digit. It may contain no more than 14 integer digits and no more than 4 fractional digits. It may contain valid combinations of
Leading sign
Decimal point and
Grouping commas.
A valid entry field may have spaces on the left, the right, or both. Interior spaces are invalid.
Process: The input expression is edited and if invalid an error condition is recorded in the return code. If valid, any signs, decimal points, and commas are removed and the resulting numeric value is decimal-point aligned in a signed field. In addition, a set of input descriptors is calculated.
Output: A decimal-point aligned, signed numeric value in a PIC S9(14)V9(4) field called ALIGNED-NUMERIC-VALUE
A set of input descriptors
INTEGER-DIGIT-COUNT (0 - 14)
FRACTIONAL-DIGIT-COUNT (0 - 4)
WAS-SIGN-FOUND (N-0, YES)
WERE-COMMAS-FOUND (N-0, YES)
WAS-DECIMAL-POINT-FOUND (N-0, YES)
A RETURN-CODE with the following values
· NORMALIZATION-OK
· INVALID-FIRST-CHAR
First character is other than a digit, period, or sign
· INVALID-NONFIRST-CHAR
Nonfirst character is other than a digit, period, or comma

· NO-DIGIT-FOUND

No numeric character was entered

· TOO-MANY-INTEGER-DIGITS

More than 14 consecutive digits without a decimal point

· TOO-MANY-FRACTIONAL-DIGITS

More than 4 digits to the right of a decimal point

· TOO-MANY-DECIMAL-POINTS

More than 1 decimal point

· COMMA-RIGHT-AFTER-SIGN

Comma immediately follows a sign

· INVALID-COMMA-INTERVAL

Less than 3 consecutive-digits following a comma

More than 3 consecutive digits preceding or following a comma

· COMMA-AFTER-POINT

Comma appears to the right of a decimal point

If the value of RETURN-CODE is *not* NORMALIZATION-OK, then the values of the other output fields are *undefined*.

TECHNICAL DESIGN.

LANGUAGE: COBOL

ACCESS: PERFORM of included sub-routine

HIERARCHY: Normalize-Numeric-Exp
CHART   Left-justify Expression
                    Find Right-most Non-space
                    Validate Expression
                      Initialize Descriptor Fields
                      Set Return OK
                      Do Validation Scan
                      Wrap Up Validation Scan
                    Normalize Valid Expression
                      Save Digit
                      Delete Specials
                      Align Output Value
                      Establish Sign

NOTES:

Output Fields	Setting Procedures
Return Code (Error)	Do Validation Scan
	Wrap Up Validation Scan
Return Code (OK)	Set Return OK
Input Descriptors	Initialize Description Fields
	Do Validation Scan
	Wrap Up Validation Scan
ALIGNED-NUMERIC-VALUE	Align Output Value
	Establish Sign

Module Test Documentation for Normalize Numeric Expression

- Test Design Specification
- Test Case Specification
- Test Summary Report

Prepared by Module Developer
March 23, 1982

A2.2. Normalize Numeric Expression
Module Test-Design Specification

1. Test-Design Specification Identifier

NNE.TD.01.05   15 March 1981

NOTE: No test plan is associated with this module, because its development was not associated with any particular application project (so there is no project level test plan) and because the special projects manager decided that a specific module test plan was unnecessary. The quality support manager concurred.

2. Features to be Tested

Individual Features
2.1 Digits Only Processing
2.2 Sign Processing
2.3 Decimal Point Processing
2.4 Commas Processing
Combinations
2.5 Sign and Decimal Point
2.6 Sign and Commas
2.7 Decimal Point and Commas
2.8 Sign, Decimal Point and Commas

All of these features are specified in the functional design description contained in the *common routines* section of the programmer's guide.

3. Approach Refinements

The individual processing features of the module will be tested first with valid and invalid input. All of the combinations will then be used.

A program will be written to drive the module. A file will be created with each record containing a single input value and fields to store the resulting values. The driver program will read a record, pass the corresponding input value to the module, store the resulting values in the record and rewrite it. The current version id of the module should be stored in each rewritten record.

Before testing begins, a test-case file will be generated in the same format as the driver file. The records will contain the input values along with the *predicted* resulting values. Following a test run, the driver file will be compared with the case file. The file comparison utility program will report any differences.

Since generation of all possible input values is impractical, test-set comprehensiveness will be evaluated based upon the following criteria:

(1) Requirements coverage — has each of the requirements been satisfied?

(2) Design coverage — has each of the functional design specifications been satisfied?

(3) Domain coverage — has each of the input constraints (for example, maximum of one decimal point) been tested? Have representative values been included? Have all error messages been generated?

(4) Branch coverage — has every branch been taken at least once?

(5) Statement coverage — has every statement been executed at least once?

Appropriate checklists will be generated to evaluate criteria 1-3. Existing code instrumentation tools will be used to evaluate 4 and 5.

The test set must satisfy each component of the five criteria specified above at least once.

Test Case Selection Rationale

Input constraints

(1) No more than 14 integer digits

(2) No more than 4 fractional digits

(3) No more than one decimal point

(4) Between 1 and 3 contiguous digits to the left of each comma

(5) Exactly 3 contiguous digits to the right of each comma

(6) No commas after the decimal point

There are no relevant internal or output constraints.

Common Test-Case Characteristics

All test cases require a module driver.

4. Test Identification

Cases

  Digits Only

    Valid

14 integer digits	NNE.TC.001
centered 6 integer digits	NNE.TC.002
left justified 1 integer digit	NNE.TC.003

    Invalid

15 integer digits	NNE.TC.010
digit string with imbedded space	NNE.TC.011
digit string with leading invalid character	NNE.TC.012
digit string with imbedded invalid character	NNE.TC.013
digit string with trailing invalid character	NNE.TC.014

  Sign

    Valid

right justified + signed 14 integers	NNE.TC.020
— signed integers	NNE.TC.021

    Invalid

imbedded sign	NNE.TC.030
trailing sign	NNE.TC.031
sign alone without digits	NNE.TC.032
2 leading signs	NNE.TC.033
2 separated signs	NNE.TC.034

  Decimal Point

    Valid

leading point with 4 fractional digits	NNE.TC.040
embedded point with 1 fractional digit	NNE.TC.041
trailing point with 14 integers	NNE.TC.042

Cases
    Invalid
        5 fractional digits   NNE.TC.050
        2 points   NNE.TC.051
        point without digits   NNE.TC.052
    Commas
        Valid
            1 comma   NNE.TC.060
            4 commas with 14 integer digits   NNE.TC.061
        Invalid
            leading comma   NNE.TC.070
            4 digits to left of a comma   NNE.TC.071
            2 digits to right of a comma   NNE.TC.072
            4 digits to right of a comma   NNE.TC.073
            trailing comma   NNE.TC.074
            comma without digits   NNE.TC.075
            15 integer digits   NNE.TC.076
    Sign and Decimal Point
        Valid
            sign and trailing point with 1 digit   NNE.TC.080
            sign adjacent to point with 1 digit   NNE.TC.081
            sign and point with 14 digits   NNE.TC.082
        Invalid
            sign and point without digits   NNE.TC.090
    Sign and Commas
        Valid
            sign and comma with 14 digits   NNE.TC.100
            sign and comma with 4 digits   NNE.TC.101
        Invalid
            sign adjacent to comma   NNE.TC.110
    Decimal Point and Commas
        Valid
            comma with 14 integer digits and 4 fractional
               digits   NNE.TC.120
            one comma with 4 digits and trailing point   NNE.TC.121
        Invalid
            no digits between comma and point   NNE.TC.130
            4 digits between comma and point   NNE.TC.131
            comma following point   NNE.TC.132
    Sign, Decimal Point and Commas
        Valid
            longest valid expression   NNE.TC.140
            shortest valid expression   NNE.TC.141
            representative valid expression   NNE.TC.142
        Invalid
            15 integer and 4 fractional digits   NNE.TC.150
            14 integer and 5 fractional digits   NNE.TC.151

Procedures. There are no *formal* test procedures associated with this design.

The procedure for using the module driver is in the *test tools* section of the programmer's guide.

5. Feature Pass/Fail Criteria

Each feature must pass all of its test cases in order to pass this test.

ANSI/IEEE
Std 829-1983

A2.3. Normalize Numeric Expression
Module Test-Case Specification

1. Test Case Specification Identifier

NNE.TC.121.01   17 March 1981
One comma with 4 digits and trailing point.

2. Test Items

Normalized Numeric Expression Subroutine — This routine strips signs, commas, and decimal points from numeric expressions.

The requirements, functional design, and technical design specifications are contained in the *common routines* section of the programmer's guide.

3. Input Specifications

1,234. in NUMERIC-EXPRESSION

4. Output Specifications

+12340000 in ALIGNED-NUMERIC-VALUE
NORMALIZATION-OK in RETURN-CODE
4 in INTEGER-DIGIT-COUNT
0 in FRACTIONAL-DIGIT-COUNT
N-0 in WAS-SIGN-FOUND
YES in WERE-COMMAS-FOUND
YES in WAS-DECIMAL-POINT-FOUND

5. Environmental Needs

A module driver is required to execute this case.

6. Special Procedural Requirements

The procedure for using the module driver is in the *test tools* section of the programmer's guide.

7. Intercase Dependencies

None.

A2.4. Normalize Numeric Expression
Module Test Summary Report

1. Test Summary Report Identifier

NNE.TS.01 23 March 1981

2. Summary

After correcting three faults, the Normalize Numeric Expression Module (Revision 5) passed all tests. The routine was tested using a module driver.

The following test documents are associated with this module.

(1) Module Test Design Specification
NNE.TD.01.05
(2) Module Test Case Specifications
NNE.TC.001 — .151

3. Variances

Conditions identified during testing resulted in enhancements to the set of invalid conditions described in the original functional design. This in turn resulted in the specification of eleven additional test cases. All of these changes are included in the current documentation.

4. Comprehensiveness Assessment

The attached (but not included with example) checklists and execution trace reports demonstrate that the minimum comprehensiveness requirements specified in the test design specification have been satisfied.

5. Summary of Results

Three of the test cases (071, 073, and 131) exposed faults involving insufficient logic. Additional logic was added, some new test cases were defined and the test set was rerun. All features passed their tests.

6. Evaluation

The module passed comprehensive testing with only three faults being detected. No more than one additional fault in the first six months of use is specified.

ANSI/IEEE
Std 829-1983

7. Summary of Activities

Begin Testing 03/12/82	Est	Actual
Test Design (including cases)	2.0 days	3.0 days
Module Driver Development	1.0 days	1.5 days
Test Execution	2.0 days	2.0 days
Module Revision	2.0 days	1.5 days
Test Reporting	0.5 days	0.5 days
End Testing 03/23/82	7.5 days	8.5 days

8. Approvals

_____   _____

Development Project Manager   Date

Appendix B
Implementation and Usage Guidelines

B1. Implementation Guidelines

When the standard is adopted by an organization, it is recommended that it be implemented in phases.

(1) Initial Phase. Begin by introducing the planning and reporting documents. The test plan will provide a foundation for the whole testing process. The reporting documents will encourage the testing organization to record the appropriate data in an organized manner.

Begin by implementing test documentation at the system level. The need for rigor and control during system testing is critical. System test documentation is a key element in meeting this need.

(2) Subsequent Phases. Introduce the balance of the documents in subsequent phases. Their sequence of introduction will depend upon the results of prior phases.

The test documentation eventually will form a document hierarchy corresponding to the design hierarchy, that is, system test documentation, subsystem test documentation, and module test documentation.

B2. Additional Test-Documentation Guidelines

Develop guidelines for the documentation of the specific testing techniques used in your organization (for example, code inspections or simulation). This documentation will supplement the basic documents of the standard.

B3. Usage Guidelines

(1) In the project plan or the organization's standards, identify which test documents are required during which testing activities. Provide guidelines for using these documents in your organization.

Figure B1 (below) is an example of a specification for the test documents required for various testing activities. The amount of documentation required will vary from organization to organization.

(2) Add sections and material within sections in order to tailor each document to a particular test item and a particular test environment.

(3) Consider documenting sets of modules at the module test level. For example, if might be useful to develop a module test design specification for a set of modules which generate reports. While different test cases would be required, a common test procedure specification might be appropriate.

Documents Activities	Test Plan	Test Design Spec	Test Case Spec	Test Proc Spec	Test Item Trans Report	Test Log	Test Incident Report	Test Summary Report
Acceptance	X	X	X	X	X		X	X
Field	X	X			X		X	X
Installation	X	X	X	X	X		X	X
System	X	X	X	X	X	X	X	X
Subsystem		X	X	X	X	X	X	X
Program		X	X					X
Module		X	X					X

Fig B1
Example of a Required Test Documentation Specification

Appendix C
Related Documentation Standards

Several other standards which relate to test documentation are described below. Related testing standards can be found in Appendix D.

C1. National Standards

These references establish nationally recognized requirements for software documentation.

ANSI N413-1974, American National Standard Guidelines for the Documentation of Digital Computer Programs.[1]

ANSI/IEEE Std 100-1977, IEEE Standard Dictionary of Electrical and Electronics Terms.[2]

ANSI/IEEE Std 730-1981, Standard for Software Quality Assurance Plans.

IEEE Std 729-1983, IEEE Standard Glossary of Software Engineering Terminology.

Guide for Technical Documentation of Computer Projects, American National Standards Institute Technical Committee X3. Technical Report no 6, New York: June 1982.[3]

C2. Federal Standards

These references include standards and guidelines adopted for use by Federal agencies.

Guidelines for Documentation of Computer Programs and Automated Data Systems. Federal Information Processing Standards Pub 38. National Bureau of Standards, (FIPS PUB 38), February 1976.

C3. Military Standards

These references include standards and guidelines which may be invoked in Department of Defense contracts.

Automated Data Systems Documentation Standards, Standard 7935.1-S, Department of Defense, Sept 1977.

Tactical Digital Systems Documentation Standards SECNAVINST 3560.1, Department of the Navy, 1974.

WWMCCS CCTC Test Package Development Guidelines, Technical Memorandum TM 241-80, Defense Communications Agency, Nov 1980.

---

[1] ANSI standards are available from the Sales Department of American National Standards Institute, 1430 Broadway, New York, NY 10018.

[2] IEEE standards are available from the Institute of Electrical and Electronics Engineers, IEEE Service Center, 445 Hoes Lane, Piscataway, NJ 08854.

[3] This document is available from ANSI X3 Secretary, CBEMA, 311 1st Street NW, Suite 500, Washinton, DC 20001.

Appendix D
Annotated Bibliography

This bibliography contains two kinds of references. One set of references identifies a set of basic sources on software verification and testing. The objective is to identify a few basic references on testing for those who wish information on techniques and tools. The second set of references identifies some military testing standards which might serve as source material for those developing testing standards within their organization. These standards focus on testing rather than documentation.

D1 Basic Sources

ADRION, W.R., BRANSTAD, M.A. and CHERNIAVISKY, J.C. *Validation, Verification and Testing of Computer Software*. National Bureau of Standards: NBS Special Pub 500-75 1980.

This survey discusses testing and analysis techniques that can be used to validate software. Verification throughout the development process is stressed. Specific tools and techniques are described.

BARRY, M. *Airborne Systems Software Acquisition Engineering Guidebook for Software Testing and Evaluation*. TRW: 30323-6011-TU-00 1980.

This guidebook describes the planning and testing activities necessary to a successful software testing effort. It presents checklists and references to supplemental information in government documents and to summarized data from professional journals and books.

DEUTSCH, M.S. *Software Verification and Validation*. Prentice-Hall: 1982.

This book describes a testing methodology based upon techniques used at the Hughes Aircraft Company. It describes the application of automated verification systems and summarizes the verification activities used throughout the software life cycle. It provides insight into one effective approach to dealing with the verification of large software systems.

GLASS, R. *Software Reliability Guidebook*. Prentice-Hall: 1979.

This book defines reliability as the degree to which a software system both satisfies its re-quirements and delivers usable services. The book surveys many methodologies that are supposed to increase software reliability. These methodologies span the software life cycle requirements, design, implementation, checkout, and maintenance. The handbook rates each methodology as to its value, as a function of the degree of reliability required for the software program. The book is written for the practitioner but includes an annotated bibliography at the end of each chapter for readers desiring a more academic discussion of the topics. The section devoted to the checkout phase (testing) contains almost as much material as all the other life cycle sections combined. Test plans, procedures and reports are briefly described.

GUNTHER, R. *Management Methodology for Software Product Engineering*. John Wiley and Sons: Wiley-Interscience, 1978.

This book was selected for inclusion from the many management oriented books on software development because of its chapter devoted to managing the software product test. This chapter maps the product test groups activities into the traditional software life cycle phases. The chapter discusses software test documentation and even presents a table of contents for test plans and test logs. The author writes from his experience as a product planning manager for Amdahl Corporation.

HETZEL, W.C. Ed. *Program Test Methods*. Prentice-Hall: 1973.

This book is a collection of papers from a testing symposium held in 1972. It covers testing concepts, design of programs to facilitate testing, design of languages to facilitate testing, testing mathematical software, and testing large software systems. The book contains a comprehensive bibliography.

MILLER, E. and HOWDEN, W.E. *Tutorial: Software Testing and Validation Techniques (2nd Ed)*. IEEE Computer Society Press: Catalog no EHO 180-0, 1981.

This IEEE Tutorial is a collection of papers that represent new developments in program structure analysis, test coverage, test results analysis, test project management techniques, and test tools. The publication also includes an extensive bibliography on testing.

MYERS, G. *The Art of Software Testing.* Wiley — Interscience, John Wiley and Sons: 1979.

This book is based upon material from Software Reliability: Principles and Practices by the same author. The book emphasizes testing as an activity which tries to find errors in a program, not an activity that attempts to show that a program works. The book expands this thesis into a set of testing principles. Testing techniques and methodology are covered along with a survey of existing tools. Test documentation is not addressed. The book does a good job of defining testing terms and classifying testing techniques.

PERRY, W. *Effective Methods of EDP Quality Assurance.* Wellesly Massachusetts: QED Systems, 1977.

This handbook contains the following four sections: The Quality Assurance Function, Planning The Quality Assurance Function, Quality Assurance Reviews, and Relationships and Other QA Tests. The appendix presents a sample software QA manual. Software testing is presented as one activity requiring a QA review. The handbook presents what points should be addressed by a detailed test plan as well as the test result report. The handbook's strength is its broad coverage of all the aspects of a well organized QA group. The book addresses software testing as an important activity in software development that should be reviewed by a QA function.

POWELL, P.B. Ed. *Planning for Software Validation, Verification and Testing.* National Bureau of Standards: NBS Special Pub 1982.

The document is for those who direct and those who implement computer projects. It explains the selection and use of validation, verification, and testing (VV and T) tools and techniques. It explains how to develop a plan to meet specific software VV and T goals.

POWELL, P.B. Ed. *Software Validation, Verification, and Testing Technique and Tool Reference Guide.* National Bureau of Standards: NBS Special Pub 1982.

Thirty techniques and tools for validation, verification, and testing (VV and T) are described. Each description includes the basic features of the technique or tool, the input, the output, an example, an assessment of the effectiveness and of the learning time and training, an estimate of the needed resources, and references.

WOOLRIDGE, S. *Systems and Programming Standards.* New York: Petrocelli/Charter, 1977.

The author's major purpose is to outline the contents of a programming standards manual. Chapter 8 addresses system testing and presents the table of contents for a system test plan as well as a checklist for system testing. The presentation differs from the other references because of the book's focus on standards and procedures as contrasted to testing philosophies and software QA techniques. The book shows that testing procedures can be integrated into general software development procedures.

YEH, R. *Current Trends in Programming Methodology.* vol II Program Validation. Prentice-Hall, 1977.

This book is a selection of papers published during the first half of the seventies. The collection of papers is indexed and the volume also includes an extensive annotated bibliography. Test documentation is not covered but the book provides a reference point to theoretical treatments of software testing.

D2. Military Testing Standards

Acquisition and Support Procedures for Computer Resources in Systems. AF Regulation 800-14, vol 2, Department of the Air Force, 1975.

The volume defines the Air Force procedures for the acquisition of computer programs used in military systems. It defines a software acquisition life cycle. In chapter four, it defines the required types, levels and phases of software testing and their relationship to this life cycle. It specifies policy for software testing at the following levels: informal testing, preliminary qualification testing, formal qualification testing, and system level testing. This volume identifies the required contents for test plans and procedures and it also discusses general methods for computer program verification and validation.

Testing of Computer Software Systems. Technical Bulletin, TB 18-104, Department of the Army, September 1981.

This technical bulletin defines the Army's computer software testing methodology. It identifies required tests and test documentation. It also identifies a variety of participants in the testing process and their responsibilities.

Weapon System Software Development. MIL-STD-1679. Department of the Navy, 1978.

This specification requires quality assurance procedures at each stage of development to validate accuracy, correctness, and performance of the product programs and to verify the accuracy and conformance of program documentation. In the area of software trouble reporting, the specification requires the development and implementation of procedures for handling and reporting software problems. Section 5.8 describes various testing requirements.

An American National Standard

IEEE Guide to Software
Requirements Specifications

Sponsor

Software Engineering Technical Committee
of the
IEEE Computer Society

Approved September 30, 1983
IEEE Standards Board

Approved July 20, 1984
American National Standards Institute

Foreword

(This Foreword is not a part of ANSI/IEEE Std 830-1984, IEEE Guide to Software Requirements Specifications.)

This guide describes alternate approaches to good practice in the specification of software requirements. The requirements may be explicitly stated by the user or they may be allocated to computer software (that is, programs) by the system requirements analysis process. This guide does not suggest that a hierarchy of software requirements specifications exists, of which each, in turn, defines a smaller subset of requirements.

As a guide, this document should help:

(1) Software customers to accurately describe what they wish to obtain.

(2) Software suppliers to understand exactly what the customer wants.

(3) Individuals to accomplish the following goals:

   (a) Develop standard software requirements specifications (SRS) outline for their own organizations.

   (b) Define the form and content of their specific software requirements specifications.

   (c) Develop additional local supporting items such as an SRS quality checklist, or an SRS writer's handbook.

To the customers, suppliers and other individuals, a good SRS provides several specific benefits. It will accomplish the following goals:

(1) Establish the basis for agreement between the customers and the suppliers on what the software product is to do. The complete description of the functions to be performed by the software specified in the SRS will assist the potential user, to determine if the software specified meets their needs or how the software must be modified to meet their needs.

(2) Reduce the development effort. The preparation of the SRS forces the various concerned groups in the customer's organization to consider rigorously all of the requirements before design begins and reduces later redesign, recoding, and retesting. Careful review of the requirements in the SRS can reveal omissions, misunderstandings, and inconsistencies early in the development cycle when these problems are easier to correct.

(3) Provide a basis for estimating costs and schedules. The description of the product to be developed as given in the SRS is a realistic basis for estimating project costs and can be used to obtain approval for bids or price estimates. The SRS also provides a clear description of the required software and makes it easier to estimate and plan the necessary resources. The requirements which, together with a development plan, can be used to measure progress.

(4) Provide a baseline for validation and verification. Organizations can develop their validation and verification plans much more productively from a good SRS. As a part of the development contract, the SRS provides a baseline against which compliance can be measured. (However, that the converse is not true; a standard legal contract cannot be used as an SRS. Such documents rarely contain the detail required and are often incomplete.)

(5) Facilitate transfer. The SRS makes it easier to transfer the software product to new users or new machines. Customers thus find it easier to transfer the software to other parts of their organization, and suppliers find it easier to transfer it to new customers.

(6) Serves as a basis for enhancement. Because the SRS discusses the product but not the project that developed it, the SRS serves as a basis for later enhancement of the finished product. The SRS may need to be altered, but it does provide a solid foundation for continued production evolution.

This guide is based on a model in which the result of the software requirements specification process is an unambiguous and complete specification document. In principle, the SRS can be mechanically translated into the specified software program directly. As such, the resulting SRS document itself is the specified software, and the supplier's only duty (after completing the SRS) would be the mechanical compilation of the SRS into machine code for the target computer. The present state of the art does not support such a compiler with an optimizer of such efficiency to make it practical but this limitation need not, and should not, restrict the intermediate objective of an unambiguous SRS.

This guide is consistent with IEEE Std 729-1983, IEEE Standard Glossary of Software Engineering Terminology; ANSI/IEEE Std 730-1981, IEEE Standard for Software Quality Assurance Plans; and IEEE Std 829-1983, IEEE Standard for Software Test Documentation. This guide may be used in conjunction with those standards or separately.

This guide was prepared by the Software Requirements Working Group of the Software Engineering Standards Subcommittee of the Technical Committee on Software Engineering of the IEEE Computer Society.

At the time the guide was approved, the Software Requirements Working Group had the following membership:

At the time that it approved this guide, the Software Engineering Standards Subcommittee had the following membership:

Special representatives to the software engineering standards subcommittee were:

J. Milandin: ANSI Z1
W. G. Perry: Data Processing Manufacturers Association
R. Pritchett: EDP Auditors Association
T. L. Regulinski: IEEE Reliability Society
N. C. Farr: Nuclear Power Engineering Committee, IEEE Power Engineering Society

Suggestions for improvement of this guide are welcome. They should be provided to:

The Secretary
IEEE Standards Board
345 East 47th St
New York, New York 10017

At the time the IEEE Standards Board approved this standard on September 20, 1983 it had the following members:

James H. Beall, *Chairman*   **Edward Chelotti,** *Vice Chairman*

Sava I. Sherr, *Secretary*

J. J. Archambault	Donald H. Heirman	John P. Riganati
John T. Boettger	Irvin N. Howell	Frank L. Rose
J. V. Bonucchi	Joseph L. Koepfinger*	Robert W. Seelbach
Rene Castenschiold	Irving Kolodny	Jay A. Stewart
Edward J. Cohen	George Konomos	Clifford O. Swanson
Len S. Corey	John E. May	Robert E. Weiler
Donald C. Fleckenstein	Donald T. Michael*	W. B. Wilkens
Jay Forster		Charles J. Wylie

*Member emeritus

Contents

An American National Standard

IEEE Guide to Software
Requirements Specifications

1. Scope and Organization

1.1 Scope. This is a guide for writing software requirements specifications. It describes the necessary content and qualities of a good Software Requirements Specification (SRS) and presents a prototype SRS outline.

This guide does not specify industry-wide SRS standards nor state mandatory SRS requirements. This guide is written under the premise that the current state of the art does not warrant or support such a formal standards document.

This guide is applicable to in-house and commercial software products. Special care, however, should be used in its application because:

(1) This guide is aimed at specifying requirements of software to be developed. Application of this material to already-developed software is counter-productive.

(2) This guide does not cover the specification of requirements for software being developed using the techniques of rapid prototyping.

1.2 Organization. The remainder of this guide is organized as follows:

(1) Section 2 provides the references used throughout the guide.

(2) Section 3 provides definitions of specific terms used throughout the guide.

(3) Section 4 provides background information for writing a good SRS.

(4) Section 5 provides specific guidance for expressing software requirements.

(5) Section 6 discusses each of the essential parts of an SRS and provides alternate prototype outlines.

2. References

[1] ANSI/IEEE Std 100-1977, IEEE Standard Dictionary of Electrical and Electronics Terms.

[2] ANSI/IEEE Std 730-1981, IEEE Standard for Software Quality Assurance Plans.

[3] ANSI/IEEE Std 729-1983, IEEE Standard Glossary of Software Engineering Terminology.

[4] BRUSAW, C. T., ALRED, G. and OLIU, W., *Handbook of Technical Writing*, New York, St. Martin's Press, 1976.

[5] DASARATNY, B., *Timing Constraints of Real-Time Systems: Constructs for Expressing Them*, IEEE Real-Time Systems Symposium, Dec 1982.

[6] DAVIS, A., The Design of a Family of Applications-Oriented Requirements Languages, *IEEE Computer*, 15, 5 May 1982, pp 21–28.

[7] FREEDMAN, D. and WEINBERG, G., Handbook of Walkthroughs, *Inspections and Technical Reviews*, 3rd Ed, Little and Brown Publishers, New York.

[8] KAIN, R., Automata Theory: Machines and Languages, McGraw Hill, New York, 1972.

[9] KOHAVI, Z., Switching and Finite Automata Theory, McGraw Hill, New York, 1970.

[10] KRAMER, J., Editor, Application Oriented Specifications Glossary of Terms, *European Workshop on Industrial Computer Systems (EWICS)*, Imperial College, London, England, May 6, 1981.[1]

---

[1]Copies of this document are available from EWICS, c/o G. R. Koch, BIOMATIK Gmbh, Carl-Mez Str 81–83, D-7800 Freiburg, Federal Republic of Germany.

[11] MILLS, G., and WALTER, J., *Technical Writing*, New York, Holt, Rinehart and Winston, 4th Ed, 1978.

[12] PETERSON, J., *Petri Nets*, ACM Computing Surveys, 9, 4, Dec 1977, pp 223–252.

[13] RAMAMOORHY, C. and SO, H. H., *Software Requirements and Specifications: Status and Perspectives*, Tutorial: Software Methodology, RAMAMOORTHY, C. and YEH, R. T., Editors. IEEE Catalog no EHO 142-0, 1978, pp 43–164.

[14] TAGGART, W. M. Jr, and THARP, M. O., *A Survey of Information Requirements Analysis Techniques*, ACM Computing Surveys, 9, 4, Dec 1977, pp 273–290.

[15] TEICHROEW, D., *A Survey of Languages for Stating Requirements for Computer-Based Information Systems*, 1972 Fall Joint Computer Conference, 1972, pp 1203–1224.

3. Definitions

Except for the definitions listed below, the definitions of all terms used in this guide conform to the definitions provided in IEEE Std 729-1983 [3][2], for example, the terms requirement, requirements specification. If a term used in this guide does not appear in that Standard, then ANSI/IEEE Std 100-1977 [1], applies.

The terms listed in this section have been adopted from Section 2, [10].

contract. A legally binding document agreed upon by the customer and supplier. This includes the technical, organizational, cost and schedule requirements of a product.

customer. The person, or persons, who pay for the product and usually (but not necessarily) decides the requirements. In the context of this document the customer and the supplier may be members of the same organization.

language. A means of communication, with syntax and semantics, consisting of a set of representations, conventions and associated rules used to convey information.

partitioning. Decomposition; the separation of the whole into its parts.

---

[2]Numbers in brackets correspond to those of the references in Section 2.

supplier. The person, or persons, who produce a product for a customer. In the context of this document, the customer and the supplier may be members of the same organization.

user. The person, or persons, who operate or interact directly with the system. The user(s) and the customer(s) are often not the same person(s).

4. Background Information for Writing a Good SRS

This section provides background information necessary for writing an SRS. This includes:

(1) Examination of the nature of the SRS

(2) Environmental considerations surrounding the SRS

(3) Characteristics required for a good SRS

(4) Recommendations for joint preparation of an SRS

(5) Evolutionary aspects of the SRS

(6) The use of automated tools to develop an SRS

4.1 The SRS. The SRS is a specification for a particular software product, program, or set of programs that does certain things. See ANSI/IEEE Std 730-1981 [2], 3.4.2.1.

The description places two basic requirements on the SRS:

(1) It must say certain things. For example, software developed from an SRS that fails to specify that error messages will be provided, will probably fail to satisfy the customer.

(2) It must say those things in certain ways. For example, software developed from an SRS that fails to specify the format and content of error messages and instead is developed from a vague and non-quantifiable requirement such as *All error messages will be helpful*, will probably be unsatisfactory. What is *helpful* for one person can be a severe aggravation to another person.

For recommended contents of an SRS see Section 6.

4.2 Environment of the SRS. It is important to consider the part that the SRS plays in the total software project. The provisions in ANSI/IEEE Std 730-1981 [2], define the minimum required documents for a software project. See [2], 3.4.2.

ANSI/IEEE Std 730-1981 [2] also identifies the other useful documents. See [2], 3.4.3.

Since the SRS has a definite role to play in this documentation scheme, SRS writers should be careful not to go beyond the bounds of that role. This means the following requirements should be met:

(1) The SRS must correctly define all of the software requirements, but no more.

(2) The SRS should not describe any design, verification, or project management details, except for required design constraints.

Such a properly written SRS limits the range of valid solutions but does not specify any particular design and thus provides the supplier with maximum flexibility.

4.3 Characteristics of A Good SRS. The previous sections describe the types of information that should be contained in an SRS. The following concepts deal with particular characteristics. A good SRS is:

(1) Unambiguous
(2) Complete
(3) Verifiable
(4) Consistent
(5) Modifiable
(6) Traceable
(7) Usable during the Operation and Maintenance Phase

4.3.1 Unambiguous. An SRS is unambiguous if — and only if — every requirement stated therein has only one interpretation.

(1) As a minimum, this requires that each characteristic of the final product be described using a single unique term.

(2) In cases where a term used in a particular context could have multiple meanings, the term must be included in a glossary where its meaning is made more specific.

4.3.1.1 Natural Language Pitfalls. Requirements are often written in a natural language (for example, English). SRS writers who use a natural language must be especially careful to review their requirements for ambiguity. The following examples are taken from Section 2, [7].

(1) The specification *The data set will contain an end of file character*, might be read as:

(a) There will be one and only one end of file character

(b) Some character will be designated as an end of file character

(c) There will be at least one end of file character

(2) The specification *The control total is taken from the last record*, might be read as:

(a) The control total is taken from the record at the end of the file

(b) The control total is taken from the latest record

(c) The control total is taken from the previous record

(3) The specification *All customers have the same control field*, might be read as:

(a) All customers have the same value in their control field

(b) All customer control fields have the same format

(c) One control field is issued for all customers

(4) The specification *All files are controlled by a file control block*, might be read as:

(a) One control block controls the entire set of files

(b) Each file has its own block

(c) Each file is controlled by a control block, but one control block might control more than one file

4.3.1.2 Formal Requirements Specifications Languages. One way to avoid the ambiguity inherent in natural language is to write the SRS in a formal requirements specification language.[3]

(1) One major advantage in the use of such languages is the reduction of ambiguity. This occurs, in part, because the formal language processors automatically detect many lexical, syntactic, and semantic errors.

(2) One major disadvantage in the use of such languages is the length of time required to learn them.

4.3.2 Complete. An SRS is complete if it possesses the following qualities:

(1) Inclusion of all significant requirements, whether relating to functionality, performance, design constraints, attributes or external interfaces.

(2) Definition of the responses of the software to all realizable classes of input data in all realizable classes of situations. Note that it is important to specify the responses to valid and invalid input values.

(3) Conformity to any SRS standard that applies to it. If a particular section of the standard is not applicable, the SRS should

---

[3]For detailed discussion on this topic, suggested readings are [6], [13], [14], and [15].

include the section number and an explanation of why it is not applicable.

(4) Full labeling and referencing of all figures, tables, and diagrams in the SRS and definition of all terms and units of measure.

4.3.2.1 Use of TBDs. Any SRS that uses the phrase *to be determined* (TBD) is not a complete SRS.

(1) The TBD is, however, occasionally necessary and should be accompanied by:

(a) A description of the conditions causing the TBD (for example, why an answer is not known) so that the situation can be resolved.

(b) A description of what must be done to eliminate the TBD.

(2) Any project documents that are based on an SRS that contains TBDs, should:

(a) Identify the version or state the specific release number of the SRS associated with that particular document.

(b) Exclude any commitments dependent upon the sections of the SRS that are still identified as TBDs.

4.3.3 Verifiable. An SRS is verifiable if and only if every requirement stated therein is verifiable. A requirement is verifiable if and only if there exists some finite cost-effective process with which a person or machine can check that the software product meets the requirement.

(1) Examples of nonverifiable requirements include statements such as:

(a) *The product should work well*, or *The product should have a good human interface.* These requirements cannot be verified because it is impossible to define the terms *good* or *well.*

(b) *The program shall never enter an infinite loop.* This requirement is non-verifiable because the testing of this quality is theoretically impossible.

(c) *The output of the program shall usually be given within 10 s.* This requirement is non-verifiable because the term *usually* cannot be measured.

(2) An example of a verifiable statement is *The output of the program shall be given within 20 s of event* X, *60% of the time; and shall be given within 30 s of event* X, *100% of the time.* This statement can be verified because it uses concrete terms and measurable quantities.

(3) If a method cannot be devised to determine whether the software meets a particular requirement, then that requirement should be removed or revised.

(4) If a requirement is not expressible in verifiable terms at the time the SRS is prepared, then a point in the development cycle (review, test plan issue, etc) should be identified at which the requirement must be put into a verifiable form.

4.3.4 Consistent. An SRS is consistent if and only if no set of individual requirements described in it conflict. There are three types of likely conflicts in an SRS:

(1) Two or more requirements might describe the same real world object but use different terms for that object. For example, a program's request for a user input might be called a *prompt* in one requirement and a *cue* in another.

(2) The specified characteristics of real world objects might conflict. For example:

(a) The format of an output report might be described in one requirement as *tabular* but in another as *textual.*

(b) One requirement might state that all lights shall be green while another states that all lights shall be blue.

(3) There might be a logical or temporal conflict between two specified actions. For example:

(a) One requirement might specify that the program will add two inputs and another specify that the program will multiply them.

(b) One requirement might state that A must always follow B, while another requires that A and B occur simultaneously.

4.3.5 Modifiable. An SRS is modifiable if its structure and style are such that any necessary changes to the requirements can be made easily, completely, and consistently. Modifiability generally requires an SRS to:

(1) Have a coherent and easy-to-use organization, with a table of contents, an index, and explicit cross-referencing.

(2) Not be redundant; that is, the same requirement should not appear in more than one place in the SRS.

(a) Redundancy itself is not an error, but it can easily lead to errors. Redundancy can occasionally help to make an SRS more readable, but a problem can arise when the redundant document is updated. Assume, for instance, that a certain requirement is stated in two places. At some later time, it is determined that the requirement should be altered, but the change is made in only one of the two locations. The SRS then becomes inconsistent.

(b) Whenever redundancy is necessary, the SRS should include explicit cross-references to make it modifiable.

4.3.6 Traceable. An SRS is traceable if the origin of each of its requirements is clear and if it facilitates the referencing of each requirement in future development or enhancement documentation. Two types of traceability are recommended:

(1) Backward traceability (that is, to previous stages of development) depends upon each requirement explicitly referencing its source in previous documents.

(2) Forward traceability (that is, to all documents spawned by the SRS) depends upon each requirement in the SRS having a unique name or reference number.

When a requirement in the SRS represents an apportionment or a derivative of another requirement, both forward and backward traceability should be provided. Examples include:

4.3.6.1 The allocation of response time to a data base function from the overall user response time requirement.

4.3.6.2 The identification of a report format with certain functional and user interface requirements.

4.3.6.3 A software product that supports legislative or administrative needs (for example, tax computations, reporting of an overhead ratio). In this case, the exact legislative or administrative document that is being supported should be identified.

The forward traceability of the SRS is especially important when the software product enters the operation and maintenance phase. As code and design documents are modified, it is essential to be able to ascertain the complete set of requirements that may be affected by those modifications.

4.3.7 Usable During the Operation and Maintenance Phase. The SRS must address the needs of the operation and maintenance phase, including the eventual replacement of the software.

(1) Maintenance is frequently carried out by personnel not associated with the original development. Local changes (corrections) can be implemented by means of a well-commented code. For changes of wider scope, however, the design and requirements documentation is essential. This implies two actions

(a) The SRS should be modifiable as indicated in 4.3.5.

(b) The SRS should contain a record of all special provisions that apply to individual components such as:

(i) Their criticality (for example, where failure could impact safety or cause large financial or social losses).

(ii) Their relation to only temporary needs (for example, to support a display that may be retired soon).

(iii) Their origin (for example, function X is to be copied from an existing software product in its entirety).

(2) Knowledge of this type is taken for granted in the developing organization but is frequently missing in the maintenance organization. If the reason for or origin of a function is not understood, it is frequently impossible to perform adequate software maintenance on it.

4.4 Joint Preparation of the SRS. The software development process begins with supplier and customer agreement on what the completed software must do. This agreement, in the form of an SRS, should be jointly prepared. This is important because usually neither the customer nor the supplier is qualified to write a good SRS by himself.

(1) Customers usually do not understand the software design and development process well enough to write a usable SRS.

(2) Suppliers usually do not understand the customer's problem and field of endeavor well enough to specify requirements for a satisfactory system.

The customer and the supplier need to work together to produce a well written and completely understood SRS.[4]

4.5 SRS Evolution. The SRS may need to evolve as the development of the software product progresses.

(1) It may be impossible to specify some details at the time the project is initiated. For example, it may be impossible to define during the Requirements Phase, all of the screen formats for an interactive program in a manner that guarantees that they will not be altered later.

(2) Additional changes may ensue as deficien-

---

[4]This guide does not specifically discuss style, language usage, or techniques of good writing. It is quite important, however, that an SRS be well written; for guidance, please refer to general technical writing guides such as [1] and [11].

cies, shortcomings, and inaccuracies are discovered in the SRS, as the product evolves.

Two major considerations in this process are:

4.5.1 The requirements should be specified as completely and thoroughly as possible, even if evolutionary revisions can be forseen as inevitable. For example, the desired screen formats should be specified as well as possible in the SRS as a basis for later design.

4.5.2 A formal change process should be initiated to identify, control, track, and report projected changes, as soon as they are initially identified. Approved changes in requirements should be incorporated in the SRS in such a way as to:

(1) Provide an accurate and complete audit trail of changes.

(2) Permit the review of current and superseded portions of the SRS.

4.6 Tools for Developing an SRS. The most obvious way to create an SRS is to write it in a natural language (for example, English). But because natural languages are rich, although imprecise, a number of more formal methods have been devised to assist SRS writers.

4.6.1 Formal Specification Methodologies. The degree to which such formal methodologies may be useful in preparing an SRS depends upon a number of factors:

(1) The size and complexity of the program

(2) Whether a customer contract requires it

(3) Whether the SRS is a vehicle for contracts or merely an internal document

(4) Whether the SRS document will become the top level of the design document

(5) What computer facilities are available to support such a methodology

No attempt is made here to describe or endorse any particular tool.[5]

4.6.2 Production Tools. A computer-based word processor is a most useful production aid. Usually, an SRS will have several authors, will undergo several revisions, and will have several reorganizations. A word processor that manages the text as a computer file facilitates this process.

Almost all computer systems have a word processor and often a document preparation package is associated with it. This automates paragraphing and referencing, the printing of headings and subheadings, the compilation of tables of contents and indexes, etc, all of which help in the production of a more readable SRS.

4.6.3 Representation Tools. Some words in the SRS, especially nouns and verbs, refer specifically to entities and actions in the system. There are several advantages to identifying them as such.

(1) It is possible to verify that an entity or action always has the same name everywhere in the SRS. Thus *calculate trajectory* would not co-exist with *determine flight path.*

(2) It is possible to identify every place in the specification where a particular entity or action is described.

In addition, it may be desirable to formalize the English structure in some way to allow automated processing of the content of the SRS. With such constraints it becomes possible to:

4.6.3.1 Display the requirements in some tabular or graphical way.

4.6.3.2 Automatically check the SRS requirements in hierarchical layers of detail, where each layer is complete in itself but may also be expanded upon in a lower hierarchical layer or be a constituent of an upper hierarchical layer.

4.6.3.3 Automatically check that the SRS possesses some or all of the characteristics described in 4.3.

5. Software Requirements

Each software requirement in an SRS is a statement of some essential capability of the software to be developed. The following subsections describe:

(1) Methods used to express software requirements

(2) Annotation of the software requirements

(3) Common pitfalls encountered in the process

5.1 Methods Used To Express Software Requirements. Requirements can be expressed in a number of ways:

(1) Through input/output specifications

(2) By use of a set of representative examples

(3) By the specification of models

5.1.1 Input/Output Specifications. It is often effective to specify the required behavior of a software product as a sequence of inputs and outputs.

---

[5]For detailed discussion on this topic, see, for example, [6], [13], [14], and [15].

5.1.1.1 Approaches. There are at least three different approaches based on the nature of the software being specified:

(1) Some software products (such as reporting systems) are best specified by focusing on required outputs. In general, output-focused systems operate primarily on data files. User input usually serves to provide control information and trigger data file processing.

(2) Others are best specified by focusing on input/output behavior. Input/output-focused systems operate primarily on the current input. They are required to generate the *matching* output (as with data conversion routines or a package of mathematical functions).

(3) Some systems (such as process control systems) are required to remember their behavior so that they can respond to an input based on that input and past inputs; that is, behave like a finite state machine. In this case the focus is on both input/output pairs and sequences of such pairs.

5.1.1.2 Difficulties. Most software products can receive an infinite number of sequences as input. Thus, to completely specify the behavior of the product through input/output sequences would require that the SRS contain an infinitely long set of sequences of inputs and required outputs. With this approach, therefore, it may be impossible to completely specify every conceivable behavior that is required of the software.

5.1.2 Representative Examples. One alternative is to indicate what behavior is required by using representative examples of that behavior. Suppose, for example, that the system is required to respond with a "1" every time it receives a "0". Clearly, a list of all possible sequences of inputs and outputs would be impossible. However, by using representative sequences one might be able to fully understand the system's behavior. This system's behavior might be described by using this representative set of four dialogues:[6]

0101
010101010101
01
010101

These dialogues provide a good idea of the required inputs and outputs but they do not specify the system's behavior completely.

5.1.3 Models. Another approach is to express the requirements in the form of a model.[7] This can be an accurate and efficient way to express complex requirements.

At least three generalized types of models are in common usage:

(1) Mathematical
(2) Functional
(3) Timing

Care should be taken to distinguish between the model for the application; that is, a linear programming model (with a set of linear inequalities and an objective function) and the model for the software which is required to implement the application model. See 5.1.3.5.

5.1.3.1 Mathematical Models. A mathematical model is a model that uses mathematical relations to describe the software's behavior. Mathematical models are especially useful for particular application areas, including navigation, linear programming, econometrics, signal processing and weather analysis.

A mathematical model might specify the response discussed in 5.1.2 like this:

$(01)*$

where $*$ means that the parenthesized character string is repeated one or more times.

5.1.3.2 Functional Models. A functional model is a model that provides a mapping from inputs to outputs. Functional models, for example, finite state machines or Petri nets can help identify and define various features of the software or can demonstrate the intended operation of the system.

A functional model might specify the response, previously described by the mathematical model, in the form of a finite state machine as shown in Fig 1. In this figure, the incoming arrow points to the starting state. The double lined box represents the accepting state. The notation X/Y on the lines indicates that when X is accepted as an input, Y is produced as an output.

5.1.3.3 Timing Models. A timing model is a model that has been augmented with timing constraints. Timing models are quite useful for specifying the form and details of the software's behavior, particularly for real-time systems or for human factors of any system.

---

[6] Each of the four sample dialogues given here (one per line) represents a sequence of one-character user inputs and one-character system outputs.

[7] For details on using modeling techniques, see [5], [8], [9], and [12].

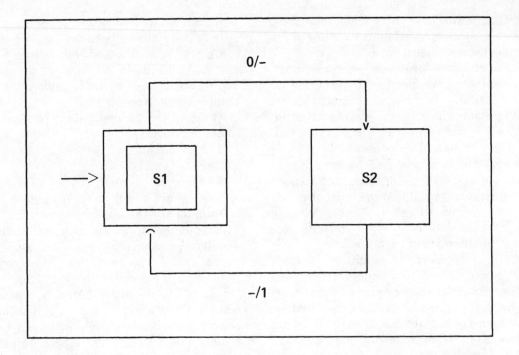

Fig 1
A Functional Model Specifying Any Sequence of Alternating 0s and 1s

A timing model might add these constraints to the model shown in Fig 1.

(1) The stimulus 0 will occur within 30 s of the arrival in state S1

(2) The response 1 will occur within 2 s of the arrival in state S2

5.1.3.4 Other Models. In addition to the aforementioned, specific applications have particularly helpful models. For example, a compiler specification might employ attribute grammars, or a payroll system might use tables. It is to be noted that the use of a formal requirements language for an SRS usually implies a need for the use of a particular model.

5.1.3.5 Cautions. Whatever type of model is used:

(1) It must be rigorously defined, either in the SRS or in a document referenced in the SRS. This definition should specify

(a) The required ranges of the model's parameters

(b) The values of constraints it uses

(c) The required accuracy of results

(d) The load capacity

(e) The required execution time

(f) Default or failure response

(2) Care must be taken to keep a model definition within the domain of requirements.

Whenever an SRS uses a model:

(a) It means that the model provided an especially efficient and accurate way to specify the requirements

(b) It does not mean that the implementation of the software product must be based on that model.

A model that works effectively for explaining requirements in a written document may not be optimal for the actual software implementation.

5.2 Annotation of the Software Requirements. Typically, all of the requirements that relate to a software product are not equally important. Some requirements may be essential, especially for life-critical applications, while others may be just *nice to have*.

(1) Each requirement in the SRS should be annotated to make these differences in relative importance clear and explicit.

(2) Annotating the requirements in this manner, helps:

(a) Customers to give more careful consideration to each requirement, which often clarifies any hidden assumptions they may have.

(b) Developers to make correct design decisions and devote appropriate levels of effort to the different parts of the software product.

5.2.1 Stability. One method of annotating requirements uses the dimension of stability. A requirement may be considered *stable* when it is thought that the needs which it addresses will not change during the expected life of the software, or it may be considered *volatile* and subject to change.

5.2.2 **Degree of Necessity.** Another way to annotate is to distinguish classes of requirements as mandatory, desirable, and optional.

(1) Mandatory implies that the software will not be acceptable unless these requirements are provided in an agreed manner.

(2) Desirable implies that these are requirements that would enhance the software product, but would not make it unacceptable if they are absent.

(3) Optional implies a class of functions that may or may not be worthwhile, which gives the supplier the opportunity to propose something which exceeds the SRS.

5.2.3 **Annotation Caution.** Prior to annotating the requirements, a thorough understanding of the contractual implications of such annotations, should be obtained.

5.3 **Common Pitfalls Encountered in Expressing Requirements.** An essential point about the SRS is that it should specify the results that must be achieved by the software, not the means of obtaining those results.

(1) The basic issues that the requirements writer must address are these:

(a) *Functionality* — what the software is supposed to do

(b) *Performance* — the speed, availability, response time, recovery time of various software functions, etc

(c) *Design Constraints Imposed on an Implementation* — any required standards in effect, implementation language, policies for data base integrity, resource limits, operating environment(s), etc

(d) *Attributes* — considerations of portability, correctness, maintainability, security, etc

(e) *External Interfaces* — interactions with people, hardware, other software and other hardware

(2) The requirements writer should avoid placing either design or project requirements in the SRS. The requirements writer should clearly distinguish between identifying required design constraints and projecting a design.

5.3.1 **Embedding Design in the SRS.** Embedding design specifications in the SRS unduly constrains the software designs and artificially places potentially dangerous requirements in the SRS.

(1) The SRS must specify what functions are to be performed on what data to produce what results at what location for whom. The SRS should focus on the services to be performed. The SRS should not normally specify design items such as

(a) Partitioning the software into modules

(b) Allocating functions to the modules

(c) Describing the flow of information or control between modules

(d) Choosing data structures

(2) It is not always practical to consider the design as being completely isolated from the SRS. Security or safety considerations may impose requirements that reflect directly into design constraints; for example, the need to

(a) Keep certain functions in separate modules

(b) Permit only limited communication between some areas of the program

(c) Compute check sums for critical quantities

In general, it must be considered that the selection of an appropriate high-level design for the software may require vast amounts of resources (perhaps as much as 10% to 20% of the total product development cost). There are two alternatives:

(1) Ignore the warning in this guide and specify the design in the SRS. This will mean that either a potentially inadequate design is stated as a requirement (because insufficient time was spent in arriving at it), or an exorbitant amount of time is spent during the requirements phase (because an entire design analysis is performed before SRS completion).

(2) Use the advice in 5.1.3 of this guide. State the requirements using a *model* design used solely to assist in the description of the requirements and not intended to serve as the actual design.

5.3.2 **Embedding Project Requirements in the SRS.** The SRS should address the software product, not the process of producing the software product.

(1) Project requirements represent an understanding between a customer and a supplier about the contractual matters pertaining to the production of software (and thus should not be

included in the SRS). These normally include such items as:

    (a) Cost
    (b) Delivery schedules
    (c) Reporting procedures
    (d) Software development methods
    (e) Quality assurance
    (f) Validation and verification criteria
    (g) Acceptance procedures

(2) Project requirements are specified in other documents, typically in a computer program development plan or a statement of work. The requirements for only the software product itself are given in the SRS.

6. An SRS Prototype Outline

This section discusses each of the essential parts of the SRS. These parts are arranged in Table 1 in an outline that can serve as a prototype for any SRS.

Software suppliers and customers should tailor the content requirements of this guide based on the particular package being specified, and individual companies might base their own SRS standards upon it. Remember that while an SRS does not have to follow this outline or use the names for its parts, any good SRS must include all of the information discussed here.

6.1 Introduction (Section 1 of the SRS). The following subsections of the SRS should provide an overview of the entire SRS.

Table 1
Prototype SRS Outline

Table of Contents
1. Introduction
   1.1 Purpose
   1.2 Scope
   1.3 Definitions, Acronyms, and Abbreviations
   1.4 References
   1.5 Overview
2. General Description
   2.1 Product Perspective
   2.2 Product Functions
   2.3 User Characteristics
   2.4 General Constraints
   2.5 Assumptions and Dependencies
3. Specific Requirements
   (See 6.3.2 of this guide for alternate organizations of this section of the SRS.)
Appendixes
Index

6.1.1 Purpose (1.1 of the SRS). This subsection should accomplish the following:

(1) Delineate the purpose of the particular SRS

(2) Specify the intended audience for the SRS

6.1.2 Scope (1.2 of the SRS). This subsection should:

(1) Identify the software product(s) to be produced by name; for example, Host DBMS, Report Generator, etc

(2) Explain what the software product(s) will, and, if necessary, will not do

(3) Describe the application of the software being specified. As a portion of this, it should:

    (a) Describe all relevant benefits, objectives, and goals as precisely as possible. For example, to say that one goal is to provide *effective reporting capabilities* is not as good as saying *parameter-driven, user-definable reports with a 2 h turnaround and on-line entry of user parameters.*

    (b) Be consistent with similar statements in higher-level specifications (for example, the System Requirement Specification), if they exist.

6.1.3 Definitions, Acronyms, and Abbreviations (1.3 of the SRS). This subsection should provide the definitions of all terms, acronyms, and abbreviations required to properly interpret the SRS. This information may be provided by reference to one or more appendixes in the SRS or by reference to other documents.

6.1.4 References (1.4 of the SRS). This subsection should:

(1) Provide a complete list of all documents referenced elsewhere in the SRS, or in a separate, specified document.

(2) Identify each document by title, report number — if applicable — date, and publishing organization.

(3) Specify the sources from which the references can be obtained.

This information may be provided by reference to an appendix or to another document.

6.1.5 Overview (1.5 of the SRS). This subsection should:

(1) Describe what the rest of the SRS contains

(2) Explain how the SRS is organized

6.2 The General Description (Section 2 of the SRS). This section of the SRS should describe the general factors that affect the product and its requirements.

This section usually consists of five subsections, as follows:

(1) Product Perspective
(2) Product Functions
(3) User Characteristics
(4) General Constraints
(5) Assumptions and Dependencies

It should be made clear that this section does not state specific requirements; it only makes those requirements easier to understand.

6.2.1 Product Perspective (2.1 of the SRS). This subsection of the SRS puts the product into perspective with other related products or projects.

(1) If the product is independent and totally self-contained, it should be stated here.

(2) If the SRS defines a product that is a component of a larger system or project — as frequently occurs — then this subsection should:

(a) Describe the functions of each component of the larger system or project, and identify interfaces

(b) Identify the principal external interfaces of this software product.

NOTE: This is not a detailed description of these interfaces; the detailed description is provided elsewhere in the SRS.

(c) Describe the computer hardware and peripheral equipment to be used.

NOTE: This is an overview description only.

A block diagram showing the major components of the larger system or project, interconnections, and external interfaces can be very helpful.

This subsection should not be used to impose a specific design solution or specific design constraints on the solution. This subsection should provide the reasons why certain design constraints are later specified as part of the Specific Requirements Section of the SRS.

6.2.2 Product Functions (2.2 of the SRS). This subsection of the SRS should provide a summary of the functions that the software will perform. For example, an SRS for an accounting program might use this part to address *customer account maintenance, customer statement and invoice preparation* without mentioning the vast amount of detail that each of those functions requires.

Sometimes the function summary that is necessary for this part can be taken directly from the section of the higher-level specifica-

tion (if one exists) that allocates particular functions to the software product. Note that, for the sake of clarity:

(1) The functions should be organized in a way that makes the list of functions understandable to the customer or to anyone else reading the document for the first time.

(2) Block diagrams showing the different functions and their relationships can be helpful. Remember, however, that such a diagram is not a requirement on the design of a product itself; it is simply an effective explanatory tool.

This subsection should not be used to state specific requirements. This subsection should provide the reasons why certain specific requirements are later specified as part of the Specific Requirements Section(s) of the SRS.

6.2.3 User Characteristics (2.3 of the SRS). This subsection of the SRS should describe those general characteristics of the eventual users of the product that will affect the specific requirements.

Many people interact with a system during the operation and maintenance phase of the software life cycle. Some of these people are users, operators, and maintenance and systems personnel. Certain characteristics of these people, such as educational level, experience, and technical expertise impose important constraints on the system's operating environment.

If most users of the system are occasional users, a resulting specific requirement might be that the system contains reminders of how to perform essential functions rather than assuming that the user will remember these details from the last session or from reading the user's guide.

This subsection should not be used to state specific requirements or to impose specific design constraints on the solution. This subsection should provide the reasons why certain specific requirements or design constraints are later specified as part of the Specific Requirements Section(s) of the SRS.

6.2.4 General Constraints (2.4 of the SRS). This subsection of the SRS should provide a general description of any other items that will limit the developer's options for designing the system. These can include:

(1) Regulatory policies
(2) Hardware limitations; for example, signal timing requirements
(3) Interfaces to other applications
(4) Parallel operation
(5) Audit functions

(6) Control functions

(7) Higher-order language requirements

(8) Signal handshake protocols; for example, XON –XOFF, ACK – NACK.

(9) Criticality of the application

(10) Safety and security considerations

This subsection should not be used to impose specific requirements or specific design constraints on the solution. This subsection should provide the reasons why certain specific requirements or design constraints are later specified as part of the Specific Requirements Section of the SRS.

6.2.5 Assumptions and Dependencies (2.5 of the SRS). This subsection of the SRS should list each of the factors that affect the requirements stated in the SRS. These factors are not design constraints on the software but are, rather, any changes to them that can affect the requirements in the SRS. For example, an assumption might be that a specific operating system will be available on the hardware designated for the software product. If, in fact, the operating system is not available, the SRS would then have to change accordingly.

6.3 The Specific Requirements (Section 3 of the SRS). This section of the SRS should contain all the details the software developer needs to create a design. This is typically the largest and most important part of the SRS.

(1) The details within it should be defined as individual specific requirements, following the guidelines described in Section 3 of this guide (verifiable, unambiguous, etc)

(2) Background should be provided by cross-referencing each specific requirement to any related discussion in the Introduction, General Description, and Appendixes portions of the SRS, whenever possible.

(3) One way to classify the specific requirements is as follows:

(a) Functional Requirements

(b) Performance Requirements

(c) Design Constraints

(d) Attributes

(e) External Interface Requirements

The important points to be recognized are that:

(1) Specific requirements should be organized in a logical and readable fashion.

(2) Each requirement should be stated such that its achievement can be objectively verified by a prescribed method.

6.3.1 Information Required as Part of the Specific Requirements

6.3.1.1 Functional Requirements. This subsection of the SRS should specify how the inputs to the software product should be transformed into outputs. It describes the fundamental actions that must take place in the software.

For each class of function or sometimes for each individual function, it is necessary to specify requirements on inputs, processing, and outputs. These are usually organized with these four subparagraphs:

(1) Introduction. This subparagraph should provide a description of the purpose of the function and the approaches and techniques employed. It should contain any introductory or background material which might clarify the intent of the function.

(2) Inputs. This subparagraph should contain:

(a) A detailed description of all data input to this function to include:

(i) The sources of the inputs

(ii) Quantities

(iii) Units of measure

(iv) Timing

(v) The ranges of the valid inputs to include accuracies and tolerances.

(b) The details of operator control requirements should include names and descriptions of operator actions, and console or operator positions. For example, this might include required operator activities such as form alignment — when printing checks.

(c) References to interface specifications or interface control documents where appropriate.

(3) Processing. This subparagraph should define all of the operations to be performed on the input data and intermediate parameters to obtain the output. It includes specification of:

(a) Validity checks on the input data

(b) The exact sequence of operations to include timing of events

(c) Responses to *abnormal* situations, for example:

(i) Overflow

(ii) Communication failure

(iii) Error handling

(d) Parameters affected by the operations

(e) Requirements for degraded operation

(f) Any methods (for example, equations, mathematical algorithms, and logical operations) which must be used to transform the system inputs into corresponding outputs. For example, this might specify:

(i) The formula for computing the withholding tax in a payroll package

(ii) A least squares curve fitting technique for a plotting package

(iii) A meteorological model to be used for a weather forecasting package

(g) Validity checks on the output data

(4) Outputs. This subparagraph should contain:

(a) A detailed description of all data output from this function to include:

(i) Destinations of the outputs

(ii) Quantities

(iii) Units of measure

(iv) Timing

(v) The range of the valid outputs is to include accuracies and tolerances

(vi) Disposition of illegal values

(vii) Error messages

(b) References to interface specifications or interface control documents where appropriate

In addition, for those systems whose requirements focus on input/output behavior, the SRS should specify all of the significant input/output pairs and sequences of pairs. Sequences will be needed when a system is required to remember its behavior so that it can respond to an input based on that input and past behavior; that is, behave like a finite state machine.

6.3.1.2 Performance Requirements. This subsection should specify both the static and the dynamic numerical requirements placed on the software or on human interaction with the software, as a whole.

(1) Static numerical requirements may include:

(a) The number of terminals to be supported

(b) The number of simultaneous users to be supported

(c) Number of files and records to be handled

(d) Sizes of tables and files

Static numerical requirements are sometimes identified under a separate section entitled *capacity*.

(2) Dynamic numerical requirements may include, for example, the numbers of transactions and tasks and the amount of data to be processed within certain time periods for both normal and peak workload conditions.

All of these requirements should be stated in measurable terms, for example, *95% of the transactions shall be processed in less than 1 s,*

rather than, *operator shall not have to wait for the transaction to complete.*

NOTE: Numerical limits applied to one specific function are normally specified as part of the processing subparagraph description of that function.

6.3.1.3 Design Constraints. Design constraints can be imposed by other standards, hardware limitations, etc.

6.3.1.3.1 Standards Compliance. This subsection should specify the requirements derived from existing standards or regulations. They might include:

(1) Report format

(2) Data naming

(3) Accounting procedures

(4) Audit Tracing. For example, this could specify the requirement for software to trace processing activity. Such traces are needed for some applications to meet minimum government or financial standards. An audit trace requirement might, for example, state that all changes to a payroll data base must be recorded in a trace file with before and after values.

6.3.1.3.2 Hardware Limitations. This subsection could include requirements for the software to operate inside various hardware constraints. For example, these could include:

(1) Hardware configuration characteristics (number of ports, instruction sets, etc)

(2) Limits on primary and secondary memory

6.3.1.4 Attributes. There are a number of attributes that can place specific requirements on the software. Some of these are indicated below. These should not be interpreted to be a complete list.

6.3.1.4.1 Availability. This could specify the factors required to guarantee a defined availability level for the entire system such as checkpoint, recovery and restart.

6.3.1.4.2 Security. This could specify the factors that would protect the software from accidental or malicious access, use, modification, destruction, or disclosure. Specific requirements in this area could include the need to:

(1) Utilize certain cryptographical techniques

(2) Keep specific log or history data sets

(3) Assign certain functions to different modules

(4) Restrict communications between some areas of a program

(5) Compute checksums for critical quantities

6.3.1.4.3 Maintainability. This could specify the requirements to ensure that the software could be maintained. For example, as a part of this,

(1) Specific coupling metrics for the software modules could be required

(2) Specific data/program partitioning requirements could be specified for micro-devices

6.3.1.4.4 Transferability/Conversion. This could specify the user procedures, user interface compatibility constraints (if any) etc, required to transport the software from one environment to another.

6.3.1.4.5 Caution. It is important that required attributes be specified so that their achievement can be objectively verified by a prescribed method.

6.3.1.5 External Interface Requirements

6.3.1.5.1 User Interfaces. This should specify:

(1) The characteristics that the software must support for each human interface to the software product. For example, if the user of the system operates through a display terminal, the following should be specified:

(a) Required screen formats

(b) Page layout and content of any reports or menus

(c) Relative timing of inputs and outputs

(d) Availability of some form of programmable function keys

(2) All the aspects of optimizing the interface with the person who must use the system. This may simply comprise a list of do's and don'ts on how the system will appear to the user. One example might be a requirement for the option of long or short error messages. Like all others, these requirements should be verifiable and for example, *a clerk typist grade 4 can do function X in Z min* after 1 h *of training* rather than *a typist can do function X.* (This might also be specified in the Attributes section under a section titled *Ease of Use.*)

6.3.1.5.2 Hardware Interfaces. This should specify the logical characteristics of each interface between the software product and the hardware components of the system. It also covers such matters as what devices are to be supported, how they are to be supported, and protocols. For example, terminal support might specify full screen support as opposed to line by line.

6.3.1.5.3 Software Interfaces. This should specify the use of other required software products (for example, a data management system, an operating system, or a mathematical package), and interfaces with other application systems (for example, the linkage between an accounts receivable system and a general ledger system).

For each required software product, the following should be provided:

(1) Name

(2) Mnemonic

(3) Specification number

(4) Version number

(5) Source

For each interface, this part should:

(1) Discuss the purpose of the interfacing software as related to this software product.

(2) Define the interface in terms of message content and format. It is not necessary to detail any well-documented interface, but a reference to the document defining the interface is required.

6.3.1.5.4 Communications Interfaces. This should specify the various interfaces to communications such as local network protocols, etc.

6.3.1.6 Other Requirements. Certain requirements may, due to the nature of the software, the user organization, etc, be placed in separate categories as indicated below.

6.3.1.6.1 Data Base. This could specify the requirements for any data base that is to be developed as part of the product. This might include:

(1) The types of information identified in 6.3.1.1

(2) Frequency of use

(3) Accessing capabilities

(4) Data element and file descriptors

(5) Relationship of data elements, records and files

(6) Static and dynamic organization

(7) Retention requirements for data

NOTE: If an existing data base package is to be used, this package should be named under *Interfaces to Software* and details of using it specified there.

6.3.1.6.2 Operations. This could specify the normal and special operations required by the user such as:

(1) The various modes of operations in the user organization; for example, user-initiated operations

(2) Periods of interactive operations and periods of unattended operations

(3) Data processing support functions

(4) Backup and recovery operations

NOTE: This is sometimes specified as part of the User Interfaces section.

6.3.1.6.3 Site Adaptation Requirements.
This could:

(1) Define the requirements for any data or initialization sequences that are specific to a given site, mission, or operational mode, for example, grid values, safety limits, etc.

(2) Specify the site or mission-related features that should be modified to adapt the software to a particular installation.

6.3.2 Organizing The Specific Requirements.
This subsection is often the largest and most complex of all the parts of the SRS.

(1) It may be necessary to organize this section into subdivisions according to the primary classes of functions to be performed by the software. For example, consider a large interactive accounting system. This may be broken down at the top level into operational software (which supports near-real-time transactions), support software (logging functions, disk backup, loading tapes, etc), and diagnostic software (primarily hardware and communications support), and at the next level into accounts receivable, accounts payable, etc.

(2) It should be remembered, however, that the purpose of this subdivided organization is to improve the readability of the SRS, not to define the high level design of the software being specified.

The best organization for Section 3, Specific Requirements, in an SRS, depends on the application area and the nature of the software product being specified. Tables 2 through 4 show four possible organizations.

(1) In Prototype Outline 1 (Table 2), all the Functional Requirements are specified, then the four types of interface requirements are specified, and then the rest of the requirements are specified.

(2) Prototype Outline 2 (Table 3) shows the four classes of interface requirements applied to each individual Functional Requirement. This is followed by the specification of the rest of the requirements.

(3) In Prototype Outline 3 (Table 4), all of the issues addressed by the Functional Requirements are specified, then the other requirements that apply to them are specified. This pattern is then repeated for each of the External Interface Requirement Classifications.

**Table 2
Prototype Outline 1 for SRS Section 3**

```
3.  Specific Requirements
    3.1  Functional Requirements
         3.1.1  Functional Requirement 1
                3.1.1.1  Introduction
                3.1.1.2  Inputs
                3.1.1.3  Processing
                3.1.1.4  Outputs
         3.1.2  Functional Requirement 2
         . . . .
         3.1.n  Functional Requirement n
    3.2  External Interface Requirements
         3.2.1  User Interfaces
         3.2.2  Hardware Interfaces
         3.2.3  Software Interfaces
         3.2.4  Communications Interfaces
    3.3  Performance Requirements
    3.4  Design Constraints
         3.4.1  Standards Compliance
         3.4.2  Hardware Limitations
         . . . .
    3.5  Attributes
         3.5.1  Security
         3.5.2  Maintainability
         . . . .
    3.6  Other Requirements
         3.6.1  Data Base
         3.6.2  Operations
         3.6.3  Site Adaptation
         . . . .
```

**Table 3
Prototype Outline 2 for SRS Section 3**

```
3.  Specific Requirements
    3.1  Functional Requirements
         3.1.1  Functional Requirement 1
                3.1.1.1  Specification
                         3.1.1.1.1  Introduction
                         3.1.1.1.2  Inputs
                         3.1.1.1.3  Processing
                         3.1.1.1.4  Outputs
                3.1.1.2  External Interfaces
                         3.1.1.2.1  User Interfaces
                         3.1.1.2.2  Hardware
                                    Interfaces
                         3.1.1.2.3  Software
                                    Interfaces
                         3.1.1.2.4  Communication
                                    Interfaces
         3.1.2  Functional Requirement 2
         . . . .
         3.1.n  Functional Requirement n
    3.2  Performance Requirements
    3.3  Design Constraints
    3.4  Attributes
         3.4.1  Security
         3.4.2  Maintainability
         . . . .
    3.5  Other Requirements
         3.5.1  Data Base
         3.5.2  Operations
         3.5.3  Site Adaption
         . . . .
```

Table 4
Prototype Outline 3 for SRS Section 3

```
3.  Specific Requirements
    3.1  Functional Requirements
         3.1.1  Functional Requirement 1
                3.1.1.1  Introduction
                3.1.1.2  Inputs
                3.1.1.3  Processing
                3.1.1.4  Outputs
                3.1.1.5  Performance Requirements
                3.1.1.6  Design Constraints
                         3.1.1.4.1  Standards
                                    Compliance
                         3.1.1.4.2  Hardware
                                    Limitations
                         . . . .
                3.1.1.7  Attributes
                         3.1.1.7.1  Security
                         3.1.1.7.2  Maintainability
                         . . . .
                3.1.1.8  Other Requirements
                         3.1.1.8.1  Data Base
                         3.1.1.8.2  Operations
                         3.1.1.8.3  Site Adaption
                         . . . .
         3.1.2  Functional Requirement 2
                . . . .
         3.1.n  Functional Requirement n
    3.2  External Interface Requirements
         3.2.1  User Interfaces
                3.2.1.1  Performance Requirements
                3.2.1.2  Design Constraints
                         3.2.1.2.1  Standards
                                    Compliance
                         3.2.1.2.2  Hardware
                                    Limitations
                         . . . .
                3.2.1.3  Attributes
                         3.2.1.3.1  Security
                         3.2.1.3.2  Maintainability
                         . . . .
                3.2.1.4  Other Requirements
                         3.2.1.4.1  Data Base
                         3.2.1.4.2  Operations
                         3.2.1.4.3  Site Adaption
                         . . . .
         3.2.2  Hardware Interfaces
         3.2.3  Software Interfaces
         3.2.4  Communications Interfaces
```

Table 5
Prototype Outline 4 for SRS Section 3

```
3.  Specific Requirements
    3.1  Functional Requirement 1
         3.1.1  Introduction
         3.1.2  Inputs
         3.1.3  Processing
         3.1.4  Outputs
         3.1.5  External Interfaces
                3.1.5.1  User Interfaces
                3.1.5.2  Hardware Interfaces
                3.1.5.3  Software Interfaces
                3.1.5.4  Communication Interfaces
         3.1.6  Performance Requirements
         3.1.7  Design Constraints
         3.1.8  Attributes
                3.1.8.1  Security
                3.1.8.2  Maintainability
                . . . .
         3.1.9  Other Requirements
                3.1.9.1  Data Base
                3.1.9.2  Operations
                3.1.9.3  Site Adaption
                . . . .
    3.2  Functional Requirement 2
         . . . .
    3.n  Functional Requirement n
```

(4) In Prototype Outline 4 (Table 5), the interface requirements and the rest of the requirements are specified as they pertain to each Functional Requirement.

The organization of the Specific Requirements Section of the SRS should be chosen with the goal of properly specifying the requirements in the most readable manner.

6.4 Supporting Information. The supporting information; that is, the Table of Contents, the Appendixes, and the Index, make the SRS easier to use.

(1) The Table of Contents and Index are quite important and should follow the generally accepted rules for good documentation practices.[8]

(2) The Appendixes are not always considered part of the actual requirements specification and are not always necessary. They might include:

(a) Sample I/O formats, descriptions of cost analysis studies, or results of user surveys.

(b) Supporting or background information that can help the readers of the SRS.

(c) A description of the problems to be solved by the software.

(d) The history, background, experience and operational characteristics of the organization to be supported.

(e) A cross-reference list, arranged by milestone, of those incomplete software requirements that are to be completed by specified milestones. (See 4.3.2 and 4.3.3 (4).)

(f) Special packaging instructions for the code and the media to meet security, export, initial loading, or other requirements.

(3) When Appendixes are included, the SRS should explicitly state whether or not the Appendixes are to be considered part of the requirements.

---

[8]See, for example: [4] and [11].

24

ANSI/IEEE
Std 983-1986

An American National Standard

IEEE Guide for Software Quality Assurance Planning

983

Sponsor

**Software Engineering Standards Subcommittee
of the
Technical Committee on Software Engineering
of the
IEEE Computer Society**

Approved September 19, 1985

IEEE Standards Board

Approved February 20, 1986

American National Standards Institute

Foreword

(This Foreword is not a part of IEEE Std 983-1986, IEEE Guide for Software Quality Assurance Planning.)

The purpose of this guide is to recommend approaches to good Software Quality Assurance practices in support of ANSI/IEEE Std 730-1984, IEEE Standard for Software Quality Assurance Plans. This guide is meant to supplement ANSI/IEEE Std 730-1984 by presenting the current consensus of those in the software development community who have expertise or experience in generating, implementing, evaluating, and modifying Software Quality Assurance plans. This guide is not offered as a detailed procedures manual for establishing and operating Software Quality Assurance programs. This guide does not constitute further requirements than those stated in ANSI/IEEE Std 730-1984. An organization can claim compliance with ANSI/IEEE Std 730-1984 without following completely, or in part, this guide. Detailed information regarding specific software quality assurance activities may be found in other IEEE Standards. These are referenced where appropriate. While this guide quotes major portions of ANSI/IEEE Std 730-1984, the standard is not quoted in its entirety. ANSI/IEEE Std 730-1984 users are advised to consult that standard directly.

In accordance with ANSI/IEEE Std 730-1984, the practices herein are directed toward the development and maintenance of critical software, that is, where failure could impair safety or cause large financial losses. Determination of this criticality lies in the "eyes of the beholder." The specific application and situation of each user must be carefully considered. Should there be doubt, it is suggested that the software be considered critical. For software that is definitely noncritical, or software already developed, a subset of the requirements stated in ANSI/IEEE Std 730-1984 is appropriate.

This guide serves the three groups discussed in the Foreword to ANSI/IEEE Std 730-1984: the user, the developer, and the public.

(1) The user, whether external or internal to the developing organization, has a need for the software product that meets its identified requirements. Thus, the user cannot afford to rely solely on the developer's tests at the conclusion of the software development effort. Should the software product fail to meet requirements at that point, the user's need still exists and a major portion of the development time has been lost. The user, therefore, needs to have a reasonable degree of confidence that the product is in the process of acquiring required attributes during software development.

(2) The developer needs a software quality assurance standard which establishes responsibility and accountability. It is unreasonable to expect a complete reorientation from project to project. Not only is it not cost-effective, but unless there exists a stable framework on which to base changes, improvements cannot be made.

(3) The public, which may be affected by the use of the software, has a vested interest in software development. This public includes, for example, depositors at a bank and passengers using a reservation system. The public has a right to expect that software developers have acted in a reasonable and prudent professional manner to provide the required software attributes. At some later date, the user, the developer, or both may be required to show that they did, in fact, act in such a reasonable and prudent professional manner.

This guide is addressed to readers who have professional experience in quality assurance, or in software development, but not necessarily in both. For example, this guide should be useful to the following individuals:

(1) A quality assurance person with the responsibility for developing or implementing a Software Quality Assurance Plan for a project

(2) A software development project manager desiring to initiate Software Quality Assurance procedures on a project

(3) A purchaser or user of a software product who wants to evaluate a seller's Software Quality Assurance Plan or to specify a Software Quality Assurance Plan

(4) An independent evaluator, such as an EDP auditor

(5) The person with accountability for the implementation of a Software Quality Assurance Plan

In the body of this guide, the use of "shall" is to be understood as referring to an item or activity that is mandated by ANSI/IEEE Std 730-1984. The use of "should" is to be understood as referring to a recommended item or activity. The use of "may" is to be understood as referring to an item or activity that can be advised under some circumstances, but for which there is not a professional consensus. The use of "could" is to be understood as suggesting the existence of several possibilities, the selection among which will be specific to the project and not driven by specific quality assurance considerations.

This guide was prepared and balloted by the Software Engineering Standards Subcommittee of the Software Engineering Technical Committee of the IEEE Computer Society. At the time it approved this standard, the subcommittee had the following membership:

George D. Tice, Jr., *Chairperson*

Joel Hebert, *Treasurer*   **Laurel V. Kaleda,** *Secretary*
A. Frank Ackerman, *Vice Chairperson*   **Robert M. Poston,** *Vice Chairperson*
John W. Horch, *Vice Chairperson*   **Leonard Tripp,** *Vice Chairperson*
Thomas M. Kurihara, *Vice Chairperson*

William L. Anderson	Carolyn M. Harrison	Jock A. Rader
Roy W. Bass	Clark M. Hay	Jean-Claude Rault
Nestore G. Biasi	Madeleine C. Heidkamp	Lawrence K. Reed
Michael A. Blackledge	Leslie R. Heselton, III	Donald J. Reifer
John F. Boucher	Charles R. Hollocker	Steven M. Rowan
William L. Bryan	Samual Horvitz	Frank Salvia
Fletcher J. Buckley	Lawrence M. Johmann	Hans Schaefer
Une H. Butenhoff	Harry Kalmbach	Robert W. Schillato
C. L. Carpenter	Michael R. Kirchner	Max J. Schindler
Jung K. Chung	George A. Klammer	Norman F. Schneidewind
Won L. Chung	Joseph J. Klock	Robert G. Schueppert
Corey Clinger	Dwayne L. Knirk	David J. Schultz
David Collard	Albert M. Lerner	Leonard W. Seagren
Christopher M. Cooke	Richard C. Lewis	Anthony E. Severino
Gilmore G. Cooke	F. C. Lim	Ronald L. Skelton
John D. Cooper	Gary S. Lindsay	Marian P. Smith
A. J. Cote, Jr.	Ben Livson	Wayne Smith
Richard Cotter	Alan Cheuk-Wai Ma	Thomas Q. Stevenson
Steward G. Crawford	Henry A. Malec	William G. Sutcliffe
Robert C. Crombe	William A. Mandeville	Michael H. Taint
George D. Darling	Ben Manny	Barbara J. Tante
Noah Seth Davis	Paulo Cesar Marcondes	E. Frank Testa
James A. Dobbins	Philip C. Marriott	Richard H. Thayer
Irving Doshay	Roger J. Martin	J. Rush Thompson
David C. Doty	Werner R. MaHersdorff	Paul U. Thompson
Gene E. Dufoe	Leroy M. May	Terrence L. Tillmanns
Patricia W. Duggett	Belden Menkus	George W. Trever
Robert E. Dwyer	Walter Merenda	Henry J. Trochesset
John D. Earls	Dennis F. Meronek	C. L. Troyanowski
Leo G. Egan, Jr.	Gene T. Morun	William S. Turner, III
Caroline L. Evans	David G. Mullens	David Usechak
John W. Fendrich	Saied Najafi	R. L. Van-Tilbury
Glenn S. Fields	Jainendra K. Navlakha	Udo Voges
Heinz H. Frey	Dennis E. Nickle	Ralph Wachter
Edward L. Gibbs	Olebernt Olavesen	Andrew H. Weigel
Michael J. Gooding	David E. Perr	Paul A. Willis
Robert M. Gross	Poul Grao Petersen	David L. Winningham
Russell T. Gustin	Donald J. Pfeiffer	Charles Wortz
Virl E. Haas	Patricia B. Powell	Robert H. Yacobellis

Special representatives to the Software Engineering Standards Subcommittee were as follows:

H. R. Berlack: Electronic Industry Association
N. C. Farr: Nuclear Power Engineering Committee,
  IEEE Power Engineering Society
A. Ferlan: American Society for Quality Control

S. R. Jarocki: EDP Auditors Association
J. Milandin: ANSI Z1
W. E. Perry: Data Processing Manufacturers Association
T. L. Regulinski: IEEE Reliability Society

The working group that developed this standard had the following membership:

George D. Tice, Jr., *Chairperson*   **A. Frank Ackerman,** *Co-Chairperson*

Alphonso J. Barr	Eugene Gouldman	Dennis E. Nickle
William Belke	Joseph Guidos	George O'Connell
Nestore G. Biasi	Russel Gusten	Robert M. Poston
Margaret Bornett	Carolyn M. Harrison	Patricia B. Powell
Vincent Boyer	Joel Hebert	Peter Ron Prinzivalli
Eric J. Braude	George Heblinger	Jane Radatz
Fletcher J. Buckley	John Hoelzel	Hans Reiche
Robert A. Burch	Charles R. Hollocker	Lenard B. Robertson
William Burns	Robert Hood	James Ronback
John Center	John W. Horch	Miney Roseberry
Richard Chilausky	Philip Jacobs	Hans Schaefer
Peter Clemens	Laurel V. Kaleda	Roger Scholten
Joan Colbert	Myron S. Karasik	David J. Schultz
James V. Dinkey	Robert Kessler	Robert W. Shillato
Paul Doyle	Joseph J. Klock	J. Michael Smith
Walter DuBlanica	John S. Kopec	Andi Stout
Robert L. Erickson	Richard W. Kubica	Barbara J. Taute
Charles Feather	Robert Lane	Nina C. Thomas
Arthur Ferlan	Albert M. Lerner	Don Thorne
David Gelperin	Venetta Mallory	William S. Turner, III
Jean A. Gilmore	Philip C. Marriott	Donald Willett
Shirley Gloss-Soler	Charles F. Martiny	James Zoog
Edward Gonzales	Gerald Neidhart	

When the IEEE Standards Board approved this standard on September 19, 1985, it had the following membership:

John E. May, *Chairman*   **John P. Riganati,** *Vice Chairman*

Sava I. Sherr, *Secretary*

James H. Beall	Daniel L. Goldberg	Lawrence V. McCall
Fletcher J. Buckley	Kenneth D. Hendrix	Donald T. Michael*
Rene Castenschiold	Irvin N. Howell	Frank L. Rose
Edward Chelotti	Jack Kinn	Clifford O. Swanson
Edward J. Cohen	Joseph L. Koepfinger*	J. Richard Weger
Paul G. Cummings	Irving Kolodny	W. B. Wilkens
Donald C. Fleckenstein	R. F. Lawrence	Charles J. Wylie
Jay Forster		

*Member emeritus

Contents

An American National Standard
IEEE Guide for Software Quality Assurance Planning

1. Scope and References

1.1 Scope. The purpose of this guide is to explain and clarify the contents of each section of a Software Quality Assurance Plan (SQAP) that satisfies the requirements of ANSI/IEEE Std 730-1984 [2].[1] The guide does not constitute further requirements than those stated in ANSI/IEEE Std 730-1984 [2]. An organization can claim compliance with ANSI/IEEE Std 730-1984 [2] without following completely, or in part, this guide.

This guide presents the current consensus of those in the software development community with expertise or experience in generating, implementing, evaluating, and modifying a SQAP. Section 3 of this guide describes the content of each section in a SQAP that satisfies ANSI/IEEE Std 730-1984 [2]. Each subsection of Section 3 quotes the applicable wording from the standard. Section 4 provides guidance for implementing a SQAP on a software project, or within a software development organization. Section 5 provides guidance for evaluating the contents and the implementation of a SQAP. Section 6 provides guidance for the procedures used to modify an existing SQAP. The Appendix presents a summary of the contents of a SQAP. This guide is applicable to the development and maintenance of all software, recognizing that the application of these recommendations should be tailored to the specific software product item. The user of this guide should be aware that efforts are underway to provide standards and guides that cover many areas. Prior to implementation, a check should be made with the Secretary, IEEE Standards Board, for further detailed guidance in this area.

1.2 References.

[1] ANSI/IEEE Std 729-1983, IEEE Standard Glossary of Software Engineering Terminology.

[2] ANSI/IEEE Std 730-1984, IEEE Standard for Software Quality Assurance Plans.[2]

[3] ANSI/IEEE Std 828-1983, IEEE Standard for Software Configuration Management Plans.

[4] ANSI/IEEE Std 829-1983, IEEE Standard for Software Test Documentation.

[5] ANSI/IEEE Std 830-1984, IEEE Guide to Software Requirements Specifications.

2. Definitions and Acronyms

2.1 Definitions. The definitions listed below establish meaning in the context of this guide. Other definitions can be found in ANSI/IEEE Std 729-1983 [1] and ANSI/IEEE Std 730-1984 [2].

conventions. Requirements employed to prescribe a disciplined, uniform approach to providing consistency in a software *product,* that is, uniform patterns or forms for arranging data.

practices. Requirements employed to prescribe a disciplined, uniform approach to the software development *process.*

standards. Mandatory requirements employed and *enforced* to prescribe a disciplined, uniform

---

[1] The numbers in brackets correspond to those of the references listed in Section 1.2.

[2] ANSI/IEEE publications are available from the Sales Department, American National Standards Institute, 1430 Broadway, New York, NY 10018, and the Institute of Electrical and Electronics Engineers, Service Center, 445 Hoes Lane, Piscataway, NJ 08854.

approach to software development, that is, mandatory conventions and practices are in fact standards.

techniques. Technical and managerial procedures that aid in the evaluation and improvement of the software development process.

2.2 Acronyms. The following alphabetical contractions appear within the text of this guide:

CCB	Change control board (in this document refers to change control board for a SQAP)
CDR	Critical design review
CI	Configuration item
PDR	Preliminary design review
SCM	Software configuration management
SCMP	Software configuration management plan
SDD	Software design description
SDP	Software development plan
SPM	Standards and procedures manual
SQA	Software quality assurance
SQAP	Software quality assurance plan
SRR	Software requirements review
SRS	Software requirements specification
SVVP	Software verification and validation plan
SVVPR	Software verification and validation plan review
SVVR	Software verification and validation report
UDR	User documentation review

3. Contents of a Software Quality Assurance Plan

"The organization responsible for Software Quality Assurance shall prepare a Software Quality Assurance Plan (also referred to as the Plan) that includes the sections listed below. The sections should be ordered in the described sequence. If there is no information pertinent to a section, the following statement shall appear below the section heading. *This section is not applicable to this plan,* together with the appropriate reasons for the exclusion.

(1) Purpose
(2) Reference Documents
(3) Management

(4) Documentation
(5) Standards, Practices, and Conventions
(6) Reviews and Audits
(7) Software Configuration Management
(8) Problem Reporting and Corrective Action
(9) Tools, Techniques, and Methodologies
(10) Code Control
(11) Media Control
(12) Supplier Control
(13) Records Collection, Maintenance, and Retention

"Additional sections may be added at the end, as required. Some of the material may appear in other documents. If so, then reference to those documents should be made in the body of the plan." [2][4]

For example, portions of the required information may be contained in a separate Software Configuration Management Plan (SCMP) or in a Software Development Plan (SDP). These sections should reference those particular plans. Those plans should be reviewed to ensure that they provide all the required information.

3.1 Purpose. "This section shall delineate the specific purpose and scope of the particular Software Quality Assurance Plan (SQAP). It shall list the name(s) of the software product items covered by the SQAP and the intended use of the software." [2]

The following questions should be addressed in this section:

(1) *Which software products are covered by this SQAP?* Specific names and abbreviations should be supplied for these products.

(2) *What is the intended use of the software covered by this SQAP?* How is the software to be utilized? How critical is this software? Is it part of a larger system; if so, how is it related to the system?

(3) *Why is this SQAP being written?* Is this Plan being written in response to an internal or external requirement? Why is this SQAP needed?

(4) *What documents form the basis of this SQAP?* Describe the extent to which this SQAP is based on ANSI/IEEE Std 730-1984 [2]. Identify any other documents on which this SQAP is based, eg, military or corporate quality assurance standards and guidelines.

---

[4] The quoted material appearing in this standard has been extracted from ANSI/IEEE Std 730-1984 [2].

(5) *What is the rationale behind departures from documents mentioned in 3.1(4)?* Which product or development attributes warrant additional or stricter practices or procedures? Which attributes warrant more lenient practices or procedures?

3.2 Reference Documents. "This section shall provide a complete list of documents referenced elsewhere in the text of the plan." [2]

Clearly identify the sources from which the documents can be obtained.

3.3 Management. "This section shall describe the organization, tasks, and responsibilities." [2]

Section 3.3.1 shall describe each major element of the organization which influences the quality of the software. Section 3.3.2 shall list the tasks covered by this plan. Section 3.3.3 shall identify specific organizational responsibilities for each task. This description should also identify the management position which retains overall authority and responsibility for software quality.

3.3.1 Organization. "This paragraph shall depict the organizational structure that influences the quality of the software. This shall include a description of each major element of the organization together with the delegated responsibilities. Organizational dependence or independence of the elements responsible for SQA from those responsible for software development and use shall be clearly described or depicted." [2]

The organizational element(s) responsible for the software quality assurance functions covered by the SQAP may be developers knowledgeable in quality assurance techniques and tools; a dedicated quality assurance element serving a number of projects; or a series of separate organizational elements, each of which implements one or more SQA functional activities. The SQAP should state the organizational and functional boundaries of the SQA element. This should not be construed to indicate that a specific SQA organization must be established nor that a SQA organizational element must perform specific tasks.

If the SQA element is not attached to the software development element, the plan should state this clearly and explain any interrelationships that exist between these and other elements. If the SQA element is attached to other elements, the plan should explain its structure and interrelationships.

A pictorial organizational structure should be included with a written explanation amplifying the nature and degree of relationships with all organizational elements responsible for software product quality and development. The written explanation should include:

(1) A description of each element which interacts with the SQA element

(2) Delegated responsibilities of interacting elements

(3) Reporting relationships among the interacting elements

(4) Identification of the organizational element with product release authority

(5) Identification of the organizational element which approves the SQAP

(6) The method by which conflicts are to be resolved among the elements

The written explanation may also include:

(7) The size of the SQA element

(8) An explanation of any deviations from organizational SQA policies, procedures, or standards

The description of the organizational structure should be complete so that all the tasks addressed in the SQAP can be directly related to the structure.

3.3.2 Tasks. "This paragraph shall describe the tasks associated with that portion of the software life cycle covered by this plan with special emphasis on software quality assurance activities. The sequence of the tasks shall be indicated." [2]

The basic tasks are described in 3.4 through 3.13. All of the tasks in these sections may not be applicable to a specific project, in which event they may be omitted. Any omissions or deviations from ANSI/IEEE Std 730-1984 [2] should be explained. Any additional tasks, along with additional sections to the Plan, should be included. Any deviations from corporate software quality assurance policies should be explained. This section of the SQAP should also designate the personnel responsible for publication, distribution, maintenance, and implementation of the SQAP.

Each task should be defined with entrance and exit criteria, that is, what is needed to initiate the task, and what is the output of the task. The output of each task should be defined in such a way that its achievement or completion can be objectively determined in a prescribed manner. Additionally, this section could include a table indicating the staffing levels for the listed tasks.

While it is strongly recommended that a Software Development Plan (SDP) (see 3.4.3.1) be prepared, if an SDP is not available, this section should provide schedule information outlining the development cycle.

3.3.3 Responsibilities. "This paragraph shall identify the specific organizational elements responsible for each task." [2]

If two or more elements share responsibility for a task, their respective responsibilities should be identified. The management position accountable for overall software quality should be identified. This section of the SQAP should also designate the personnel responsible for publication, distribution, and maintenance of the SQAP. It should indicate the review and approval cycle, indicating signature authority as required. It should show the number of controlled copies and describe the method of control, if applicable. It should designate the personnel responsible for distributing the SQAP and describe the methods and responsibilities for the promulgation, approval, distribution, and incorporation of changes.

3.4 Documentation. "This section shall:

(1) Identify the documentation governing the development, verification, and validation, use, and maintenance of the software.

(2) State how the documents are to be checked for adequacy. The statement shall include identification of the review or audit by which the adequacy of each document shall be confirmed, with reference to Section 6 of the Plan." [2]

Section 6 of the Plan is discussed in 3.6 of this guide.

3.4.1 Purpose. The SQAP should identify the documentation that will be prepared during the development, verification and validation, use, and maintenance of the software. The SQAP should identify the organizational elements responsible for the origination, verification, maintenance, and control of the required documentation. The SQAP should also identify the specific reviews, audits, and associated criteria required for each document, including references as appropriate to 3.6, Reviews and Audits.

The following subsections should describe the format and content of each of the documents used. If this information is provided in another document, only a reference should be given. Organizational policies, procedures, and standards may determine additional information requirements.

3.4.2 Minimum Documentation Requirements. "To ensure that the implementation of the software satisfies the requirements, the following documentation is required as a minimum . . ." [2]

ANSI/IEEE Std 730-1984 [2] requires the following documents:

(1) Software Requirements Specification (SRS)

(2) Software Design Description (SDD)

(3) Software Verification and Validation Plan (SVVP)

(4) Software Verification and Validation Report (SVVR)

(5) User Documentation

These documents will provide the basis for a logical and systematic approach to the development and operation of the software. A brief description of each document follows.

3.4.2.1 Software Requirements Specification (SRS). "The SRS shall clearly and precisely describe each of the essential requirements (functions, performances, design constraints, and attributes) of the software and the external interfaces. Each requirement shall be defined such that its achievement is capable of being verified and validated objectively by a prescribed method, for example, inspection, demonstration, analysis, or test." [2]

The SRS is usually developed from one or more completed documents such as a user requirements statement, operational requirements, statement of work, or contract. It specifies in detail the requirements as agreed upon by the developer and the requester or user. The SQAP should identify what standards or guides apply to the content and format of the SRS. ANSI/IEEE Std 830-1984 [5] describes the necessary content and qualities of an SRS.

The SRS is subject to the Software Requirements Review (SRR) described in 3.6.

3.4.2.2 Software Design Description (SDD). "The SDD shall describe the major components of the software design including data bases and internal interfaces. An expansion of this description shall be included to describe each subcomponent of the major components." [2]

The SDD is a technical description of how the software will meet the requirements set forth in the SRS. Its most important function is to describe a decomposition of the system as a whole, into components (subsystems, segments, etc) that are complete and well-bounded.

The SDD describes major system features such as data bases, diagnostics, external and internal interfaces, and overall structure. It involves descriptions of the operating environment, monitors, timing, system throughput, tables, sizing, modeling, etc. The SQAP should identify the standards and conventions that apply to the content and format of the SDD, as well as the procedures to be used in developing the SDD.

The SDD is subject to the Preliminary Design Review (PDR) and the Critical Design Review (CDR) described in 3.6.

For each component in the system, the SDD should consist of items such as:

(1) A textural description of the component's:
  (a) Inputs
  (b) Outputs
  (c) Calling sequence
  (d) Function or task
  (e) Algorithms
(2) A list of other components called
(3) A list of all calling components
(4) Allowed and tolerable range of values for all inputs
(5) Allowed and expected range of values for all outputs
(6) Assumptions, limitations, and side effects

3.4.2.3 Software Verification and Validation Plan (SVVP).

"The SVVP shall describe the methods (for example, inspection, demonstration, analysis, or test) to be used:

(1) To verify that
  (a) The requirements in the SRS are implemented in the design expressed in the SDD.
  (b) The design expressed in the SDD is implemented in the code.
(2) To validate that the code, when executed, complies with the requirements expressed in the SRS." [2]

The SVVP describes the overall plan for the verification and validation of the software. The tasks, methods, and criteria for verification and validation are described. The SVVP specifies minimum test documentation requirements. ANSI/IEEE Std 829-1983 [4] may be consulted.

The SQAP should identify which standards and conventions apply to the content and format of the SVVP. A section of the SVVP should include a verification matrix where requirements are listed with their corresponding SVVP section. The contents of the SVVP will be evaluated at the Software Verification and Validation Plan Review (SVVPR) described in 3.6.

3.4.2.4 Software Verification and Validation Report (SVVR).

"The SVVR shall describe the results of the execution of the SVVP. This shall include the results of all reviews, audits, and tests required by the SQA plan." [2]

The SVVR summarizes the observed status of the software as a result of the execution of the SVVP. It outlines any major deficiencies found; provides the results of reviews, audits, and tests; indicates the status of planned corrective actions; and should recommended whether the software is, or is not, ready for operational use.

3.4.2.5 User Documentation.

"The User Documentation (eg, manual, guide, etc) shall specify and describe the required data and control inputs, input sequences, options, program limitations, and other activities/items necessary for successful execution of the software. All error messages shall be identified and corrective actions described. A method of describing user-identified errors/problems to the developer/owner of the software shall be described." [2]

The User Documentation should be composed of the following items:

(1) User instructions which contain an introduction, a description of the user's interaction with the system, and a description of any required training for using the system (see, also, Training Manual, 3.4.4.4)
(2) A system narrative purpose and description
(3) Input/output specifications
(4) Samples of original source documents and examples of all input formats (forms or displays)
(5) Samples of all outputs (forms, reports, or displays)
(6) Data entry instructions that contain instructions for data preparation, data keying, data verification, data proofing, and error correction
(7) References to all documents or manuals intended for use by the users
(8) A description of the system's limitations
(9) A description of all error situations which can occur and how to react

A User Documentation Review (UDR) is described in 3.6.3.1

3.4.3 Other Documentation. "Other documentation may include the following:

(1) Software Development Plan
(2) Software Configuration Management Plan
(3) Standards and Procedures Manual." [2]

3.4.3.1 Software Development Plan (SDP). The SDP should identify all technical and managerial activities associated with computer program development. The SDP should specify the following items:

(1) Activity description
(2) Activity deliverables and associated completion criteria
(3) Prerequisite deliverables from prior activities, if any
(4) Schedule and interrelationships among activities
(5) Assignment of responsibility for each activity

3.4.3.2 Software Configuration Management Plan (SCMP). The SCMP should describe the methods to be used for:

(1) Identifying the software configuration items
(2) Controlling and implementing changes
(3) Recording and reporting change implementation status
(4) Conducting configuration audits

The SCMP may be a separate document or a section of the SQAP. The ANSI/IEEE Std 828-1983 [3] provides minimum acceptable requirements for the content of an SCMP.

3.4.3.3 Standards and Procedures Manual (SPM). The SPM should provide details on standards and procedures to be followed for specific activities. As a minimum, the information described in 3.5 should be included.

3.4.4 Additional Suggested Documentation. The attributes, context, and environment of the product could dictate inclusion of additional documents, such as but not limited to the following:

(1) User Requirements Statement
(2) External Interface Specification
(3) Internal Interface Specification
(4) Operations Manual
(5) Installation Manual
(6) Maintenance Manual

(7) Training Manual
(8) Training Plan

3.4.4.1 User Requirements Statement. The User Requirements Statement should include, but is not limited to:

(1) A service request which contains the identity of the requester, the software product name and title, the date the software product was requested and is required, a description of what the software product should do, an abstract of the need for the software product, privacy or security considerations, and a list of potential users of the software product.
(2) A list of the objectives that are to be satisfied by the software product, as well as any other needs (administrative, timing, SQA, etc) and restraints the user perceives as necessary.
(3) Any studies done to define resource requirements (ie, hardware, software, personnel, plant and facilities, or environmental), feasibility, or cost-benefits analyses.

3.4.4.2 External Interface Specification. The External Interface Specification should contain information about files and other interconnections to all other software products outside the system to be developed. Consideration should be given to human interfaces, hardware interfaces, environmental constraints, and files or transactions coming from or going to other systems.

3.4.4.3 Internal Interface Specification. The Internal Interface Specification should contain information about files and other interconnections among all the components within the system. Consideration should be given to such subjects as transfer of control between modules, passing of data between modules, physical interfaces, and common data bases.

3.4.4.4 Operations Manual. The Operations Manual should be composed of at least the following items:

(1) Operating instructions that contain:
  (a) An introduction
  (b) Run schedules
  (c) Setup requirements
  (d) Job control procedures
  (e) Error procedures
  (f) Security procedures
  (g) Distribution procedures
  (h) Backup and recovery procedures
  (i) Restart procedures

(2) Specifications for the system, including environmental requirements

(3) Input/output specifications

(4) Auditing controls

3.4.4.5 Installation Manual. An Installation Manual should contain instructions for the installation of the software product, file conversion instructions, use of user-controlled installation options, and instructions for performing an installation test.

3.4.4.6 Maintenance Manual. A Maintenance Manual should contain instructions for software product support and maintenance, such as procedures for correcting defects and installation of enhancements. This document should refer to the Problem Reporting System (see 3.8) and the SCMP (see 3.4.3.2).

3.4.4.7 Training Manual. The Training Manual should contain information necessary for training users and operators of the system. It should contain, but is not limited to:

(1) An introduction

(2) How to use the system

(3) Preparing input

(4) Data input descriptions

(5) Data control descriptions

(6) How to run the system

(7) Output distributions

(8) Description of output data and interpretations

3.4.4.8 Training Plan. The development of software products that require complex or unfamiliar interactions with users and operators should include a comprehensive plan for training. The Training Plan should include:

(1) A description of the population to be trained and the learning objectives for each population

(2) An estimate of the amount of resources necessary for training development, delivery, and time expenditures

(3) Procedures for evaluating the effectiveness of the training and for making modifications to the training plan

3.5 Standards, Practices, and Conventions. "This section shall:

(1) Identify the standards, practices, and conventions to be applied.

(2) State how compliance with these items is to be monitored and assured." [2]

3.5.1 Purpose. This section of the SQAP should identify the standards, practices, and conventions to be employed and specify the phases of the life cycle to which they apply. It should also indicate which individual or organizational element will be responsible for the enforcement, evaluation, and maintenance of the standards, practices, and conventions, and specify how compliance will be monitored and assured.

3.5.2 Content of Sections. "The subjects covered shall include the basic technical, design, and programming activities involved, such as documentation naming and coding, programming languages, and unit testing. As a minimum, the following information shall be provided:

(1) Documentation standards

(2) Logic structure standards

(3) Coding standards

(4) Commentary standards." [2]

The SQAP should reference or include a listing of the standards, practices, and conventions to be used on the project. As a minimum, the standards, practices, and conventions should address requirements, design, implementation, test, and documentation.

3.5.2.1 Requirements. Specify the standards, practices, and conventions to be used during requirements analysis. Use formal requirements statement languages, either textual or graphic, whenever possible. Provision should be made for a scheme that uniquely identifies each requirement. This facilitates traceability during the subsequent phases.

3.5.2.2 Design. Specify the standards, practices, and conventions to be used during the preliminary design phase where the overall structure of the software system is defined. Give serious consideration to the use of graphic techniques and top-down design.

For detailed design, state what standards, practices, and conventions will be used for specifying the internal structure of each program module, and the interfaces among them. Address such matters as naming conventions and argument list standards. Give serious consideration to requiring the use of a program design language.

3.5.2.3 Implementation. Specify the standards, practices, and conventions to be used during the implementation phase. Address such topics as the end-use computer, programming language(s), module size, declaration statement conventions, naming and labeling conventions, component layout standards, and the use of structured coding techniques (or structuring precompilers). Consider data conversion techniques for new systems that are replacing old ones. Standards for the inclusion of comment statements should also be covered here. Use standard support software and software tools whenever possible or state reasons for the use of nonstandard support software and tools.

3.5.2.4 Test. Specify the standards, practices, and conventions to be used during the testing phase. This includes unit, integration, system and acceptance testing, as well as regression testing. ANSI/IEEE Std 829-1983 [4] describes an integrated set of test documents.

Address criteria for test repeatability and test coverage such as testing every requirement, user procedure, and program statement. Specify techniques for tracing the test coverage to the test set. Indicate whether any support software will be required, and state how and from where this software will be obtained.

3.5.2.5 Documentation. Specify the standards, practices, and conventions to be used in preparing software documentation. Cite any external (eg, military, user, etc) standards with which the documents must comply. Include any standards, practices, and conventions which apply to the deliverable program source listings or executable code. Include any standards, practices, and conventions which apply to documentation for deliverable tools.

3.6 Reviews and Audits. "This section shall:

(1) Define the technical and managerial reviews and audits to be conducted.
(2) State how the reviews and audits are to be accomplished." [2]

3.6.1 Purpose. The software items produced by the software development effort should be reviewed and audited on a planned basis to determine the extent of progress and to evaluate the technical adequacy of the work and its conformance to system requirements. Technical reviews and audits should be conducted to evaluate the status and quality of the software development effort and to assure the use of required documentation. Completion of audits provides the basis for making decisions during the course of software development. Completion of reviews provides assurance that design integrity is maintained, technical deficiencies are identified, and

necessary changes have been identified and implemented.

This section should identify the specific technical and managerial reviews and audits to be conducted with respect to the software development plans, schedules, and environment. It should describe the procedures to be used in the conduct of reviews and audits, and it should identify the participants and their specific responsibilities. These review and audit procedures should identify specific responsibility for the preparation of a report upon the completion of each review. This section should identify by position or job title who is to prepare these reports, the report format, who is to receive the reports, and associated management responsibilities. The review and audit procedures should also describe the follow-up actions to assure that the recommendations made during the reviews and audits are properly implemented. This section should indicate the interval of time between performance of the review or audit and performance of the follow-up. It should also identify those responsible for performing follow-up actions.

3.6.2 Minimum Requirements. "As a minimum, the following reviews shall be conducted": [2]

(1) Software Requirements Review (SRR)
(2) Preliminary Design Review (PDR)
(3) Critical Design Review (CDR)
(4) Software Verification and Validation Plan Review (SVVPR)
(5) Functional Audit
(6) Physical Audit
(7) In-Process Audits
(8) Managerial Reviews

Tailoring or inclusion of additional reviews and audits should be made as local, contractual, or project-specific conditions dictate.

An example of the relationships and timing of these reviews and audits to the software development process is presented in Fig 1.

3.6.2.1 Software Requirements Review (SRR). "The SRR is held to ensure the adequacy of the requirements stated in the Software Requirements Specification." [2]

The SRR is an evaluation of the Software Requirements Specification (SRS). The SRR is conducted to assure the adequacy, technical feasibility, and completeness of the requirements stated in the SRS. The SRR should evaluate the SRS for the attributes required by

Typical Software Development Phases (per ANSI/IEEE Std 729-1983 [1])	Required Software Development Products (Documentation per 3.4.2)	Required SQA Audits and Reviews[2] per 3.6.2
Requirements	SQAP[1] SRS SVVP[4]	SRR In-Process Audit[3] SVVPR[4] Managerial Review[3]
Design	Preliminary SDD	PDR[5] In-Process Audit
	SDD	CDR[5]
	User Documentation[5]	UDR[5]
Implementation	Software items with documentation	In-Process Audit
Test	Test Documentation[6]	Functional Audit
Installation and Checkout[7]	Deliverable items SVVR	Physical Audit
Operation and Maintenance[8]	Products depend on scope of maintenance. Major modifications will have some or all of the above products.	Review depends on scope of required products.

**Fig 1
Example of Relationships and Timing of Required Reviews and Audits**

NOTES:
[1] This includes any referenced documents.
[2] Results of these activities are reports that identify what was reviewed, the deficiencies found, and conclusions. A report generated by a review meeting also includes recommendations as to what needs to be done to resolve the deficiencies. (The items subject to review are the software development products.)
[3] In-process audits and managerial reviews are scheduled as required throughout the software life cycle. For additional assistance see Section 5.
[4] The SVVP completion and SVVPR should be accomplished prior to the PDR.
[5] A UDR may be held independently of other reviews or in conjunction with the PDR and the CDR (a UDR is not an ANSI/IEEE Std 730-1984 [2] requirement).
[6] Refer to ANSI/IEEE Std 829-1983 [4].
[7] In the event this phase is not utilized in the SQAP, move the required products and audit to the test phase.
[8] This phase is in addition to typical software development phases to show that the SQA effort can be an iterative process.

ANSI/IEEE Std 830-1984 [5] (unambiguous, complete, verifiable, consistent, modifiable, traceable, and usable during the operation and maintenance phase). The review assures that sufficient detail is available to complete the software design.

The SQAP should indicate the organizational element responsible for conducting the SRR. All organizational elements that contribute or are impacted by the requirements should partici-

pate. These may include software design, software test, software quality assurance, system engineering, customers, users, marketing, manufacturing, etc.

The SQAP should indicate, but not be limited to, the following items as review requirements for the SRR:

(1) Traceability and completeness of the requirement from the next higher level specifi-

cation (such as a system specification or user requirements specification)

(2) Adequacy of rationale for any derived requirements

(3) Adequacy and completeness of algorithms and equations

(4) Correctness and suitability of logic descriptions that may be warranted

(5) Compatibility of external (hardware and software) interfaces

(6) Adequacy of the description of and approach to the human—machine interface

(7) Consistency in the use of symbols and in the specification of all interfaces

(8) Availability of constants and tables for calculations

(9) Testability of the software requirements

(10) Adequacy and completeness of the verification and acceptance requirements

(11) Completeness and compatibility of interface specification and control documentation

(12) Freedom from unwarranted design detail

Additional items to be considered as review requirements for the SRR could include:

(1) Trade-off and design studies that have applicability for decisions on:
  (a) Data base design
  (b) Programming language usage
  (c) Space allocation
  (d) Operations system or executive design, or both

(2) The general description of the size and operating characteristics of all support software (eg, operational program, maintenance and diagnostic programs, compilers, etc)

(3) A description of requirements for the operation of the software and identification of functional requirements such as functional simulation, environmental recording and analysis, exercise configuration, etc.

The results of the review should be documented in an SRR Report that identifies all deficiencies identified in the review and provides a plan and schedule for corrective action. After the SRS is updated to correct any deficiencies, it should be placed under configuration control to establish the baseline to be used for the software design effort.

3.6.2.2 Preliminary Design Review (PDR). "The PDR is held to evaluate the technical adequacy of the preliminary design of the

software as depicted in a preliminary version of the Software Design Description." [2]

The PDR is held to evaluate the technical adequacy of the preliminary design before the beginning of detailed design. The review assesses the progress, consistency, and technical adequacy of the selected design approach; checks the design's compatibility with the functional and performance requirements of the SRS; and verifies the existence and compatibility of the interfaces between the software, hardware, and end users. The PDR is also conducted to determine that the preliminary SDD defines a suitable software design that fulfills the requirements contained in the SRS.

The SQAP should indicate the organizational element responsible for conducting the PDR. All organizational elements that impose requirements or are impacted by the design should participate in the review. These groups could include system engineering, software development, software test, software quality assurance, the customers, users, etc.

The following items could be specified in the SQAP as review requirements for the PDR:

(1) All detailed functional interfaces with other software, system equipment, communication systems, etc, for adequate identification of interface design and design solution adequacy

(2) The software design as a whole, emphasizing allocation of software components to functions, functional flows, storage requirements and allocations, software operating sequences, and the design of the data base

(3) An analysis of the design for compatibility with critical system timing requirements, estimated running times, and other performance requirements

(4) The human factor requirements and the human—machine interfaces for adequacy and consistency of design

(5) Testability of the design, such as the existence of data store and processes that support behavior and state determination

(6) Test concepts, requirements, documentation, and tools, for adequacy

(7) Technical accuracy and currency of all available test documentation and its compatibility with the test requirements of the SRS

The results should be documented in a PDR Report which identifies all deficiencies discovered during the review and a plan and schedule for corrective action. The updated preliminary

SDD document should be placed under configuration control to establish the baseline for the detailed software design effort.

3.6.2.3 Critical Design Review (CDR).
"The CDR is held to determine the acceptability of the detailed software designs as depicted in the Software Design Description in satisfying the requirements of the Software Requirements Specification." [2]

The CDR is an evaluation of the completed Software Design Description (SDD). The CDR evaluates the technical adequacy, completeness, and correctness of the detailed design of the software before the start of coding. The purpose of the CDR is to evaluate the acceptability of the detailed design, to establish that the detailed design satisfies the requirements of the SRS, to review compatibility with the other software and hardware with which the product is required to interact, and to assess the technical, cost, and schedule risks of the product design.

The SQAP should indicate the organizational element responsible for conducting the CDR. All other organizational elements that impose requirements or are impacted by the design should participate. These groups could include system engineering, software development, software test, software quality assurance, customers, users, etc.

The following items could be specified in the SQAP as review requirements for the CDR:

(1) The compatibility of the detailed design with the SRS

(2) Available data in the form of logic diagrams, algorithms, storage allocation charts, and detailed design representations (eg, flow chart, program design language) to establish design integrity

(3) Compatibility and completeness of interface requirements

(4) All external and internal interfaces, including interactions with the data base

(5) Technical accuracy and currency of all available test documentation and its compatibility with the test requirements of the SRS

(6) The requirements for the support and test software and hardware to be used in the development of the product

(7) The final design, including function flow, timing, sizing, storage requirements, memory maps, data base, and other performance factors

The results of the review should be documented in a CDR Report which identifies all

deficiencies discovered during the review and a plan and schedule for corrective actions. The updated SDD document, when placed under configuration control, establishes the baseline for coding.

3.6.2.4 Software Verification and Validation [Plan] Review (SVVPR).
"The Software Verification and Validation [Plan] Review is held to evaluate the adequacy and completeness of the verification and validation methods defined in the SVVP." [2]

The SVVPR is an evaluation of the completed Software Verification and Validation Plan (SVVP). Since the SVVP may be developed incrementally, multiple reviews may be required. These reviews are held to assure that the verification and validation methods described in the SVVP are adequate and will provide complete evaluation data.

The SQAP should indicate the organizational element responsible for conducting the Software Verification and Validation Plan Review. All organizational elements that impose requirements or are impacted by the SVVP should participate. These groups could include system engineering, software development, software design, software test, software quality assurance, customers, users, etc.

The following items should be specified in the SQAP as the SVVPR requirement criteria:

(1) All verification and validation methods, along with completion criteria to assure traceability to, and compatibility with, the functional and performance requirements expressed in the SRS

(2) Reports to adequately document results of all reviews, audits, and tests based on the requirements listed in the SVVP

(3) Adequate descriptions of the software configuration to be tested, including test support software and hardware

(4) Test plans and test designs to assure that all requirements are tested

(5) Test procedures and test cases to assure that test inputs and success criteria are adequately defined and that test instructions are clear and concise

(6) A test schedule identifying which tests are to be done, when, and by whom

The results of the review should be documented in an SVVPR Report which identifies all deficiencies discovered during the review, and which provides a plan and schedule for corrective action. The updated SVVP, when placed under configuration control, establishes the baseline for the software verification and validation effort.

3.6.2.5 Functional Audit. "This audit is held prior to the software delivery to verify that all requirements specified in the Software Requirements Specification have been met." [2]

The Functional Audit compares the code with the documented software requirements as stated in the current SRS. Its purpose is to assure that the code addresses all, and only, the documented requirements stated in the SRS.

The SQAP should indicate the organizational element responsible for the Functional Audit. The results are to be documented in the Functional Audit Minutes, which identify all discrepancies found and the plans for their resolution.

Input to the Functional Audit should consist of:

(1) Software Requirements Specification (SRS)

(2) Software Verification and Validation Report (SVVR)

(3) Software Verification and Validation Plan Review (SVVPR) Minutes

3.6.2.6 Physical Audit. "This audit is held to verify that the software and its documentation are internally consistent and are ready for delivery." [2]

The Physical Audit compares the code with its supporting documentation. Its purpose is to assure that the documentation to be delivered correctly describes the code.

The SQAP should indicate the organizational element responsible for conducting the Physical Audit. The results of the Physical Audit are to be documented in the Physical Audit Minutes which identify all discrepancies and the plans for their resolution. Once the discrepancies have been resolved, the software can be delivered.

Input to the Physical Audit should consist of:

(1) Software Design Description (SDD)
(2) Software products
(3) Associated documentation

3.6.2.7 In-Process Audits. "In-process audits of a sample of the design are held to verify consistency of the design, including:

(1) Code versus design documentation

(2) Interface specifications (hardware and software)

(3) Design implementations versus functional requirements

(4) Functional requirements versus test descriptions." [2]

In-process audits of samples of the product development items are held as required by the SQAP. The SQAP should indicate the organizational element responsible for conducting the in-process audits. Software inspections may be included as part of the in-process audit activity. The objective is to verify the consistency of the product as it evolves through the development process by determining that:

(1) Hardware and software interfaces are consistent with design requirements in the SRS

(2) The functional requirements of the SRS are fully tested by the SVVP

(3) The design of the product, as the SDD is evolving, satisfies the functional requirements of the SRS

(4) The code is consistent with the SDD

The results of all in-process audits are measures of how well the process is working. They should be documented in in-process audit reports, which identify all discrepancies found and the plans for their resolution.

3.6.2.8 Managerial Reviews. "These reviews are held periodically to assess the execution of this [SQA] plan. These reviews shall be held by an organizational element independent of the unit being audited, or by a qualified third party." [2]

The planned frequency and structure of the managerial reviews should be stated in the SQAP. They should be conducted at the direction of an appropriate level of management independent of the SQA effort.

A managerial review results in a statement as to the adequacy of the SQAP and its execution. Each review should be documented by a report summarizing the review findings, including any exceptions to the process stated in the SQAP, and any recommended changes or improvements.

Section 5 provides guidance for evaluating the contents and the implementation of a SQAP.

3.6.3 Other. Other reviews may also be conducted.

3.6.3.1 User Documentation Review (UDR). The UDR is held to determine the technical adequacy of the documentation approach and design as described in draft versions of the User Documentation.

The SQAP should indicate the organizational element responsible for conducting the UDR. All organizational elements that are affected or impacted by the User Documentation should participate in the review. These groups may include system engineering, software, development, software test, software quality assurance, customers, users, etc.

The following items could be specified in the SQAP as the UDR requirement criteria:

(1) The methods used to validate that the software product matches the user documentation

(2) Test plans, test procedures, and test cases to assure that all user documentation is tested in conjunction with the software

The UDR can be held independently of other reviews or in conjunction with the Preliminary Design Review (PDR) and the Critical Design Review (CDR).

The results of the review should be documented in a UDR Report, which identifies all deficiencies discovered during the review and which provides a plan and schedule for connective action. The updated user documentation should be placed under configuration management prior to the physical audit described in 3.6.2.6.

3.7 Software Configuration Management.

"This section shall document the methods to be used for identifying the software product items, controlling and implementing changes, and recording and reporting change implementation status. This documentation shall either be provided explicitly in this section or by reference to an existing software configuration management plan." [2]

The SQAP should describe the tasks and methodology required to assure that adequate Software Configuration Management (SCM) procedures and controls are documented and are being implemented correctly. It is not necessary that the SQA function prepare the Software Configuration Management Plan (SCMP).

The material to be supplied in this section is specified in ANSI/IEEE Std 828-1983 [3].

3.8 Problem Reporting and Corrective Action. "This section shall:

(1) Describe the practices and procedures to

be followed for reporting, tracking, and resolving software problems.

(2) State the specific organizational responsibilities concerned with their implementation." [2]

Problems encountered during software development or operation may result in defects in the software, hardware, or operations. Because of their diversity, the determination of the sources of a problem and its appropriate corrective action requires a centrally controlled system for monitoring problems and determining systemic causes.

The purposes of a software problem reporting and corrective action system are to:

(1) Assure that problems are documented, corrected, and not forgotten

(2) Assure that problem reports are assessed for their validity

(3) Provide feedback to the developer and the user on problem status

(4) Provide data for measuring and predicting software quality and reliability

These goals should be satisfied by the problem reporting and corrective action system described in the SQAP.

The SQAP should include methods to be used to assure that reported software problems are being properly controlled. The SQAP should describe the organizational element(s), provisions, and procedures for documenting, validating, tracking, and reporting the status of software problems and the appropriate corrective action.

Validating, tracking, and resolving software problems require the coordination of various groups within the organization. The SQAP should specify the groups responsible for authorizing and implementing problem reporting and corrective actions. It should also identify the point in the development process where generation of problem reports is to begin.

3.9 Tools, Techniques, and Methodologies.

"This section shall identify the special software tools, techniques, and methodologies employed on the specific project that support Quality Assurance, state their purposes, and describe their use." [2]

The SQAP shall identify the tools, techniques, and methodologies to be used to support software quality assurance. It should list or reference those tools, techniques, and methodologies which are available, and those that need to be acquired or developed. The responsible organization(s) should also be identified.

3.9.1 Tools. SQA software tools aid in the evaluation or improvement of software quality. Typical tools include, but are not limited to, operating system utilities, debugging aids, documentation aids, structuring preprocessors, file comparators, structure analyzers, standards auditors, simulators, execution analyzers, performance monitors, statistical analysis packages, test drivers, test case generators, and static or dynamic test tools.

3.9.2 Techniques. SQA techniques are technical and managerial procedures that aid in the evaluation and improvement of software quality. Such techniques include standards, software inspections, requirements tracing, requirements and design verification, reliability measurements and assessments, and rigorous or formal logic analysis.

3.9.3 Methodologies. SQA methodologies are integrated sets of the above techniques.

3.10 Code Control. "This section shall define the methods and facilities used to maintain and store controlled versions of identified software. This may be implemented in conjunction with a Computer Program Library." [2]

Code control can be interpreted as the ways and means necessary to protect or ensure the validity of a completed code. Once an appropriate baseline has been established, the code should be placed under configuration management in a computer program library. The SQAP should specify controls and security measures for software change and for protection from inadvertent alteration after the code has been baselined. It should define or reference the procedures and organizational responsibility for controlling the developed code.

The SQAP should specify a code control procedure that:

(1) Defines the specific software to be controlled

(2) Describes a standard method for identifying, labeling, and cataloging the software

(3) Lists the physical location of the software under control

(4) Describes the location, maintenance, and use of all backup copies

(5) Describes procedures for distributing a copy

(6) Identifies the documentation which is affected by changes

(7) Describes procedures for implementing a new version

3.11 Media Control. "This section shall state the methods and facilities to be used to protect computer program physical media from unauthorized access or inadvertent damage or degradation." [2]

Computer program media can be defined as those media on which computer data are stored. Typically, the storage media are disks or tapes, but could include cards, diskettes, listings, or other forms in which the data reside.

The media control methods and facilities should ensure that:

(1) The software is stored and retrieval is guaranteed

(2) Offsite storage and retrieval are provided for critical software and copies of baselined code

(3) The software is accessible only to those with the need of access

(4) The environment is controlled so that the physical media on which the software is stored do not degrade

The SQAP should reference or specify procedures and practices that pertain to the above items. For example, a backup procedure for software could indicate the schedule for backup, the type of media on which it will be placed, the location of the storage, the environment of the storage area, and the method to retrieve the backed-up software. A security system may be in place that allows access to software only through an authorization process. The SQAP should delineate the organizational elements responsible for administering and reviewing media control methods and facilities. The method for identifying, labeling, and data logging may be the same in both code and media control.

3.11.1 Unauthorized Access. Several methods are available which will provide adequate protection from unauthorized access of computer program media. The primary method is to provide a permanent labeling or identification scheme within the storage media. When the disk or tape is used on a computer, this technique can provide adequate password control or access protection. Other methods include a limited access program library, encryption, external markings, and proprietary statements identifying a controlled program. The physical security of all media must also be considered.

SQA activities to verify appropriateness and implementation of access procedures should be documented in the SQAP. Areas of concern include: identifying the programs requiring limited access, adherence to label and file restrictions, ensuring use of adequate external labeling restrictions, and providing a controlled environment such as a program library.

3.11.2 Inadvertent Damage or Degradation. Damage or degradation of the media can be minimized by providing adequate configuration management techniques, safe storage locations such as fireproof vaults, and packaging practices that are antistatic in design. Periodic reviews to ensure use of controlled environmental and cataloging practices will minimize degradation of external or physical identification of the media.

SQA activities to verify appropriateness and implementation of procedures to minimize media damage or degradation should be documented in the SQAP.

3.12 Supplier Control. "This section shall state the provisions for assuring that vendor-provided and subcontractor-developed software meets established technical requirements. As a minimum, the supplier shall be required to prepare and implement a Software Quality Assurance Plan in accordance with this standard." [2]

This section of the purchaser's SQAP should specify:

(1) The purchaser's involvement with the supplier's SQA program

(2) The purchaser's procedures for auditing the supplier's conformance to ANSI/IEEE Std 730-1984 [2] and the supplier's SQAP (an option could be to provide for an independent auditor)

(3) The actions available to the purchaser should the supplier not be in conformance with ANSI/IEEE Std 730-1984 [2] and the supplier's SQAP

3.13 Records Collection, Maintenance, and Retention. "This section shall identify the SQA documentation to be retained, shall state the methods and facilities to be used to assemble, safeguard and maintain this documentation and shall designate the retention period." [2]

3.13.1 Records Collection. The type of records to be collected are determined by the overall objectives for record keeping. These objectives should be documented in the SQAP. Possible objectives are:

(1) To provide legal or contractual evidence that the software development process was performed in conformance with established professional practice and the customer's requirements. The documents collected for legal or contractual purposes should provide evidence that:

(a) The SQAP is being followed and conforms to the requirements of applicable standards

(b) The software meets design intent and satisfies contractual requirements

(c) Corrective action is effective

(d) Testing has been performed in accordance with test plans.

(2) To provide historical or reference data that could be used to discover long-term trends in the organization's development techniques. The documents collected for historical or reference purposes should be capable of providing data for productivity, quality, and methodology studies. The documents should provide sufficient design, implementation, and testing data so as to be useful for future development.

In addition to SQA documents, records should include program media containing the exact version of programs and materials used in performing tests to assure test repeatability at any time in the future.

3.13.2 Records Maintenance. The SQAP should specify the manner in which records will be kept, that is, hard copy, microfiche, etc. Also, it should state how records will be stored to protect them from fire, theft, or environmental deterioration. The SQAP should provide for historical archiving if applicable.

3.13.3 Records Retention. The SQAP should specify the length of retention for each type of record maintained. It is important to state in the SQAP when records should be retained and when they should be destroyed.

3.13.4 Organizational Responsibilities. The SQAP should specify the organizational element responsible for originating, collecting, maintaining, storing, and protecting records. The plan should also identify the authority for access to records, and the responsibilities for changing, purging, or destroying records. Information in this section shall be compatible and consistent with information shown in 3.3.2 and 3.3.3.

4. Implementation of a Software Quality Assurance Plan

The purpose of this section is to describe the steps necessary for successfully implementing the SQAP that has been prepared for a specific project. The following items are discussed in this section:

(1) Acceptance of the SQAP by management
(2) Acceptance of the SQAP by the software developers and others whose task responsibilities are defined in the SQAP
(3) Planning and scheduling of resources and tasks for implementation of the SQAP
(4) Training of personnel to implement the SQAP
(5) Distribution of the SQAP to implementors and interfacing personnel
(6) Execution of the SQAP

4.1 Acceptance by Management. Management acceptance and commitment to the SQAP should be obtained. This will provide the support required for implementing the tasks defined. This acceptance should include commitments for the budget and resources required to implement the SQA activities.

The SQAP should be coordinated with and agreed to by each unit of the organization having responsibilities defined within the SQAP. Acceptance of the SQAP should be indicated on the cover page by an approval signature of the person in charge of each unit. Implementation of the SQAP can be effective only if all the actions called for in the SQAP are performed with the full support of management.

4.2 Acceptance by Development Personnel. It is essential to foster a spirit of cooperation between the personnel responsible for software development and the SQA activities. An effective method of achieving this is to have the development personnel participate in the preparation of the SQAP. This will tend to increase their support of SQA in general, and of the SQAP in particular. Preliminary drafts of the SQAP should therefore be circulated within the development organization for review and comments. It may also be useful to hold walkthroughs of the SQAP with all concerned personnel. During this time they will be able to ask questions directly of the authors of the SQAP, and to make their concerns and objections known before the SQAP is officially published. In this manner, the groundwork will be laid for cooperation and mutual support between all organizations responsible for activities required by the SQAP.

4.3 Planning for Implementation of the SQAP. Planning for SQAP implementation comprises three aspects:

(1) Identification of required resources
(2) Scheduling implementation resources
(3) Assessing the risks involved

4.3.1 Resources. The four types of resources required to implement a SQAP are: personnel, equipment, facilities, and tools. The quantity and quality of these resources should be made known to the appropriate level of management.

The responsible element should identify the job classifications and skill levels of the personnel required to implement and maintain the SQAP throughout the life of the project. It should identify the hardware needed to implement the SQAP and to support it throughout the project, as well as estimates of computer time and support required. It should also identify the facilities needed for storage of media and records. When resources are identified by an element other than the SQA element, the SQA element should verify compliance with this task. The tools required for implementation should already have been identified in the SQAP itself.

4.3.2 Scheduling. Once the resources involved in implementing a SQAP have been identified, the next step is to establish a schedule for the implementation. For each task identified in the SQAP, this schedule should identify the starting and completion dates for each required resource. In a similar manner, a schedule should be established for the development or acquisition of any necessary support tools.

4.3.3 Risk Assessment. The last element of planning is risk assessment. It is essential to identify the level of risk (high, medium, or low) associated with the possible failure of each required task or the unavailability of each resource. This risk assessment should identify the resulting impact on other schedules and outline alternative actions available to mitigate the risks.

4.4 Training. The need for training of personnel designated to perform the activities defined in the SQAP should be assessed. Considerations for training should include the skills of assigned personnel; special tools, techniques, and methodology that must be used; computer resources that will be used; etc.

Existing training programs should be adapted or new training programs developed to meet the needs of the plan. Training sessions should be scheduled for personnel who will be assigned to carry out the tasks. This training should be compatible with the task schedules discussed in 4.3.2.

4.5 Distribution of the SQAP. A distribution list of all personnel who are to receive the final approved copy of the SQAP should be prepared. A copy of the published SQAP should then be distributed to each individual listed, with an attached sign-off sheet that is to be initialed by the person receiving the SQAP and returned to the organization responsible for the SQAP's publication and distribution.

4.6 Execution of the SQAP. Once the SQAP is distributed, the Software Quality Assurance element shall assure that the tasks (eg, reviews and audits) documented within the SQAP are performed at the appropriate points in the life cycle. The SQAP will specify the activity to be performed, the person(s) performing the activity, and the results to be achieved. It will reference other documents as necessary. Associated work papers of the reviews and audits must provide sufficient evidence that the steps in the SQAP have been performed and reviewed by the management accountable for the SQAP. This will permit an objective determination of how well the SQA objectives have been met.

5. Evaluation of a Software Quality Assurance Plan

5.1 Purpose. The SQA element should make provision for periodic or on-going evaluation of the SQAP. Evaluating the SQAP involves examining it from two different viewpoints:

(1) Evaluating the plan's content (initially and after all revisions)
(2) Evaluating the use and management of the SQAP

The evaluation of the SQAP's content is an assessment of how the SQAP complies with ANSI/IEEE Std 730-1984 [2], internal development and quality assurance standards, and contractual documents. Evaluation of the completeness and applicability of the SQAP is facilitated by the questions presented in 5.2.1.

These questions provide an overview of the state of the SQAP.

The evaluation of the use and management of the SQAP is an assessment of the specific project's implementation of the SQAP. Section 5.2.2 contains some suggestions for this ongoing activity.

5.2 Methodology

5.2.1 SQAP Evaluation. The following questions should be asked in evaluating the overall approach of the SQAP:

(1) Are all the mandatory requirements per ANSI/IEEE Std 730-1984 [2] addressed in the SQAP?
(2) Are all contractual and company SQAP standards addressed in the SQAP?
(3) Does the SQAP specify compliance with any standards in addition to ANSI/IEEE Std 730-1984 [2]? If so, does the SQAP meet the requirements of those standards?
(4) Are all exceptions to mandatory requirements noted and adequately justified?
(5) Is the content of the SQAP adequate to achieve its stated objectives?

Additional questions which can be used in support of the evaluation of specific SQAP sections are:

(1) Purpose
(a) Are the specific purpose and scope of the SQAP described?
(b) Are the software product items covered by the SQAP completely described?
(c) Is the intended use of the software items described?
(2) Referenced Documents
(a) Are all documents referenced by the SQAP listed in this section?
(3) Management
(a) Are the structures of all the organizations that influence the quality of the software depicted?
(b) Are the management activities completely described?
(c) Are the tasks and responsibilities of the organizations that influence the quality of the software listed?
(4) Documentation
(a) Does the section describe all necessary software documentation?
(b) Does this section describe the methodologies to be used for checking documentation adequacy with reference to 3.6?
(c) Are the methodologies adequate?

(5) Standards, Practices, and Conventions

(a) Does this section identify all standards, practices, and conventions to be applied to the software?

(b) Are compliance and monitoring procedures identified?

(c) Are (a) and (b) adequate?

(6) Reviews and Audits

(a) Does this section define all necessary reviews and audits for the documentation described in 3.4?

(b) Are the methodologies for all reviews and audits described?

(c) Are (a) and (b) adequate?

(7) Software Configuration Management (SCM)

(a) Does the SCM information in this section, or contained in a separate SCMP, conform to ANSI/IEEE Std 828-1983 [3]?

(b) If the SCM/SCMP is not in conformance with ANSI/IEEE Std 828-1983 [3], is it adequate for this particular SQAP?

(8) Problem Reporting and Corrective Action

(a) Does this section describe problem reporting and corrective action procedures to be used for this project?

(b) Does this section state specific organizational responsibilities?

(c) Are the procedures adequate?

(9) Tools, Techniques, and Methodologies

(a) Are all tools, techniques, and methodologies to be used for SQA purposes fully described?

(b) Are they adequate?

(10) Code Control

(a) Does this section contain a description of all methods and facilities to be used for code control?

(b) Are they adequate?

(11) Media Control

(a) Does this section contain a description of all methods and facilities to be used for media control?

(b) Are they adequate?

(12) Supplier Control

(a) Are all procedures for interfacing between each supplier's SQAP and this SQAP fully described?

(b) Are they adequate?

(13) Records Collection, Maintenance, and Retention

(a) Are all records collection, maintenance, and retention procedures fully described?

(b) Are they adequate?

5.2.2 Implementation Evaluation. At several points in the product life cycle, usually major project milestones, the SQAP and its implementation should be evaluated by means of a managerial review. This will help assure that the project and its SQAP evolve together. As the project proceeds through the software life cycle, there are likely to be changes in the product scope. As the development plan changes, the SQAP and its implementation should also be reviewed to determine if any changes are required.

The use of the SQAP should be evaluated in terms of the tasks and responsibilities detailed in the SQAP (3.3.2 and 3.3.3). This evaluation should review the status of each task and the adequacy of the actions taken in terms of both product quality results and the schedules actually achieved for the tasks.

5.2.3 Evaluation Process Relationship. The evaluation process will have a cause–effect relationship as shown in Fig 2. A SQAP evalu-

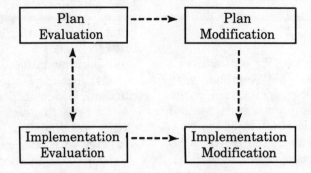

**Fig 2
Cause–Effect Graph of SQAP Evaluation and Modification**

ation, whether formal or informal, may have the effect of causing SQAP modification or causing an implementation evaluation. A SQAP modification may necessitate a corresponding implementation modification. An implementation evaluation may cause an implementation change to bring the use and management into compliance with the SQAP.

6. Modification of the Software Quality Assurance Plan

The previous section addressed the evaluation of a SQAP and the determination of any necessary changes to it. This section will describe a mechanism for implementing such changes.

6.1 Purpose. The purpose of this section is to provide a method for modifying an existing SQAP. Only if there is a provision for systematic modification of a SQAP can its users have confidence in its continued usability.

There are several reasons why a SQAP, once approved and implemented, may subsequently need to be modified. First, the SQAP may contain deficiencies. Second, it may be necessary to adjust to changes in the environment of the SQAP. For example, a new set of system requirements may require stricter or more detailed testing to assure that they are satisfied. Third, changes in the management structure of the project may make portions of the SQAP (eg, reporting lines or sign-off authorities) obsolete. Finally, the advent of new technology may make modification desirable, as for example, when new SQAP tools or techniques must be incorporated.

6.2 Scope. This section addresses methods for proposing, reviewing, and instituting modifications to a SQAP. It does not cover modifications to the manner in which the SQAP is used, managed, or controlled; provisions for these are made either within the SQAP itself or in project management directives.

6.3 Methodology. As with any document, there are five steps in the modification of a SQAP:

(1) Identify alternative options
(2) Recommend proposed change
(3) Review proposed change
(4) Incorporate approved change
(5) Release and promulgate change

Steps (1) and (2) will be followed in all cases. If a project SCM organization exists, then steps (3), (4), and (5) will be accomplished according to that organization's procedures. If there is no project SCM, then steps (3), (4), and (5) will be followed as described below.

6.3.1 Identify Alternative Options. Changes to a SQAP may be proposed from any of several sources, such as project management, software development, system validation, configuration management, quality assurance, or customer. They could suggest different solutions to the same problem. It is important to provide for the results of the SQAP evaluation process (see Section 5) to be routed through all of these sources in order that each of their proposed solutions may be presented and reviewed.

6.3.2 Recommend Proposed Change. A Change Control Board (CCB) should be organized to review all alternative solutions and to determine a single recommended change (or set of changes) which they believe best addresses the acknowledged requirement. Depending upon the frequency with which SQAP changes are proposed, this CCB may be either a standing or an ad hoc organization. It may be useful to set up such a group as a standing organization at the time the SQAP is first published, if numerous change requests are expected. When such requests become fewer and farther between, the CCB may be converted to an ad hoc status.

6.3.3 Review Proposed Change. Once the CCB has agreed upon a proposed change, it should be sent to all interested or potentially affected parties for their review and comments. This step is necessary to provide agreement before the change is published and distributed. The CCB should have responsibility for evaluation and incorporation of comments received from the reviewers, and for approval or rejection of the proposed change.

6.3.4 Incorporate Approved Change. If, after studying the reviewers' comments, the CCB approves the proposed change, it is incorporated into the SQAP. Standard document control procedures should be employed here, including editorial review, printing of change pages, use of vertical bars to highlight added or modified text, and control procedures to preserve previous versions of the document.

6.3.5 Release and Promulgate Change. A management official should be designated who will have sign-off authority on SQAP changes.

Once this official has approved the change page(s) for release, standard document distribution methods may be employed. Then, all that remains is to monitor the implementation of the change. This responsibility should be assigned to the appropriate management official. At this point, the evaluation process begins again (see Section 5).

Appendix

(This Appendix is not a part of IEEE Std 983-1986, IEEE Guide for Software Quality Assurance Planning.)

Table A1
Summary of SQAP Contents

Item	Shall	Should	May	ANSI/ IEEE Std 730-1984 [2]	IEEE Std 983-1986	Other Stds
• Description of specific scope and purpose of SQAP	X			3.1		
products covered by the SQAP	X			3.1	3.1(1)	
intended use	X			3.1	3.1(2)	
reason for SQAP		X		—	3.1(3)	
base documents		X		—	3.1(4)	
rationale for departures from base documents		X		—	3.1(5)	
• Reference documents list	X			3.2	3.2	
• Description of project and plan management						
Organization	X			3.3.1	3.3.1	
Tasks	X			3.3.2	3.3.2	
Responsibilities	X			3.3.3	3.3.3	
• Identification of documents to be used for development, verification, use, and maintenance of the products covered by SQAP and how they are to be evaluated	X			3.4	3.4	
SRS	X			3.4.2.1	3.4.2.1	ANSI/IEEE 830-1984 [5]
SDD	X			3.4.2.2	3.4.2.2	
SVVP	X			3.4.2.3	3.4.2.3	
SVVR	X			3.4.2.4	3.4.2.4	
User Documentation	X			3.4.2.5	3.4.2.5	
SDP			X	3.4.3(1)	3.4.3.1	
SCMP			X	3.4.3(2)	3.4.3.2	ANSI/IEEE 828-1983 [3]
SPM			X	3.4.3(3)	3.4.3.3	
User Requirements Statement			X	—	3.4.4.1	
External Interface Specification			X	—	3.4.4.2	
Internal Interface Specification			X	—	3.4.4.3	
Operations Manual			X	—	3.4.4.4	
Installation Manual			X	—	3.4.4.5	
Maintenance Manual			X	—	3.4.4.6	
Training Manual			X	—	3.4.4.7	
Training Plan			X	—	3.4.4.8	
• Identification of Standards, Practices, and Conventions, and statement of compliance check methods	X			3.5	3.5	
Documentation Standards	X			3.5.2	3.5.2	
Logic Structure Standards	X			3.5.2	3.5.2	
Coding Standards	X			3.5.2	3.5.2	
Commentary Standards	X			3.5.2	3.5.2	
Requirements Standards		X		—	3.5.2.1	
Design Standards		X		—	3.5.2.2	
Implementation Standards		X		—	3.5.2.3	

Item	Shall	Should	May	ANSI/ IEEE Std 730-1984 [2]	IEEE Std 983-1986	Other Stds
Test Standards		X		—	3.5.2.4	ANSI/IEEE 829-1983 [4]
Documentation Standards		X		—	3.5.2.5	
• Definition of technical reviews and audits and means of accomplishment	X			3.6.1	3.6	
• Conduct the following reviews:	X			3.6.2	3.6.2	
SRR	X			3.6.2.1	3.6.2.1	ANSI/IEEE 830-1984 [5]
PDR	X			3.6.2.2	3.6.2.2	
CDR	X			3.6.2.3	3.6.2.3	
SVVPR	X			3.6.2.4	3.6.2.4	
Functional Audit	X			3.6.2.5	3.6.2.5	
Physical Audit	X			3.6.2.6	3.6.2.6	
In-Process Audits	X			3.6.2.7	3.6.2.7	
Managerial Reviews	X			3.6.2.8	3.6.2.8	
UDR			X		3.6.3.1	
• Definition of software product item control procedures	X			3.7	3.7	ANSI/IEEE 828-1983 [3]
• Document methods for identification of software product items, change control, and change reporting	X			3.7	3.7	ANSI/IEEE 828-1983 [3]
• Discussion of problem reporting and corrective action	X			3.8	3.8	
• Describe tools, techniques and methodologies to be used	X			3.9	3.9	
• Definition of code control methods and facilities	X			3.10	3.10	
• Definition of media control methods and facilities	X			3.11	3.11	
Unauthorized access	X			3.11	3.11.1	
Damage and degradation	X			3.11	3.11.2	
• Provision for supplier quality assurance methods	X			3.12	3.12	
• Identification of software SQA records collection, maintenance, and retention	X			3.13	3.13	
Document record types and objectives		X		—	3.13.1	
Maintenance	X			3.13	3.13.2	
Retention period	X			3.13	3.13.3	
Organizational responsibility		X		—	3.13.4	
• Implementing a SQAP		X			4.0	
• Evaluating a SQAP		X			5.0	
• Modifying a SQAP		X			6.0	

Acknowledgments

The following organizations provided support for the development of this standard:

AT&T Bell Laboratories
AT&T Information Systems
AT&T Technologies
Bell Canada
B. L. Rosenberg and Co
Boeing Aerospace Co
CAP Gemini/DASD
Central Institute for Industrial Research
Computer Sciences Corp
Cox Cable Communications Inc
Data General Corp
Defense Mapping Aerospace Center
E-Systems, Inc
EG&G Idaho, Inc
Federal Aviation Agency
General Electric Co
IBM Corp
Itek Applied Technology
Lockheed Electronics
Logicon, Inc
Loral Electric Systems
Martin Marietta Engineering Systems
McLaughlin Research, Inc
Medtronic, Inc
National Bureau of Standards
Naval Air Development Center
Naval Surface Weapons Center

NCR Corp
Northern Telecom Limited
Northeast Utilities
Northrop Corp
OASAS Limited
Paradyne Corp
Perkin Elmer
Planning Research Corp
Programming Environments, Inc
PRP Systems, Inc
Raytheon Data Systems
RCA
SAI Comsystems
Science Applications, Inc
Software Quality Engineering
Sperry
Tektronix, Inc
Teledyne Brown Engineering
Teledyne Geotech
Texas Instruments
Time, Inc
Union Carbide Nuclear Division
US Air Force Communications Computer Programming Center
US Army Computer Systems Command
US Nuclear Regulatory Commission
Veatch, Rich & Nadler

(This support does not constitute or imply approval or endorsement of this standard.)

IEEE Recommended Practice for Ada*
As a Program Design Language

Sponsor

**Technical Committee on Software Engineering of the
IEEE Computer Society**

990

Foreword

(This Foreword is not a part of IEEE Std 990-1987, IEEE Recommended Practice for Ada As a Design Language.)

Software Engineering is an emerging field. As part of that process, the Department of Defense initiated, and ANSI approved, ANSI/MIL-STD-1815A-1983, which defines the Ada* Programming Language. In recent years, there has been a growing demand for the use of Ada as a Program Design Language (PDL). Recognizing that an adequate definition of an Ada PDL did not exist, a project was approved in March 1983 to provide that definition as part of a voluntary consensus process. This recommended practice is the result of that process.

This is one of an evolving set of integrated software engineering standards; for example,
ANSI/IEEE Std 729-1983, IEEE Standard Glossary of Software Engineering Terminology
ANSI/IEEE Std 730-1984, IEEE Standard for Software Quality Assurance Plans
ANSI/IEEE Std 828-1983, IEEE Standard for Software Configuration Management Plans
ANSI/IEEE Std 829-1983, IEEE Standard for Software Test Documentation
ANSI/IEEE Std 830-1983, IEEE Guide for Software Requirement Specifications
ANSI/IEEE Std 983-1986, IEEE Guide for Software Quality Assurance Planning
ANSI/IEEE Std 1008-1987, IEEE Standard for Software Unit Testing
This recommended practice may be used either in conjunction with those standards or separately.

As a recommended practice, this document should be helpful to PDL designers, PDL evaluators, software designers, and other members of the software engineering community concerned with the use of Ada as a PDL.

Members of the Executive Steering Committee were as follows:

Robert M. Blasewitz, *Chairman*   **Mark S. Gerhardt,** *Vice-Chairman*
Susan P. Mardinly, *Executive Chairman*
Dianna H. Peet, *Secretary*

Michael J. Devlin   Michael Gordon   Charlene Hayden
Debbie Faith   Thomas J. Walsh

*Ada is a registered trademark of the United States Government, Department of Defense, (Ada Joint Program Office).

The Ada as a PDL Working Group had the following members:

Robert M. Blasewitz, *Chairman*

George H. Alessi
Ed Amoroso
Christine M. Anderson
John A. Anderson
Peter G. Anderson
Grebenc Andrej
Barbara Ardary
Jeannine Arsenault
John Bailey
James Baldo, Jr
Richard W. Baldwin
Leo Beltracchi
Mordechai Ben Menachem
Yechiel Ben Naftali
John C. Bennett
Victor G. Berecz
Ed Bevard
Lee Blaine
William Bogdan
Roy Bollinger
Graham D. Boose
Robert Borland
Jack Boudreaux
Carol Brade
James Bradley
Eric J. Braude
Christine L. Braun
Alton L. Brintzenhoff
Dwight R. Brooks
Jerry R. Brookshire
Al Brown
Fletcher J. Buckley
Ruck Byrne
Jim Cain
Lorie J. Call
Robert Calland
Miguel A. Carrio
Virginia L. Castor
Phil Caverly
Ann Chase Charles
R. Childress
Antonio M. Cicu
James H. Cistone
Rita Coco
Gerald Cohen
Richard L. Conn
Jack W. Crenshaw
John J. Cupak, Jr
Patricia W. Daggett
B. K. Daniels
Adriam Davidoviciv
Theodore F. DeMuro
Phil A. J. DeVicci
Michael J. Devlin
C.J. DiPietro
Jack Dozier
Einar Dragstedt
Lawrence E. Druffel
Walter DuBlanica
Robert Eachus
Michael W. Evans
Richard E. Fairley
Debbie Faith
Jeffrey K. Farmer
Sal Fazzolari
Hal C. Ferguson

Kathy A. Fieldstad
Charles A. Finnell
Herman A. Fischer
Gerald Fisher
Larry Fishtahler
A.M. Foley
Alain Fontaine
Kevin Fosso
Helene Freedman
Jean Friedman
Bob Fritz
Sigrid Fritz
Vivian M. Gaetano
Michael J. Gagnon
Michel Galinier
Gary Garb
Forrest Karl Gardner
William Gardner
Anthony Gargaro
Dale Gaumer
Charles L. Gausche
William X. Gebele
David Gelperin
Mark S. Gerhardt
Larry D. Gilchrist
Shirley A. Gloss-Soler
Philip Goldstein
Michael Gordon
D.J. Gorman
Allain Griesemer
Thomas A. Grobicki
Howard Hamer
Richard M. Hanchett
Larry E. Hanlan
Ralph V. Harris
Michele Hartman
Charlene R. Hayden
Marlow Henne Herman
Ness Richard F. Hilliard
Warren Hoffnung
Michael Olin Hogan
Maretta T. Holden
Michael Horton
Mary Inglis
Jonathan James
Vicki Johnson
Lesa Kaitz
Gilbert H. Kemp
Robert Knapper
Martin Koenekamp
Shai Koenig
John F. Kramer, Jr
Bill Krueger
Arthur F. Krummenoeh
Joseph A. Krupinski
Mike Kuchinski
Joan Kundig
Carole J. Kuruma
Frank X. Laslo
Cony Lau
C. Crissman Laubach, III
Chris Laudbach
Carol LeDoux
Raymond C. Leber
Min Lee
Roger Lee

Larry Lindley
Steven Litvintchouk
Warren Loper
Michael E. Luken
Paul Maguire
Mark Maiocco
Allen Malberg
Sue Mardinly
D.H. Martin
Robert F. Mathis
Cathy Maxson
R.D. McCamy
Robert D. McClure
Ed McCronen
Gregory McFarland
Raymond J. McGlynn
George McPherson
Loren Meck
Mike Meirink
Louis Minham
James Moloney
David Moore
John I. Moore, Jr
William L. Morrison
A.J. Murfin
J.O. Neilson
Thomas Newsome
Edward Ng
Robert F. Owens
Eddie Paramore
Bruce R. Parker
Michael Patrick
Dianna H. Peet
George Petrovay
Larry Pochetti
Tim Portor
John Privitera
Thomas S. Radi
Stan F. Ralph
Salim Ramji
Kim T. Rawlinson
Ann Reedy
Alan Reiblein
Donald J. Reifer
Patrick J. Reilly
Herbert L. Resnick
Carol Righini
John W. Roberts
Kenneth Roberts
Mike Rockenhause
Paul Rogoway
Helen E. Romanowsky
Steven M. Rowan
R.C. Roy
David Rudd
Ruth Rudolph
Richard Rupolo
John L. Rymer
Mark Sadler
Sabina Saib
Arthur E. Salwin
Burnett H. Sams
Jack Schaefer
David F. Schick
Richard Schneider
Harvey E. Schock, Jr

The following persons were on the balloting committee that approved this standard for submission to the IEEE Standards Board:

A. Frank Ackerman
William W. Agresti
Dock Allen
Dennis R. Allison
Charles J. Antwelli
Barbara Ardary
Wolf Arfuidson
Tom Armbruster
James Baldo
Geoff R. Baldwin
Karl G. Balke
Bryce M. Bardin
John G.P. Barnes
B.C. Bass
Richard E. Batty
August A. Bauer
Leo Beltracchi
Frank Belz
Mordechai Ben-Menachem
Victor G. Berecz
H. Ronald Berlack
Brett L. Binns
Michael A. Blackledge
Robert M. Blasewitz
John J. Blyskal
Barry W. Boehm
William Bogdan
William Boyden
Carl Brandon
Jerry R. Brookshire
Al Brown
Fletcher J. Buckley
Harry Carl
David J. Carlson
Ingemar Carlson
A.J. Carvalho III
Janice A. Chelini
John Chihorek
Nhan V. Chu
Won L. Chung
Antonio M. Cicu
James H. Cistone
Suzette N. Clafton
John R. Clark
Donald R. Clarson
Corey Clinger
Richard T. Close
Peter Coad, Jr
Norman Cohen
Benjamin J. Consilvio
Chrisopher M. Cooke
Bard S. Crawford
James A. Darling
Sid David
Thomas Davis
Phil A.J. DeVicci
Vincent P. De-vito
Robert J. Decker
Michael J. Devlin
David G. Doty
Einar Dragstedt
Walter Du-Blanica
Robert E. Dwyer
Theodore J. Dzik
John D. Earls
Lange Brian Eliot
Richard E. Fairly
Raouf H. Farag
John W. Fendrich

Hal C. Ferguson
Glenn S. Fields
Gerry Fisher
A.M. Foley
Julian Forster
Kenneth A. Foster
Deborah L. Franke
Craig D. Fuget
Alfred Ganz
Leonard B. Gardner
Anthony Gargaro
David Gelperin
Edward L. Gibbs
Luther E. Gifford
Shirley A. Gloss-Soler
Marty Goldberg
Michael Gordon
Jacob Vadim Gore
Robert M. Grahm
Benjamin W. Green
Thomas A. Grobicki
Robert S. Grossman
Lawrence M. Gunther
Virl E. Haas
Harry E. Hansen, Jr
Hal M. Hart
Clark M. Hay
Paul L. Hazan
Jeffrey M. Hickey
L.J. Hoffman
Robert Hofkin
C.F. Howard
Henry B. Hoyle
Wendy J. Hudson
Charles J. Huller
James H. Ingram
Garland M. Jett, Jr
David Johnson III
Owen K. Kato
Mansour Kavianpour
Judith S. Kerner
Glenn M. Kersnick
Robert A. Kessler
Duane E. Kiefer
Genevieve M. Knight
Joseph A. Krupinski
Joan Kundig
Thomas M. Kurihara
Robert G. Kurkjian
Robin B. Lake
Robert A.C. Lane
Gregory N. Larsen
Randal Leavitt
Raymond C. Leber
David H. Lee
John A.N. Lee
James M. Lepsch
Ear Leung
Ben Livson
Paul E. MacNeil
Kartic C. Majumdar
Armand Marchesin
Sue Mardinly
Borut Maricic
Uchida Mark-Rene
Gregory C. Marr
Thomas H. Maryanski
Paul A. Mauro
C. Mazza

Maurice B. McEoy
Gregory McFarland
Raymond J. Mc-glynn
James McKelvey
Philip N. Merritt
Ben W. Miller
Robert P. Miller
Siba N. Mohanty
James Moody
Charles S. Mooney
John I. Moore, Jr
Nancy Moore
Gene T. Morun
Stephen V. Mroczek
David G. Mullens
Jose L. Munoz
W.M. Murray
Myron L. Nack
Hironobu Nagano
Jainendra K. Navlakha
Geraldine Rajcul Neidhart
States L. Nelson
Thomas Newsome
Dennis E. Nickle
T.L. Norman
John C. Norrell
Tim O'Bannon
James E. O'Day
Bruce R. Parker
Judson F. Parker
Michael Patrick
Robert L. Patton, Jr
Dianna H. Peet
Paul Peterson
Ramona Pfau
Ronald N. Pipes
Tim Porter
Ian Pyle
Edward Purvis
James E. Quelle
Sandra J. Raddue
Jock A. Rader
Thomas S. Radi
Salim Ramji
John Reddan
Larry K. Reed
T.D. Regulinski
Donald J. Reifer
Helen E. Romanowsky
Steven M. Rowan
Daniel M. Roy
Ruth Rudolph
Frances A. Ruhlman
John L. Rymer
H. Saha
Paul J. Sakson
Arthur E. Salwin
Jean E. Sammet
Burnett H. Sams
Raymond E. Sandborgh
Julio Gonzalez Sanz
Stephen R. Schach
Franz P. Schauer
Peter E. Schilling
Lee O. Schmidt
Norman F. Schneidewind
Wolf A. Schnoege
Leonard W. Seagren
Devdoot D. Sen

Contents

IEEE Recommended Practice for Ada As a Program Design Language

1. Introduction

1.1 Scope. This document provides recommendations reflecting the state of the art and alternate approaches to good practice for characteristics of Program Design Languages (PDLs) based on the syntax and semantics of the Ada Programming Language. In this recommended practice, these are referred to as Ada PDLs.

1.2 Scope Restrictions. This recommended practice addresses the characteristics of an Ada PDL and not the use of an Ada PDL. Although certain capabilities are recommended to be provided by an Ada PDL, this document does not state how a designer will design, nor how the design is to be documented, using an Ada PDL. While certain capabilities are recommended for an Ada PDL, specification of the ways to use those capabilities is beyond the scope of this document.

While it is widely recognized that graphic representations may enhance the design activity, there is no clear consensus concerning graphic representations at this time. As such, this document is principally concerned with the aspects of textual representations.

This recommended practice does not specify:

(1) A single PDL syntax

(2) The programming languages in which a design may be implemented

(3) A specific methodology to be used in conjunction with an Ada PDL

(4) The method by which a PDL text is represented, stored, or processed

This recommended practice does not provide:

(1) A tutorial on the use of:

(a) The Ada Programming Language, to include an exhaustive list of Ada constructs

(b) An Ada PDL

(2) A survey of PDLs or a history of their use

(3) A means for quantitatively determining the cost effectiveness of using an Ada PDL

1.3 Terminology. Where recommendations are made that represent the position of the IEEE, the verb *should* is used. Where alternate approaches are provided and no firm recommendations are made, the verb *may* is used.

1.4 Cautions. These are as follows:

(1) This document focuses on Ada PDLs. The use of a design language that is consistent with this recommended practice for other areas—for example, system requirements or hardware requirements—is not prohibited by this document. However, the reader is warned that there may very well be other substantial considerations in these uses, and that these considerations are beyond the scope of this recommended practice.

(2) An Ada PDL may be used to document a design when the implementation is projected to be in a Programming Language other than Ada. Users should be aware that an Ada PDL may not have the ability to represent such a design.

(3) Personnel associated with the use of a PDL should take special care to ensure that the designers do not become preoccupied with the details of the implementation when they should be designing. This may require special training, additional informal reviews, etc.

1.5 Examples. Examples are incorporated into the text of this recommended practice to enhance clarity and to promote understanding. All examples are explicitly identified. Examples should not be construed as recommended implementations.

2. Definitions and References

2.1 Definitions. The definitions listed in this section establish meaning in the context of this recommended practice. Other definitions can be found in: ANSI/IEEE Std 729-1983 [1][1] and ANSI/MIL-STD-1815A-1983 [2].

design element. A basic component or building block in a design.

design unit. A logically related collection of design elements. In an Ada PDL, a design unit is represented by an Ada compilation unit.

2.2 References. This standard shall be used in conjunction with the following publications:

[1] ANSI/IEEE Std 729-1983, IEEE Standard Glossary of Software Engineering Terminology.[2,3]

[2] ANSI/MIL-STD-1815A-1983 Reference Manual for the Ada Programming Language.[4]

3. Characteristics

3.1 General Methodology Support. A specific Ada PDL may support more than one design methodology. For example, both rapid prototyping and object-oriented design may be supported by the same Ada PDL. This is because no single development methodology is known to be superior for all applications and for all development organizations.

3.1.1 Abstraction. An Ada PDL should support the extraction of essential concepts while supporting the suppression of nonessential details.

3.1.2 Decomposition. An Ada PDL should support the division of a large software system into smaller, more manageable pieces while maintaining a fixed level of detail.

3.1.3 Information Hiding. An Ada PDL should support isolating and making inaccessible certain details that ought not to affect other parts of the software system.

3.1.4 Stepwise Refinement. An Ada PDL should support the progressive addition of detail to a software design.

3.1.5 Modularity. An Ada PDL should support the development of the design from standardized units.

3.2 Specific Design Support

3.2.1 Algorithm Design. An Ada PDL should support algorithm design. For example, depending on the intended usage, the PDL may support the use of structured control flow, computations, finite state machines, and Petri nets.

3.2.2 Data Structure Design. An Ada PDL should support data structure design. Specifically, an Ada PDL should support:

(1) Data structure definition

(2) Formalization of data structures

(3) Identification of constraints on acceptable values

(4) Identification of allowable operations on objects

(5) Location of points of access to data objects

(6) Modification of data objects

(7) Specification of data structure scope, duration, and storage methodology (for example, stored in shared memory, files, stack, etc) and constraints (for example, size limitations).

3.2.3 Connectivity. An Ada PDL should support the identification of explicit connections, including dependencies.

(1) The following should be formally described by the PDL:

(a) Ordering of component execution. As a part of this, the PDL should support the expression of:

(i) Sequential invocation of computational processes

(ii) Initiation and termination of parallel processes

(iii) Synchronization of parallel processes

(b) Data definition dependencies

---

[1] The numbers in brackets correspond to those of the references in 2.2 of this section.

[2] ANSI documents are available from the Sales Department, American National Standards Institute, 1430 Broadway, New York, NY 10018.

[3] See, specifically, Algorithm, Data Structure, Design, Design Language, Design Methodology, Life Cycle, Process, Program Design Language, and Software Life Cycle.

[4] See, specifically, Ada Programming Language, Compilation Unit, Generic Unit, Object, Package, Program Unit, Subprogram, Task, and Type.

(c) Data flow

(d) Possible error conditions and their associated consequences

(e) Interfaces between design units and between design elements

(f) Asynchronous interrupts

(2) The following may be formally describable by the Ada PDL:

(a) How the hardware works

(b) How interacting systems are expected to behave

3.2.4 Adaptability. The Ada PDL may have the capability to:

(1) Be adjusted under controlled forms to allow for national characters in a language other than English

(2) Implement restriction of certain syntax and semantics for particular applications (see 3.4.1.)

(3) Support graphic representations of the design being described

3.3 Other Support. The PDL may support the expression of Product and Management Information.

3.3.1 Product Information. Examples include:

(1) Performance. This may include critical timing, frequency, capacity, and other constraints.

(2) Fault Tolerance. This may include error detection/diagnosis and error handling, backup and recovery, reliability, and redundancy.

(3) Security. This may include multilevel security constraints, set/use access restrictions, breach detection and handling, and the identification of the security classification(s) of the material itself.

(4) Distribution. This may include geographic distribution of processing, data storage, and access.

(5) Adaptation. This may include accommodations to be made to support differing levels of user expertise.

(6) Assumptions. Description of a context within which an algorithm exists. For example, a function that does division may be built on the assumption that the denominator is not zero.

(7) History. This may include design decisions and alternate, rejected solutions to the chosen design, together with a rationale for the choice.

(8) Traceability. This may include traceability of:

(a) Detailed Design to Preliminary or Top-

Level Design, and further to the Software Requirements specifications

(b) Preliminary, or Top-Level Design to Detailed Design

(c) Applicable standards

3.3.2 Management Information. Examples include:

(1) Organizational information, such as division of work and assignment of tasks to team members

(2) Planning information, such as milestone definitions, resource estimation, dependencies that affect the development process itself, and scheduling

(3) Status information, such as milestone completion

(4) Configuration Management information, to include Configuration Identification and Change Control restrictions

3.4 Ada Relationships. The PDL should be related to the Ada Programming Language in the following respects:

3.4.1 Conformance. An Ada PDL should conform syntactically and semantically to ANSI/MIL-STD-1815A-1983 [2]. Specifically, an Ada PDL should be processible by a validated Ada compiler without error.

(1) An Ada PDL may be processible by other tools: for example, a PDL Preprocessor. Preprocessing should not be required prior to error-free processing by a validated Ada compiler.

(2) There is no requirement that an Ada PDL provide the full capabilities of the Ada Programming Language. A conforming subset should be adequate for the application and is allowable, for example, to prevent the use of:

(a) Untranslatable Ada constructs when designing for a target language other than Ada

(b) Inefficient control structures when developing embedded computer systems software

(c) Excessively detailed design constructs during high-level design, for example, use of representation specifications

3.4.2 Extensions. Commentary text may be used to extend the expressive capability of an Ada PDL beyond the semantics of Ada.

Two forms of comments are available:

(1) Unstructured comments

(2) Structured comments

3.4.2.1 Unstructured Comments. Unstructured comments may be used for:

(1) Natural language explanation of statements made in Ada

(2) Any information required in the design process where formal structures are not required: for example, for human-to-human communication

The user of unstructured comments should be aware that tools can process unstructured comments only in very primitive ways (for example, storage, retrieval, and crossreferencing).

3.4.2.2 Structured Comments. Structured comments (also known as annotations):

(1) May be used to provide design information in additional design-oriented semantics.

(2) Should be consistent with the Ada language. For example, in compound constructs, the end of the construct should mirror the beginning:

```
--*High Level Design
--*
--*
--*End High Level Design
```

(3) Are identified by a sentinel character, word, or phrase immediately following the double dash that indicates a comment to an Ada complier, for example, "--keyword" or "--*".

(a) The sentinel has two functions:

(i) To highlight the comment as belonging to the formal structure of the PDL, alerting any reader that the information is of special significance

(ii) To direct PDL processing tools toward information upon which the tools may be required to act

(b) Associated with the sentinel are semantic rules that indicate:

(i) Whether the comment applies to the preceding or the following Ada construct

(ii) What constructs are allowed after the sentinel, based on the context in which the sentinel appears

3.4.2.3 Replication Constraints. All concepts that can be reasonably expressed in noncommentary Ada should be so expressed. Information that can be provided in the Ada portion of the PDL should not be replicated within the commentary text by Ada constructs or by any other means.

The following organizations supported working group members in the development of this recommended practice:

Ada Joint Program Office
AT&T Bell Laboratories
BDM Corporation
Bendix Corporation
Boeing-Vertol
Burroughs Corporation
Canadian Marconi Company
Comptek Research, Inc
Computer Sciences Corporation
Control Data Corporation
Convex Computer Corporation
Digital Equipment Corporation
Federal Aviation Administration
Federal Department of Transportation
Ford Aerospace & Communications Division
General Dynamics
General Electric Company
General Research Corporation
Grumman Aerospace Corporation
GTE Government Systems Division
GTE Sylvania
SSD Harris Corporation
Hughes Aircraft Company
IBM
I.C.L. Intermetrics
Johns Hopkins Applied Physics Lab

Kearfott Softech, Inc
Litton Data Systems
Lockheed Electronics Company
M/A Com—Linkabit
Magnavox
Martin Marietta Aerospace
MITRE
National Bureau of Standards
Naval Air Development Center
Naval Avionics Center
NBC
Norden Systems
Prior Data Sciences, Ltd
Raytheon Company
RCA SAI Comsystems
SDC
Singer
Sperry
SYSCON Corporation
Teledyne Brown Engineering
Texas Instruments
Transport Canada
U.S. Air Force
U.S. Army
U.S. Navy
Vitro Corporation

An American National Standard

IEEE Standard Taxonomy for Software Engineering Standards

Sponsor

**Software Engineering Subcommittee
of the
Technical Committee on Software Engineering
of the
IEEE Computer Society**

1002

Approved December 11, 1986

IEEE Standards Board

Approved June 4, 1987

American National Standards Institute

Foreword

(This Foreword is not a part of ANSI/IEEE Std 1002-1987, IEEE Standard Taxonomy for Software Engineering Standards.)

Software Engineering is an emerging field. As part of that process a set of software engineering standards is being developed. They are used to:

(1) Improve communications between and among software engineers and others.

(2) Achieve economy of cost, human effort, and essential materials.

(3) Institutionalize practical solutions to recurring problems.

(4) Achieve predictability of cost and quality.

(5) Establish norms of acceptable professional practice.

To support the development, integration, and use of software engineering standards, a need for a taxonomy is recognized. A project was approved in June 1983 to define a taxonomy as part of a voluntary consensus process. This document is the result of that process.

This is one of an evolving set of integrated IEEE Software Engineering standards, recommended practices, and guides. The set currently includes:

ANSI/IEEE Std 729-1983, IEEE Standard Glossary of Software Engineering Terminology

ANSI/IEEE Std 730-1984, IEEE Standard for Software Quality Assurance Plans

ANSI/IEEE Std 828-1983, IEEE Standard for Software Configuration Management Plans

ANSI/IEEE Std 829-1983, IEEE Standard for Software Test Documentation

ANSI/IEEE Std 830-1984, IEEE Guide to Software Requirements Specifications

ANSI/IEEE Std 983-1986, IEEE Guide for Software Quality Assurance Planning

ANSI/IEEE Std 1008-1987, IEEE Standard for Software Unit Testing

This standard may be used in conjunction with this set of standards or separately.

The taxonomy can be applied, but is not limited to, project, program, organization, industrial, national, and international standards. As a document, this standard should be useful to those who develop, use, manage, and evaluate software engineering standards. The taxonomy provides a:

(1) Comprehensive scheme for classifying software engineering standards, recommended practices, and guides.

(2) Framework for identifying the need for new software engineering standards, recommended practices, and guides.

(3) Comprehensive scheme for analyzing a set of software engineering standards, recommended practices, and guides appropriate for a given industry, company, program, project, or particular work assignment.

(4) Framework for comparing sets of software engineering standards, recommended practices, and guides to support the selection of the most useful set for a particular software product.

The application of the taxonomy to achieve the above purposes is described in the appendix.

Keywords applicable to this standard are: nomenclature standard, notation standard, software engineering.

The sponsor for this standard was the Software Engineering Standards Subcommittee of the Software Engineering Technical Committee of the IEEE Computer Society, John W. Horch, Chairman.

Special representatives to the Software Engineering Standards Subcommittee were:

P.W. Abrahams	S.R. Jarocki	W.F. Mitchell
H.R. Berlack	R.R. Jones	W.E. Perry
A. Ferlan	J.A.N. Lee	T.L. Regulinski
	J. Milandin	P.E. Schilling

The working group that developed this standard had the following membership:

Leonard L. Tripp, *Chairperson*   **Perry R. Nuhn,** *Co-Chairperson*
Ralph G. Wachter, *Co-Chairperson*

A. Frank Ackerman	Paul Howley	Robert C. Olsen
Eleanor Antreasian	John Horch	Sharon R. Cobb-Pierson
Joan P. Bateman	Harry Kalmbach	Robert B. Poston
H. Ronald Berlack	Louis B. Kiersky	Max J. Schindler
Richard L. Chilausky	Thomas M. Kurihara	David Schultz
Francois Coallier	John B. Lane	Leonard W. Seagren
Stewart Crawford	F. C. Lim	John Selman
James Darling	Phillip C. Marriott	David M. Siefert
John W. Fendrich	Virginia Marting	Dave Simkins
Mehmet Ficici	Dan G. McNicholl	R. van Tilburg
Craig D. Fuget	Mordechai Ben-Menachim	William S. Turner, III
David Gelperin	Fred Mervine	Clyde E. Willis
Jeff van Gilder	Manijeh Moghis	Paul A. Willis
	Dennis E. Nickle	

When the IEEE Standards Board approved this standard on December 11, 1986, it had the following membership:

John E. May, *Chairman*   **Irving Kolodny,** *Vice Chairman*
Sava I. Sherr, *Secretary*

James H. Beall	Jack Kinn	Robert E. Rountree
Fletcher J. Buckley	Joseph L. Koepfinger*	Martha Sloan
Paul G. Cummings	Edward Lohse	Oley Wanaselja
Donald C. Fleckenstein	Lawrence V. McCall	J. Richard Weger
Jay Forster	Donald T. Michael*	William B. Wilkens
Daniel L. Goldberg	Marco W. Migliaro	Helen M. Wood
Kenneth D. Hendrix	Stanley Owens	Charles J. Wylie
Irvin N. Howell	John P. Riganati	Donald W. Zipse
	Frank L. Rose	

*Member emeritus

The following persons were on the balloting committee that approved this document for submission to the IEEE Standards Board:

A. Frank Ackerman
Jagdish C. Agrawal
Richard L. Aurbach
K. Ramesh Babu
James Baldo, Jr
H. Jack Barnard
Roy W. Bass
Leo Beltracchi
Yechiel Ben-Naftali
Victor G. Berecz
H.R. Berlack
J. Emmett Black
Michael A. Blackledge
Ron Blair
Kevin W. Bowyer
Kathleen L. Briggs
Fletcher J. Buckley
Margaret Butler
Homer C. Carney
Ronald R. Carter
Robert N. Charette
Tsun S. Chow
Jung K. Chung
Peter Coad, Jr
Francois Coallier
Christopher M. Cooke
A.J. Cote, Jr
Stewart Crawford
George D. Darling
Taz Daughtrey
P.O. Denny
Harpal S. Dhama
Mike Dotson
William P. Dupros
Michael Dutton
Robert E. Dwyer
Mary Eads
John D. Earls
Michael Edward
L.G. Egan
Steven R. Eisen
Caroline L. Evans
David W. Favor
John W. Fendrich
Robert G. Ferreol
Glenn S. Fields
Gordon Force
J. Forster
Deborah L. Franke
C.R. Frederick
Carl Friedlander

Ismael Fuentes-Crespo
Micheel Galinier
Leonard B. Gardner
David Gelperin
James L. Gildersleeve
Shirley Gloss-Soler
Ole Golubjatnikov
J. Kaye Grau
Andrej Grebenc
Thomas Griest
Victor M. Guarnera
Lawrence M. Gunther
David A. Gustafson
Russell Gustin
Howard Hamer
Hans-Ludwig Hansen
George B. Hawthorne
Clark M. Hay
Terry L. Hengl
Charles P. Hollocker
John W. Horch
Cheng Hu
Shang-Sheng Jeng
David Johnson, III
Laurel V. Kaleda
Constantine Kaniklidis
Myron S. Karasik
Adi N. Kasad
Ron Kenett
R.A. Kessler
Joseph A. Krupinski
Hirayr M. Kudyan
Joan Kundig
T.M. Kurihara
Robin B. Lake
Lak-Ming Lam
John B. Lane
Robert A.C. Lane
William P. LaPlant, Jr
Greg Larsen
Jack A. Latimer
Jay Levenson
Leon S. Levy
Paul Lieberaz
F.C. Lim
Bertil Lindberg
David Linsson
William M. Lively
John M. Long
John Lowell
L.J. Mablack

Bill Macre
Andy Mahindru
Henry Malec
Paulo Cesar Marcondes
Stuart Marcotte
Philip C. Marriott
Nicholas L. Marselos
Roger J. Martin
Robert F. Martini
Ivano Mazza
J.A. McCall
John McKissick, Jr
Glen A. Meldrum
Belden Menkus
Ben W. Miller
Manijeh Moghis
Charles S. Mooney
Joyce E. Mortison
Gene T. Morun
Dale N. Murray
Myron L. Nack
Hironobu Nagano
Saied Najafi
Gerry Neidhart
Brian Nejmeh
Dennis E. Nickle
I.H. Obbink
Wilma Osborne
D.J. Ostrom
David G. Owens
Thomas D. Parrish
M.T. Perkins
Donald J. Pfeiffer
R.M. Poston
Peter Ron Prinzivalli
Thomas S. Radi
Meir Razy
John Reddan
Larry K. Reed
Matthias F. Reese, III
T.D. Regulinski
Donald J. Reifer
Steven M. Rowan
R. Waldo Roth
Hom Sack
Julio Gonzalez Sanz
Stephen R. Schach
Franz P. Schauer
Max Schindler
Norman Schneidewind
Nolf A. Schnoege

Robert G. Schueppert
David J. Schultz
Gregory D. Schumacher
Leonard W. Seagren
Devdoot Sen
Gerard P. Share
Robert W. Shillato
David M. Siefert
David J. Simkins
Jacob Slonim
Marion P. Smith
Harry M. Sneed
J.G. Snodgrass
Al R. Sorkowitz
Hugh B. Spillane
Lee Sprague
G. Wayne Staley
Alan N. Sukert
William G. Sutcliffe
Richard H. Thayer
Booker T. Thomas
Paul U. Thompson
E.O. Tilford
Terrence L. Tillmanns
Lawrence F. Tracey
Glendon R. Trebble
Robert Troy
C.L. Troyanowski
Dana L. Ulery
R.L. Van Tilburg
P.M. Vater
Osmo Vikman
R. Wachter
Dolores R. Wallace
Andrew H. Weigel
R.W. Werlwas
Walter L. Whipple
Paul A. Willis
Patrick J. Wilson
Paul Wolfgang
W. Martin Wong
Dennis L. Wood
Paul R. Work
Tom Worthington
Charles Wortz
Stephen D. Yaste
Natalie C. Yopconka
Michael E. York
Marvin Zelkowitz
Peter F. Zoll

Contents

An American National Standard

IEEE Standard Taxonomy for Software Engineering Standards

1. Introduction

1.1 Scope. This document describes the form and content of a software engineering standards taxonomy. Applicability is not restricted by software application, size, complexity, criticality, or hardware environment. This taxonomy applies to standards (from the related disciplines of engineering management, systems engineering, computer hardware engineering, computer science, and information science) with which a software engineer would be reasonably acquainted. This taxonomy is application independent. For example, an accounting test standard would be placed under test standards, but the qualifier, accounting, has no significance. The document explains the various types of software engineering standards, their functional and external relationships, and the role of various functions participating in the software life cycle. The taxonomy may be used as a method for planning the development or evaluation of standards for an organization. It could also serve as a basis for classifying a set of standards or for organizing a standards manual.

1.2 Terminology. The word *shall* identifies the mandatory material within this standard. The words *should* and *may* identify optional material.

1.3 References. This standard shall be used in conjunction with the following reference:

[1] ANSI/IEEE Std 729-1983, IEEE Standard Glossary of Software Engineering Terminology.[1]

---

[1] ANSI/IEEE publications can be obtained from the Sales Department, American National Standards Institute, 1430 Broadway, New York, NY 10018, or from the Service Center, The Institute of Electrical and Electronics Engineers, 445 Hoes Lane, P.O. Box 1331, Piscataway, NJ 08855-1331.

2. Definitions

The definitions listed below establish meaning in the context of this standard. Other definitions can be found in ANSI/IEEE Std 729-1983 [1].[2] **See specifically: audit, certification, configuration management, conversion, debugging, design, design phase, implementation phase, installation and checkout phase, integration, maintenance, operation and maintenance phase, quality assurance, requirements analysis, requirements phase, retirement phase, review, software engineering, software maintenance, test phase, and testing.** For the purpose of this standard, the term "software" includes the computer programs, data, and documentation portions of both software and firmware.

code of ethics standard. A standard that describes the characteristics of a set of moral principles dealing with accepted standards of conduct by, within, and among professions.

coding. The transforming of logic and data from design specifications into a programming language.

component standard. A standard that describes the characteristics of data or program components.

concept phase. The period of time in the software life cycle during which the user needs are described and evaluated through documentation (for example, statement of needs, advance planning report, project initiation memo, feasibility studies, system definition documentation, regulations, procedures or policies relevant to the project).

---

[2] The numbers in square brackets refer to those of the references listed in 1.3.

curriculum standard. A standard that describes the characteristics of a course of study on a body of knowledge that is offered by an educational institution.

description standard. A standard that describes the characteristics of product information or procedures provided to help understand, test, install, operate, or maintain the product.

design standard. A standard that describes the characteristics of a design or a design description of data or program components.

job function. A group of engineering processes that is identified as a unit for the purposes of work organization, assignment, or evaluation. Examples are design, testing, or configuration management.

language standard. A standard that describes the characteristics of a language used to describe a requirements specification, a design, or test data.

licensing standard. A standard that describes the characteristics of an authorization given by an official or a legal authority to an individual or organization to do or own a specified thing.

manufacturing phase. The period of time in the software life cycle during which the basic version of a software product is adapted to a specified set of operational environments and is distributed to a customer base.

measurement standard. A standard that describes the characteristics of evaluating a process or product.

method standard. A standard that describes the characteristics of the orderly process or procedure used in the engineering of a product or performing a service.

nomenclature standard. A standard that describes the characteristics of a system or set of names, or designations, or symbols.

notation standard. A standard that describes the characteristics of formal interchanges within a profession.

occupational title standard. A standard that describes the characteristics of the general area of work or profession.

plan standard. A standard that describes the characteristics of a scheme for accomplishing

defined objectives or work within specified resources.

process management. The direction, control, and coordination of work performed to develop a product or perform a service. Example is quality assurance.

process standard. A standard that deals with the series of actions or operations used in making or achieving a product.

product analysis. The process of evaluating a product by manual or automated means to determine if the product has certain characteristics.

product engineering. The technical processes to define, design, and construct or assemble a product.

product management. The definition, coordination, and control of the characteristics of a product during its development cycle. Example is configuration management.

product standard. A standard that defines what constitutes completeness and acceptability of items that are used or produced, formally or informally, during the software engineering process.

product support. The providing of information, assistance, and training to install and make software operational in its intended environment and to distribute improved capabilities to users.

professional standard. A standard that identifies a profession as a discipline and distinguishes it from other professions.

report standard. A standard that describes the characteristics of describing results of engineering and management activities.

representation standard. A standard that describes the characteristics of portraying aspects of an engineering or management product.

requirement standard. A standard that describes the characteristics of a requirements specification.

resource management. The identification, estimation, allocation, and monitoring of the means used to develop a product or perform a service. Example is estimating.

software life cycle. The period of time that starts when a software product is conceived and ends when the product is no longer available for use. The software life cycle typically includes a concept phase, requirements phase, design phase, implementation phase, test phase, manufacturing phase, installation and checkout phase, operation and maintenance phase, and sometimes, retirement phase.

taxonomy. A scheme that partitions a body of knowledge and defines the relationships among the pieces. It is used for classifying and understanding the body of knowledge.

technical management. The application of technical and administrative resources to plan, organize, and control engineering functions.

technique standard. A standard that describes the characteristics of applying accumulated technical or management skills and methods in the creation of a product or performing a service.

verification and validation. The process of determining whether the requirements for a system or component are complete and correct, the products of each development phase fulfill the requirements or conditions imposed by the previous phase, and the final system or component complies with specified requirements.

3. Taxonomy of Software Engineering Standards

The taxonomy shall consist of a standards partition, software engineering partition, and a framework that relates the two partitions. Each partition results in the definition of a set of categories wherein each category has a name and a membership rule. The standards partition characterizes the roles of standards. The software engineering partition characterizes the aspects of software engineering with which a standard can be associated. The framework combines the two partitions into a two-dimensional scheme, which describes the set of possible software engineering standards. The taxonomy framework also describes how the categories are organized for classification purposes. Section 3.1 describes the standards partition, Section 3.2 describes the software engineering partition, and Section 3.3 describes the taxonomy framework and its relationships.

3.1 Standards Partition. The standards partition shall be organized by type of standard. The

**Fig 1
Partition of Standards by Type**

four types are process, product, professional, and notation standards. See Fig 1 for the complete partition.

Process standards deal with the series of actions or operations used in engineering a product or delivering a service. The actions or operations make use of methods, tools, and techniques. They give the "whos," "whats," "hows," "wheres," "whens," and levels of the work done in software engineering. Product standards are concerned with the format and content of things. The products are the documented results of the software development and maintenance activities and provide a baseline for future activities. Professional standards deal with all aspects of software engineering that identify it as a profession. An example is a curriculum for a Master of Software Engineering degree. Notation standards deal with the communication of common items among the software engineering professionals in a uniform manner. An example is a glossary. The output of a process is a product; the process is performed by people using tools and techniques within the profession.

3.2 Software Engineering Partition. The software engineering partition shall consist of two parts: job functions and software life cycle. These two parts or perspectives are used in order to compare, judge, evaluate, and determine the scope and content of software engineering standards. See Fig 2 for the software engineering

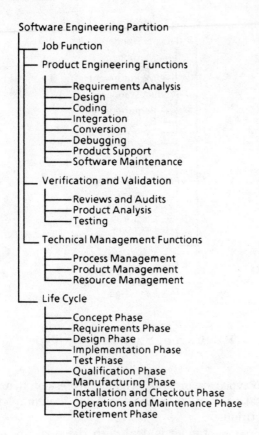

**Fig 2
Partition of Software Engineering by
Function and Life Cycle**

partition. Job functions are the identifiable processes of software engineering. Job functions often occur in parallel. For example, designs are updated as software elements are developed. No strict temporal sequence exists among the job functions since planning, execution, or follow-up within a function will certainly overlap other job functions.

Job functions are divided into three parts: product engineering functions, verification and validation functions, and technical management functions. The three parts contain the major ongoing, parallel activities of producing, checking, and controlling that are not concentrated in a single life cycle phase. The product engineering functions includes those processes that are necessary to define, produce, and support the final software product. Verification and validation functions are the technical activities that check the quality of the product. Technical management functions are those processes that structure and control the engineering functions. Project management is viewed as being related

to technical management in the following way: Typically, project management is the use, by one or more organizations, of the technical management functions of process management, product management, and resource management to develop a product within specified resources.

3.3 Taxonomy Framework. The taxonomy framework shall consist of:

(1) Names of the categories in the standards partition and the relationships among the names

(2) Names of the categories in the software engineering partition and the relationships among the names

(3) Rules for composing the framework

(4) Presentation format for the framework

The taxonomy may be presented in different ways, depending on how it can be used most effectively. The rows and columns may be reversed, higher or lower levels of classification can be shown, or only part of the table may be used.

This standard presents three versions of the taxonomy framework for use. The three versions are titled:

(a) Basic Taxonomy Framework (Version A)

(b) Basic Taxonomy Framework (Version B)

(c) Comprehensive Taxonomy Framework

The two Basic Taxonomy Frameworks have the same column labels with the row labels being somewhat different. The row labels for Version A are a selection from the job function portion of the software engineering partition that generally are present in all software life phases and the software life cycle phases. The column labels are the major categories of the standards partition. The row labels for Version B are the complete job function portion of the software engineering partition.

The two Basic Taxonomy Frameworks are illustrated in Figs 3 and 4. The frameworks are presented in the form of a two-dimensional table. An entry in one of the tables is defined by the names from the respective row label and column label of the entry. For example, in Fig 4, the most upper left table entry would be process standards for requirements analysis.

The Comprehensive Taxonomy Framework (see Fig 5) uses the full depth of both the standards partition and the software engineering partition. For presentation purposes, the framework is organized into two parts with the row labels from the standards partition and the column labels from the software engineering partition. For this framework, the entry name is defined by the names of the respective column label and row label of the entry.

The framework composition rules define the layout for the framework and how the entries in the table are composed. The rules are:

(1) The framework is displayed as a two-dimensional table with a set of labels for the rows and a set of labels for the columns.

(2) The names from either the standards partition or the software engineering partition are assigned as the source for the row labels. The remaining partition is the source for the column labels.

(3) A suitable set of names for the row and column labels is selected from the lists shown in Figs 1 and 2, starting at the left and proceeding to the desired level of detail.

(4) The scope of the framework is defined by eliminating those row-column pairs that are not feasible.

(5) An entry in the table is defined by names from the respective row and column of the entry.

Examples of how to classify standards using this taxonomy are contained in Appendix A.

			Type of Standard			
			Process Standard	Product Standard	Professional Standard	Notation Standard
Job Function	Ver & Val	Reviews & Audits				
		Product Analysis				
		Testing				
	Tech Mgmt	Process Management				
		Product Management				
		Resource Management				
S/w Life Cycle		Concept				
		Requirement				
		Design				
		Implementation				
		Test				
		Manufacturing				
		Operation and Maintenance				
		Retirement				

**Fig 3
Basic Taxonomy Framework (Version A)**

	Type of Standard			
Job Function	Process Standard	Product Standard	Professional Standard	Notation Standard
Product Engineering				
Requirements Analysis				
Design				
Coding				
Integration				
Conversion				
Debugging				
Product Support				
Software Maintenance				
Ver & Val				
Reviews and Audits				
Product Analysis				
Testing				
Tech Mgmt				
Process Management				
Product Management				
Resource Management				

Fig 4
Basic Taxonomy Framework (Version B)

ANSI/IEEE
Std 1002-1987

		Job Function													
		Product Engineering								Verification & Validation			Technical Management		
		Requirements Analysis	Design	Coding	Integration	Conversion	Debugging	Product Support	Software Maintaince	Reviews and Audits	Product Analysis	Testing	Process Management	Product Management	Resource Management
P r o c e s s	Method														
	Technique														
	Measurement														
P r o d u c t	Requirements														
	Design														
	Component														
	Description														
	Plan														
	Report														
P r o f e s s i o n	Occupational Title														
	Code of Ethics														
	Certification														
	Licensing														
	Curriculum														
N o t a t i o n	Nomenclature														
	Representation														
	Language														

(Left vertical label: Type Of Standard)

Fig 5
Comprehensive Taxonomy Framework
(Part 1)

15

	Software Life Cycle									
	Concept	Requirements	Design	Implementation	Test	Manufacturing	Installation & Checkout	Operation & Maintenance	Retirement
Type Of Standard — Process — Method									
Technique									
Measurement									
Product — Requirements									
Design									
Component									
Description									
Plan									
Report									
Profession — Occupational Title									
Code of Ethics									
Certification									
Licensing									
Curriculum									
Notation — Nomenclature									
Representation									
Language									

Fig 5 (Cont'd)
Comprehensive Taxonomy Framework
(Part 2)

16

Appendix
Taxonomy Usage Examples

(This Appendix is not a part of ANSI/IEEE Std 1002-1987, IEEE Standard Taxonomy for Software Engineering Standards, but is included for information only.)

This Appendix illustrates how the taxonomy can be used to:

(1) Classify a set of software engineering standards

(2) Annotate software engineering standards with keywords

(3) Characterize a software engineering standards program

(4) Correlate functions and software life cycle viewpoints

A1. Classification of Selected Standards

This section presents a selection of references on software engineering standards. The key for selection was that the reference is publicly available through a trade association, government agency, or national society other than IEEE. The references are listed below with their identifier. The identifiers are placed in the two tables (Figs A1 and A2). The selected standards were classified using the job function table of the Comprehensive Taxonomy Framework organized by software life cycle phase. In a complete example, there would be a job function table for each software life cycle phase. The example presented contains two tables. The first table (see Fig A1) depicts those standards that essentially have equal applicability over most software life cycle phases. The second table (see Fig A2) depicts those standards that are of special importance for the design phase of the software life cycle.

Identifier	Title
ICAM	Air Force Materials Laboratory, ICAM Documentation Standards, IDS 150120000A, December 28, 1981.
480	Department of Defense, Configuration Control-Engineering Changes, Deviations, and Waivers, DOD-STD-480A, 1978.[3]
483	Department of Defense, Configuration Management Practices for Systems, Equipment, Munitions, and Computer Programs, MIL-STD-483A, June 4, 1985.[4]
499	Department of Defense, Engineering Management, MIL-STD-499, May 1, 1974.
52779	Department of Defense, Software Quality Assurance Program Requirements, MIL-S-52779A, August 1, 1979.
490	Department of Defense, Specification Practices, MIL-STD-490, June 4, 1985.
RADC	Rome Air Development Center, RADC Computer Software Development Specification, CP 0787796100E, May 1979.
TADSTAD9	Department of Defense, Tactical Digital System Standard, Software Quality Assurance Testing Criteria, TADSTAD 9, 1978.[5]
1521	Department of Defense, Technical Reviews and Audits for Systems, Equipment, and Computer Software, MIL-STD-1521B, June 4, 1985.
2167	Department of Defense, Defense System Software Department, DOD-STD-2167, June 4, 1985.

---

[3] DOD and MIL publications are available from the Director, US Navy Publications and Printing Service, Eastern Division, 700 Robbins Avenue, Philadelphia, PA 19111.

[4] See footnote 3.

[5] Information on this publication can be obtained by writing to TAD, Chief of Materiel Command Headquarters, Washington, DC 20360.

Identifier	*Title*	
2167.1	Section 5.1	Requirements Analysis
2167.2	Sections 5.2, 5.3	Design
2167.3	Section 5.4	Coding
2167.4	Sections 5.5, 5.6	Integration and Testing
2167.5	Section 5.7	Configuration Management
2167.6	Section 5.8	Quality Evaluation
2167.7	Section 5.8.1.5	Installation and Checkout
2167.8	Sections 4.1, 4.2, 5.9	Project Management

FIPS 38   National Bureau of Standards, Guidelines for Documentation of Computer Programs and Automated Data Systems, Federal Information Processing Standards (FIPS) Publication (PUB) 38, February 15, 1976.[6]

FIPS 64   National Bureau of Standards, Guidelines for Documentation of Computer Programs and Automated Data Systems for the Initiation Phase, FIPS PUB 64, August 1, 1979.

FIPS 99   National Bureau of Standards, Guideline: A Framework for the Evaluation and Comparison of Software Development Tools, FIPS PUB 99, March 1983.

FIPS 101   National Bureau of Standards, Guideline for Lifecycle Validation, Verification, and Testing of Computer Software, FIPS PUB 101, June 1983.

FIPS 105   National Bureau of Standards, Guideline for Software Documentation Management, FIPS PUB 105, June 1984.

FIPS 106   National Bureau of Standards, Guideline on Software Maintenance, FIPS PUB 106, July 1984.

NSAC-39   Nuclear Safety Analysis Center, Verification and Validation for Safety Parameter Display Systems, NSAC-39, December 1981.

178   Radio Technical Commission for Aeronautics, Software Considerations in Airborne Systems and Equipment Certification, RTCA/DO-178A, March 22, 1985.[7]

178.1	Section 6	Development Verification and Validation
178.2	Sections 7.1, 7.2	Configuration Management
178.3	Sections 7.1, 7.3	Software Quality Assurance

9650   MITRE, Software Reporting Metrics, ESD-TR-85-145, MTR 9650, Revision 2, November 1985.

---

[6] FIPS publications are available from the Standards Processing Coordinator, Institute for Computer Sciences and Technology, National Bureau of Standards, Gaithersburg, MD 20899.

[7] RTCA publications are available from the Radio Technical Commission for Aeronautics (RTCA), 1425 K Street, NW, Suite 500, Washington, DC 20005.

Type of Standard

Job Functions		Process Standard	Product Standard	Professional Standard	Notation Standard
Product Engineering	Requirement Analysis	FIPS 99			
	Design	FIPS 99			
	Coding	FIPS 99			
	Integration	FIPS 99			
	Conversion	FIPS 99			
	Debugging	FIPS 99			
	Product Support	FIPS 99			
	Software Maintenance	FIPS 99			
V & V	Reviews and Audits	1521, 178.1, FIPS 101 NSAC-39			
	Product Analysis	178.1, FIPS 101 NSAC-39			
	Testing	TADSTAD 9, 178.1, FIPS 101, NSAC-39			
Tech Mgmt	Process Management	52779, 2167.6, 1521, FIPS 105, RADC, 2167.8,178.3	2167		
	Product Management	480, 483, 178.2, 2167.5	483, 2167		
	Resource Management	2167.8, 9650			

Fig A1

Example of General Standard Classification (Phase Independent)

Type of Standard

Job Functions		Process Standard	Product Standard	Professional Standard	Notation Standard
Product Engineering	Requirement Analysis	499*, 2167.1*	2167.1*, FIPS 64*, ICAM*		
	Design	2167.2, RADC	2167.2, FIPS 38, ICAM, 490		
	Coding	2167.3*, RADC*	2167.3*, ICAM*		
	Integration	2167.4	2167.4		
	Conversion				
	Debugging				
	Product Support				
	Software Maintenance	FIPS 106*			
V&V	Reviews and Audits	1521, 178.1, FIPS 101, NSAC-39			
	Product Analysis	178.1, FIPS 101 NSAC-39			
	Testing	TADSTAD 9, 178.1, FIPS 101, NSAC-39			
Mgmt	Process Management	52779, 2167.6, 1521, FIPS 105, RADC, 2167.8, 178.3	2167		
	Product Management	480, 483, 178.2, 2167.5	483, 2167		
	Resource Management	2167.8, 9650			

Legend *Examine for planning purposes

Fig A2
Example of General Standard Classification (Design Phase)

A2. An Approach to Annotating Software Engineering Standards with Keywords

The process of analysis, selection, and comparing of standards will benefit from a systematic means of keyword identification, which may then be incorporated into an organization's classification and retrieval procedures. An example set of keyword formation rules follows:

(1) Software engineering standards shall be classified with keywords. This shall be accomplished as part of a standard's development.

(2) Keywords shall be included in a standard's introduction. Keyword inclusion shall use the following format: "Keywords applicable to this standard are: Keyword 1, Keyword 2, . . ., Keyword n."

(3) Keywords shall be limited to words or phrases as contained in IEEE Std 1002-1987.

(4) Multiple keywords may be used in classifying a standard.

(5) Commas shall be used to separate keywords. The keyword shall will be terminated with a period.

(6) A standard shall be assigned at least one keyword from both the standards partition and software engineering partition. Within the categories of function and life cycle, multiple primary keywords may be selected.

The application of the keyword rules to some of the IEEE software engineering standards is illustrated in the following list:

Example #1. ANSI/IEEE Std 729-1983, IEEE Standard Glossary of Software Engineering Terminology. Keywords applicable to this standard are: nomenclature standard, notation standard, software engineering.

Example #2. ANSI/IEEE Std 730-1984, IEEE Standard for Software Quality Assurance Plans. Keywords applicable to this standard are: process management, product standard, software engineering, technical management.

Example #3. ANSI/IEEE Std 828-1983, IEEE Standard for Software Configuration Management Plans. Keywords applicable to this standard are: product management, product standard, technical management, software engineering.

Example #4. ANSI/IEEE Std 829-1983, IEEE Standard for Software Test Documentation. Keywords applicable to this standard are: product standard, software engineering, testing, verification and validation.

Example #5. ANSI/IEEE Std 830-1984, IEEE Guide to Software Requirements Specifications. Keywords applicable to this standard are: product engineering, product standard, requirements analysis, software engineering.

Example #6. ANSI/IEEE Std 983-1986, IEEE Guide to Software Quality Assurance Planning. Keywords applicable to this standard are: process standard, process management, technical management, software engineering.

Example #7. ANSI/IEEE Std 1008-1987, IEEE Standard for Software Unit Testing. Keywords applicable to this standard are: process standard, testing, verification and validation, software engineering.

A3. Application of Taxonomy to IEEE Software Engineering Standards (SES) Program

The IEEE Technical Committee on Software Engineering has an active program for software engineering standards. Listed below are the standards that are complete and those that are still in progress. The list of standards has been categorized by the taxonomy. To do that, three tables were created. The first table (see Fig A3) consists of the job function portion of the software engineering partition down the side and standards partition across the top. This orientation was chosen for presentation purposes.

Each entry on the standards list below was placed in the appropriate table entry. The S, R, and G refer to standard, recommended practice, and guide, respectively. The empty entries indicate possible areas for future standards.

The second and third tables use the standards partition down the side and functions across the top. The next lower level of detail was added for the standards partition. See Figs A4 and A5.

Approved Software Engineering Standards

Ref	Description
729	IEEE Standard Glossary or Software Engineering Terminology
730	IEEE Standard for Software Quality Assurance Plans
828	IEEE Standard for Software Configuration Management Plans

Ref	Description
829	IEEE Standard for Software Test Documentation
830	IEEE Guide to Software Requirements Specifications
983	IEEE Guide for Software Quality Assurance Planning
990	IEEE Guide for the Use of Ada* As a PDL
1002	IEEE Standard Taxonomy for Software Engineering Standards
1008	IEEE Standard for Software Unit Testing
1012	IEEE Standard for Software Verification and Validation Plans
1016	IEEE Recommended Practice for Software Design Descriptions

Approved Software Engineering Standards Projects

Ref	Description
P982	Standard for Software Reliability Measurement
P1028	Standard for Software Reviews and Audits
P1042	Guide for Software Configuration Management
P1044	Standard Classification of Software Errors, Faults, and Failures
P1045	Standard for Software Productivity Metrics
P1058	Standard for the Software Project Management Plan
P1059	Guide for Software Verification and Validation

Ref	Description
P1060	Standard for Software Maintenance
P1061	Standard for Software Quality Metrics
P1062	Guide for Third Party Software Acquisition
P1063	Standard for User Documentation
P1074	Standard for the Software Life Cycle Processes

A4. Job Function to Software Life Cycle Correlation

In some sense, job functions and phases can be correlated to each other. The purpose of this section is to illustrate that relationship. See Fig A6.

Note that in the product engineering and verification and validation categories each row is filled in to indicate where

(1) the planning or monitoring activity takes place (empty square)

(2) the focus of the phase and job function partially coincide (shaded square)

(3) the focus of the phase and job function directly coincide (dark square)

For product engineering and verification and validation activities, this indicates the respective phases for which these activities build, reach and stay at peak effort, and then taper off. The maintenance phase is typically a repeat of the basic software life cycle, and this is denoted in the respective column by an asterisk.

Note that for the technical management functions, activities generally happen across all phases. This is indicated by dark squares for all phases for these job functions.

---

* Ada is a registered trademark of the U.S. Government, AJPO.

Type of Standard

Job Functions		Process Standard	Product Standard	Professional Standard	Notation Standard
Product Engineering	Requirement Analysis	1074(S)	830(G)		729, 1002(S)
	Design	1074(S)	1016(R)		729(S), 990(R), 1002(S), 1016(R)
	Coding	1074(S)			729(S), 1002(S)
	Integration	1074(S)			729(S), 1002(S)
	Conversion	1074(S)			729(S), 1002(S)
	Debugging	1074(S)			729(S), 1002(S)
	Product Support	1074(S)	1063(S)		729(S), 1002(S)
	Software Maintenance	1060(S), 1074(S)			729(S), 1002(S)
V&V	Review and Audits	1028(S), 1074(S)	1012(S)		729(S), 1002(S)
	Product Analysis	1059(G)			729(S), 1002(S)
	Testing	829(S), 1008(S), 1012(S), 1074(S), 1059(G)	829(S), 1012(S)		729(S), 1002(S)
Technical Mgt	Process Management	1028(S), 1062(S), 1074(S), 983(G), 1061(S)	730(S), 1058(S)		729(S), 1002(S)
	Product Management	982(S), 1028(S), 1042(G), 1044(S), 1074(S)	828(S), 1063(S)		729(S), 1002(S)
	Resource Management	1045(S)			729(S), 1002(S)

Fig A3

Classification of IEEE Software Engineering Standards (Gross Level)

Job Function

		Product Engineering							
		Requirements Analysis	Design	Coding	Integration	Conversion	Debugging	Software Maintenance	Product Support
Process	Method	1074	1074	1074	1074	1074	1074	1060, 1074	1074
	Technique								
	Measurement								
Product	Requirement	830							
	Design		1016						
	Component								
	Description								1063
	Plan								
	Report								
Profession	Occupational Title								
	Code of Ethics								
	Certification								
	Licensing								
	Curriculum								
Notat	Nomenclature	729,1002	729,1002	729,1002	729,1002	729,1002	729,1002	729,1002	729,1002
	Representation		1016						
	Language		990						

Type of Standard

Fig A4

Classification of IEEE Software Engineering Standards (Refined Level—Part I)

| | | Job Function | | | | | |
| | | Technical Management Functions | | | Verification & Validation | | |
		Process Management	Product Management	Resource Management	Review and Audits	Product Analysis	Testing
Type of Standard — Process	Method	983,1028,1062,1074	1028,1042,1074	1074	1028,1074	1074	829,1008,1074
	Technique						
	Measurement	1061	982,1044	1045			
Product	Requirement						
	Design						
	Component						
	Description		1063				829
	Plan	730,1058	828		1012	1012	829,1012
	Report						829
Profession	Occupational						
	Code of Ethics						
	Certification						
	Licensing						
	Curriculum						
Notation	Nomenclature	729,1002	729,1002	729,1002	729,1002	729,1002	729,1002
	Representation						
	Language						

Fig A5
Classification of IEEE Software Engineering Standards (Refined Level—Part II)

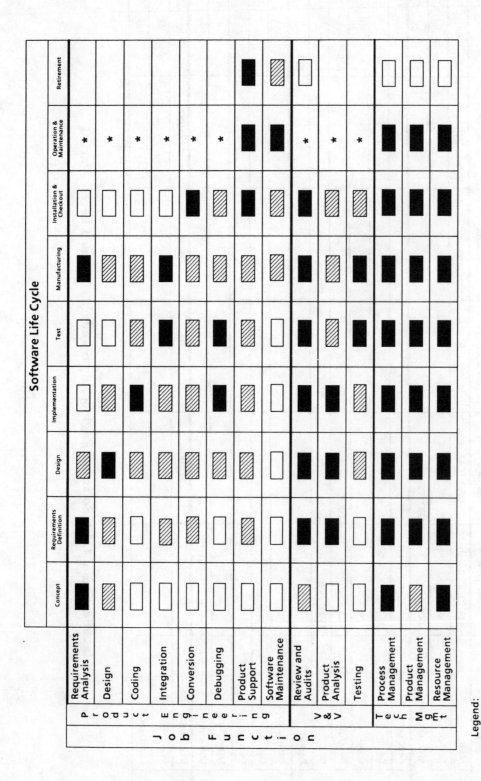

Fig A6
Job Function–Software Life Cycle Correlation

Acknowledgements

The following organizations provided support for the development of this standard:

AccuRay Corporation
Applied Physics Laboratory
AT&T Bell
Canada Bell
Northern Research
The Boeing Company
Bradley University
Computer Sciences Corporation
E-Systems
Edinboro University of Pennsylvania
Hewlett-Packard
Hughes
IBM
INCO, Inc.
ITT Corporation
McDonnell Douglas
Mervine and Pallesen
MIV-MEDA Ltd.
NCR Corporation
Northern Telecom
Pratt & Whitney Aircraft
Programming
Environments, Inc.
Sanders Associates Software
Engineering Associates Software
Quality Engineering
Teledyne Brown Engineering
Tennessee Valley Authority
The Algoma Steel Corporation, Ltd.
U.S. Department of Housing and Urban Development
U.S. Department of Transportation

This support does not constitute or imply approval or endorsement of this standard.

An American National Standard

IEEE Standard for
Software Unit Testing

Sponsor

**Software Engineering Technical Committee
of the
IEEE Computer Society**

Approved December 11, 1986

IEEE Standards Board

1008

Approved July 28, 1986

American National Standards Institute

Corrected Edition
May 1987

© Copyright 1986 by

**The Institute of Electrical and Electronics Engineers, Inc
345 East 47th Street, New York, NY 10017, USA**

Foreword

(This Foreword is not a part of ANSI/IEEE Std 1008-1987, IEEE Standard for Software Unit Testing.)

Objectives

This standard's primary objective is to specify a standard approach to software unit testing that can be used as a basis for sound software engineering practice.

A second objective is to describe the software engineering concepts and testing assumptions on which this standard approach is based. This information is contained in Appendix B. Note that Appendix B is not a part of this standard.

A third objective is to provide guidance and resource information to assist with the implementation and usage of the standard unit testing approach. This information is contained in Appendixes A, C, and D. Note that these Appendixes are not a part of this standard.

Motivation

A consensus definition of sound unit testing provides a baseline for the evaluation of specific approaches. It also aids communication by providing a standard decomposition of the unit testing process.

Audience

The primary audience for this standard is unit testers and unit test supervisors. This standard was developed to assist those who provide input to, perform, supervise, monitor, and evaluate unit testing.

Relationship with Other Software Engineering Standards

ANSI/IEEE Std 829-1983, IEEE Standard for Software Test Documentation, describes the basic information needs and results of software testing. This unit testing standard requires the use of the test design specification and test summary report specified in ANSI/IEEE Std 829-1983.

This standard is one of a series aimed at establishing the norms of professional practice in software engineering. Any of the other software engineering standards in the series may be used in conjunction with it.

Terminology

Terminology in this standard is consistent with ANSI/IEEE Std 729-1983, IEEE Standard Glossary of Software Engineering Terminology. To avoid inconsistency when the glossary is revised, its definitions are not repeated in this standard.

The *test unit* referred to in this standard is a specific case of the *test item* referred to in ANSI/IEEE 829-1983. The term *test unit* is used because of this standard's narrower scope.

The use of the term *specification, description,* or *document* refers to data recorded on either an electronic or paper medium.

The word *must* and imperative verb forms identify mandatory material within the standard. The words *should* and *may* identify optional material.

Overview

The unit testing process is composed of three *phases* that are partitioned into a total of eight basic *activities* as follows:
(1) *Perform the test planning*
   (a) Plan the general approach, resources, and schedule
   (b) Determine features to be tested
   (c) Refine the general plan
(2) *Acquire the test set*
   (a) Design the set of tests
   (b) Implement the refined plan and design

(3) *Measure the test unit*

    (a) Execute the test procedures

    (b) Check for termination

    (c) Evaluate the test effort and unit

The major dataflows into and out of the phases are shown in Fig A.

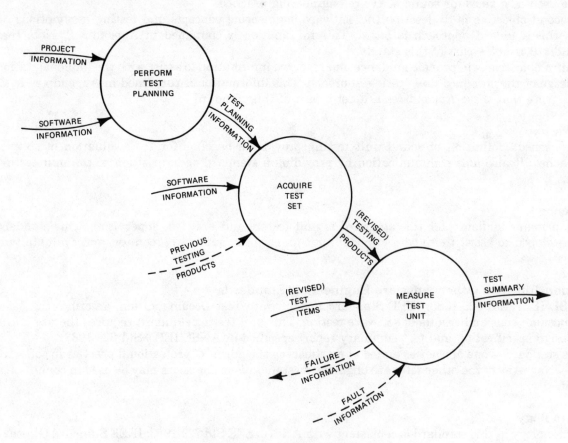

Fig A
Major Dataflows of the Software
Unit Testing Phases

Within a phase, each basic activity is associated with its own set of inputs and outputs and is composed of a series of tasks. The inputs, tasks, and outputs for each activity are specified in the body of this standard.

The set of outputs from all activities must contain sufficient information for the creation of at least two documents—a test design specification and a test summary report. Both documents must conform to the specifications in ANSI/IEEE Std 829-1983.

History

Work on this standard began in February 1983, following announcement of the formation of the task group in the technical and commercial press in late 1982. The project authorization request was approved by the IEEE Standards Board on June 23, 1983 following the second meeting. A total of seven meetings held throughout the United States at three month intervals produced the draft submitted for ballot in March 1985. A total of over 90 persons contributed to the initial development of this standard. Contributors are those individuals who either attended a working-group meeting, submitted written comments on a draft, or both.

This standard was developed by a working group with the following members:

David Gelperin, *Chairperson*   **Pat Wilburn,** *Cochairperson*

A. Frank Ackerman	Ken Foster	John Owens
Craig Adams	John Fox	William Perry
David Adams	Roger Fujii	Gerald Peterson
Jack Barnard	Ross Gagliano	Bob Poston
Wanda Beck	Mark Gerhard	Patricia Powell
Boris Beizer	Ed Gibson	Samuel T. Redwine, Jr
K. Mack Bishop	Therese Gilbertson	Sanford Rosen
Jill E. Boogaard	Gary Girard	Hans Schaefer
Milt Boyd	Keith Gordon	Eric Schnellman
Nathan B. Bradley	Paul Grizenko	Harvey Schock
Martha Branstad	Jeff Grove	Al Sema, Jr
Fletcher Buckley	Ismet Gungor	Harlan Seyfer
John W. Cain	Mark Heinrich	Victor Shtern
Christopher Cooke	Rudolph Hodges	Rick Simkin
L. L. Doc Craddock	R. A. Kessler	Wayne Smith
Palmer Craig	Tom Kurihara	Harry Sneed
Michael Cramer	Costas Labovites	Hugh B. Spillane
Dave Dahlinghaus	Frank LaMonica	Ben Sun
Noah Davids	F. C. Lim	Murray Tabachnick
Henry Davis	Philip C. Marriott	Barbara Taute
Bruce Dawson	Debra L. McCusker	Leonard Tripp
Claudia Dencker	Charlie McCutcheon	William S. Turner III
Michael Deutsch	Rudolf van Megen	John Vance
Judie Divita	Denis Meredith	Guy Vogt
Jim Dobbins	Edward Miller, Jr	Dolores Wallace
David C. Doty	William Milligan	John Walter
Bill Dupras	Marcus Mullins	John C. Wang
Jim Edwards	W. M. Murray	Cheryl Webb
Karen Fairchild	Bruce Nichols	William Wilson
Peter Farrell-Vinay	Dennis Nickle	Ed Yasi
Thom Foote-Lennox	Larry Nitzsche	Natalie C. Yopconka

The following persons were on the balloting committee that approved this document for submission to the IEEE Standards Board:

When the IEEE Standards Board approved this standard on December 11, 1986, it had the following membership:

Contents

An American National Standard

IEEE Standard for Software Unit Testing

1. Scope and References

1.1 Inside the Scope. Software unit testing is a process that includes the performance of test planning, the acquisition of a test set, and the measurement of a test unit against its requirements. Measuring entails the use of sample data to exercise the unit and the comparison of the unit's actual behavior with its required behavior as specified in the unit's requirements documentation.

This standard defines an integrated approach to systematic and documented unit testing. The approach uses unit design and unit implementation information, in addition to unit requirements, to determine the completeness of the testing.

This standard describes a testing process composed of a hierarchy of phases, activities, and tasks and defines a minimum set of tasks for each activity. Additional tasks may be added to any activity.

This standard requires the performance of each activity. For each task within an activity, this standard requires either that the task be performed, or that previous results be available and be reverified. This standard also requires the preparation of two documents specified in ANSI/IEEE Std 829-1983 [2][1]. These documents are the Test Design Specification and the Test Summary Report.

General unit test planning should occur during overall test planning. This general unit test planning activity is covered by this standard, although the balance of the overall test planning process is outside the scope of this standard.

This standard may be applied to the unit testing of any digital computer software or firmware. However, this standard does *not* specify any class of software or firmware to which it must be applied, nor does it specify any class of software or firmware that must be unit tested. This standard applies to the testing of newly developed and modified units.

This standard is applicable whether or not the unit tester is also the developer.

1.2 Outside the Scope. The results of some overall test planning tasks apply to all testing levels (for example, identify security and privacy constraints). Such tasks are not considered a part of the unit testing process, although they directly affect it.

While the standard identifies a need for failure analysis information and software fault correction, it does not specify a software debugging process.

This standard does not address other components of a comprehensive unit verification and validation process, such as reviews (for example, walkthroughs, inspections), static analysis (for example, consistency checks, data flow analysis), or formal analysis (for example, proof of correctness, symbolic execution).

This standard does not require the use of specific test facilities or tools. This standard does not imply any particular methodology for documentation control, configuration management, quality assurance, or management of the testing process.

1.3 References. This standard shall be used in conjunction with the following publications.

[1] ANSI/IEEE Std 729-1983, IEEE Standard Glossary of Software Engineering Terminology.[2]

[2] ANSI/IEEE Std 829-1983, IEEE Standard for Software Test Documentation.

---

[1] The numbers in brackets correspond to the references listed in 1.3 of this standard.

[2] These publications are available from American National Standards Institute, Sales Department, 1430 Broadway, New York, NY 10018 and from IEEE Service Center, 445 Hoes Lane, Piscataway, NJ 08854.

2. Definitions

This section defines key terms used in this standard but not included in ANSI/IEEE Std 729-1983 [1] or ANSI/IEEE Std 829-1983 [2].

characteristic. *See:* **data characteristic** or **software characteristic.**

data characteristic. An inherent, possibly accidental, trait, quality, or property of data (for example, arrival rates, formats, value ranges, or relationships between field values).

feature. *See:* **software feature.**

incident. *See:* **software test incident.**

nonprocedural programming language. A computer programming language used to express the parameters of a problem rather than the steps in a solution (for example, report writer or sort specification languages). Contrast with **procedural programming language.**

procedural programming language. A computer programming language used to express the sequence of operations to be performed by a computer (for example, COBOL). Contrast with **nonprocedural programming language.**

software characteristic. An inherent, possibly accidental, trait, quality, or property of software (for example, functionality, performance, attributes, design constraints, number of states, lines of branches).

software feature. A software characteristic specified or implied by requirements documentation (for example, functionality, performance, attributes, or design constraints).

software test incident. Any event occuring during the execution of a software test that requires investigation.

state data. Data that defines an internal state of the test unit and is used to establish that state or compare with existing states.

test objective. An identified set of software features to be measured under specified conditions by comparing actual behavior with the required behavior described in the software documentation.

test set architecture. The nested relationships between sets of test cases that directly reflect the hierarchic decomposition of the test objectives.

test unit.[3] A set of one or more computer program modules together with associated control data, (for example, tables), usage procedures, and operating procedures that satisfy the following conditions:

(1) All modules are from a single computer program

(2) At least one of the new or changed modules in the set has not completed the unit test[4]

(3) The set of modules together with its associated data and procedures are the sole object of a testing process

unit. *See:* **test unit.**

unit requirements documentation. Documentation that sets forth the functional, interface, performance, and design constraint requirements for the test unit.

3. Unit Testing Activities

This section specifies the activities involved in the unit testing process and describes the associated input, tasks, and output. The activities described are as follows:

(1) Perform test planning phase
   (a) Plan the general approach, resources, and schedule
   (b) Determine features to be tested
   (c) Refine the general plan
(2) Acquire test set phase
   (a) Design the set of tests
   (b) Implement the refined plan and design
(3) Measure test unit phase
   (a) Execute the test procedures
   (b) Check for termination
   (c) Evaluate the test effort and unit

When more than one unit is to be unit tested (for example, all those associated with a software project), the Plan activity should address the total set of test units and should not be repeated for each test unit. The other activities must be performed at least once for each unit.

Under normal conditions, these activities are sequentially initiated except for the Execute and Check cycle as illustrated in Fig 1. When per-

---

[3] A test unit may occur at any level of the design hierarchy from a single module to a complete program. Therefore, a test unit may be a module, a few modules, or a complete computer program along with associated data and procedures.

[4] A test unit may contain one or more modules that have already been unit tested.

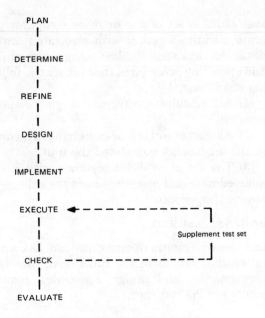

Fig 1
Unit Testing Activities

forming any of the activities except Plan, improper performance of a preceding activity or external events (for example, schedule, requirements, or design changes) may result in the need to redo one or more of the preceding activities and then return to the one being performed.

During the testing process, a test design specification and a test summary report must be developed. Other test documents may be developed. All test documents must conform to the ANSI/IEEE Std 829-1983 [2]. In addition, all test documents must have identified authors and be dated.

The test design specification will derive its information from the Determine, Refine, and Design activities. The test summary report will derive its information from all of the activities.

3.1 Plan the General Approach, Resources, and Schedule. General unit test planning should occur during overall test planning and be recorded in the corresponding planning document.

3.1.1 Plan Inputs
(1) Project plans
(2) Software requirements documentation

3.1.2 Plan Tasks
(1) *Specify a General Approach to Unit Testing.* Identify risk areas to be addressed by the testing. Specify constraints on characteristic determination (for example, features that must be tested), test design, or test implementation (for example, test sets that must be used).

Identify existing sources of input, output, and state data (for example, test files, production files, test data generators). Identify general techniques for data validation. Identify general techniques to be used for output recording, collection, reduction, and validation. Describe provisions for application software that directly interfaces with the units to be tested.

(2) *Specify Completeness Requirements.* Identify the areas (for example, features, procedures, states, functions, data characteristics, instructions) to be covered by the unit test set and the degree of coverage required for each area.

When testing a unit during software development, every software feature must be covered by a test case or an approved exception. The same should hold during software maintenance for any unit testing.

When testing a unit implemented with a procedural language (for example, COBOL) during software development, every instruction that can be reached and executed must be covered by a test case or an approved exception, except for instructions contained in modules that have been separately unit tested. The same should hold during software maintenance for the testing of a unit implemented with a procedural language.

(3) *Specify Termination Requirements.* Specify the requirements for normal termination of the unit testing process. Termination requirements must include satisfying the completeness requirements.

Identify any conditions that could cause abnormal termination of the unit testing process (for example, detecting a major design fault, reaching a schedule deadline) and any notification procedures that apply.

(4) *Determine Resource Requirements.* Estimate the resources required for test set acquisition, initial execution, and subsequent repetition of testing activities. Consider hardware, access time (for example, dedicated computer time), communications or system software, test tools, test files, and forms or other supplies. Also consider the need for unusually large volumes of forms and supplies.

Identify resources needing preparation and the parties responsible. Make arrangements for these resources, including requests for resources that require significant lead time (for example, customized test tools).

Identify the parties responsible for unit testing and unit debugging. Identify personnel requirements including skills, number, and duration.

(5) *Specify a General Schedule.* Specify a schedule constrained by resource and test unit availability for all unit testing activity.

3.1.3 Plan Outputs

(1) General unit test planning information (from 3.1.2(1) through (5) inclusive)

(2) Unit test general resource requests—if produced from 3.1.2(4)

3.2 Determine Features To Be Tested

3.2.1 Determine Inputs

(1) Unit requirements documentation

(2) Software architectural design documentation—if needed

3.2.2 Determine Tasks

(1) *Study the Functional Requirements.* Study each function described in the unit requirements documentation. Ensure that each function has a unique identifier. When necessary, request clarification of the requirements.

(2) *Identify Additional Requirements and Associated Procedures.* Identify requirements other than functions (for example, performance, attributes, or design constraints) associated with software characteristics that can be effectively tested at the unit level. Identify any usage or operating procedures associated only with the unit to be tested. Ensure that each additional requirement and procedure has a unique identifier. When necessary, request clarification of the requirements.

(3) *Identify States of the Unit.* If the unit requirements documentation specifies or implies multiple states (for example, inactive, ready to receive, processing) software, identify each state and each valid state transition. Ensure that each state and state transition has a unique identifier. When necessary, request clarification of the requirements.

(4) *Identify Input and Output Data Characteristics.* Identify the input and output data structures of the unit to be tested. For each structure, identify characteristics, such as arrival rates, formats, value ranges, and relationships between field values. For each characteristic, specify its valid ranges. Ensure that each characteristic has a unique identifier. When necessary, request clarification of the requirements.

(5) *Select Elements to be Included in the Test-ing.* Select the features to be tested. Select the associated procedures, associated states, associated state transitions, and associated data characteristics to be included in the testing. Invalid and valid input data must be selected. When complete testing is impractical, information regarding the expected use of the unit should be used to determine the selections. Identify the risk associated with unselected elements.

Enter the selected features, procedures, states, state transitions, and data characteristics in the *Features to be Tested* section of the unit's Test Design Specification.

3.2.3 Determine Outputs

(1) List of elements to be included in the testing (from 3.2.2(5))

(2) Unit requirements clarification requests—if produced from 3.2.2(1) through (4) inclusive

3.3 Refine the General Plan

3.3.1 Refine Inputs

(1) List of elements to be included in the testing (from 3.2.2(5))

(2) General unit test planning information (from 3.1.2(1) through (5) inclusive)

3.3.2 Refine Tasks

(1) *Refine the Approach.* Identify existing test cases and test procedures to be considered for use. Identify any special techniques to be used for data validation. Identify any special techniques to be used for output recording, collection, reduction, and validation.

Record the refined approach in the *Approach Refinements* section of the unit's test design specification.

(2) *Specify Special Resource Requirements.* Identify any special resources needed to test the unit (for example, software that directly interfaces with the unit). Make preparations for the identified resources.

Record the special resource requirements in the *Approach Refinements* section of the unit's test design specification.

(3) *Specify a Detailed Schedule.* Specify a schedule for the unit testing based on support software, special resource, and unit availability and integration schedules. Record the schedule in the *Approach Refinements* section of the unit's test design specification.

3.3.3 Refine Outputs

(1) Specific unit test planning information (from 3.3.2(1) through (3) inclusive)

(2) Unit test special resource requests—if produced from 3.3.2(2).

3.4 Design the Set of Tests
3.4.1 Design Inputs
(1) Unit requirements documentation

(2) List of elements to be included in the testing (from 3.2.2(5))

(3) Unit test planning information (from 3.1.2(1) and (2) and 3.3.2(1))

(4) Unit design documentation

(5) Test specifications from previous testing—if available

3.4.2 Design Tasks
(1) *Design the Architecture of the Test Set.* Based on the features to be tested and the conditions specified or implied by the selected associated elements (for example, procedures, state transitions, data characteristics), design a hierarchically decomposed set of test objectives so that each lowest-level objective can be directly tested by a few test cases. Select appropriate existing test cases. Associate groups of test-case identifiers with the lowest-level objectives. Record the hierarchy of objectives and associated test case identifiers in the *Test Identification* section of the unit's test design specification.

(2) *Obtain Explicit Test Procedures as Required.* A combination of the unit requirements documentation, test planning information, and test-case specifications may implicitly specify the unit test procedures and therefore minimize the need for explicit specification. Select existing test procedures that can be modified or used without modification.

Specify any additional procedures needed either in a supplementary section in the unit's test design specification or in a separate procedure specification document. Either choice must be in accordance with the information required by ANSI/IEEE Std 829-1983 [2]. When the correlation between test cases and procedures is not readily apparent, develop a table relating them and include it in the unit's test design specification.

(3) *Obtain the Test Case Specifications.* Specify the new test cases. Existing specifications may be referenced.

Record the specifications directly or by reference in either a supplementary section of the unit's test design specification or in a separate document. Either choice must be in accordance with the information required by ANSI/IEEE Std 829-1983 [2].

(4) *Augment, as Required, the Set of Test-Case Specifications Based on Design Information.* Based on information about the unit's design, update as required the test set architecture in accordance with 3.4.2(1). Consider the characteristics of selected algorithms and internal data structures.

Identify control flows and changes to internal data that must be recorded. Anticipate special recording difficulties that might arise, for example, from a need to trace control flow in complex algorithms or from a need to trace changes in internal data structures (for example, stacks or trees). When necessary, request enhancement of the unit design (for example, a formatted data structure dump capability) to increase the testability of the unit.

Based on information in the unit's design, specify any newly identified test cases and complete any partial test case specifications in accordance with 3.4.2(3).

(5) *Complete the Test Design Specification.* Complete the test design specification for the unit in accordance with ANSI/IEEE Std 829-1983 [2].

3.4.3 Design Outputs
(1) Unit test design specification (from 3.4.2(5))

(2) Separate test procedure specifications—if produced from 3.4.2(2)

(3) Separate test-case specifications—if produced from 3.4.2(3) or (4)

(4) Unit design enhancement requests—if produced from 3.4.2(4)

3.5 Implement the Refined Plan and Design
3.5.1 Implement Inputs
(1) Unit test planning information (from 3.1.2(1), (4), and (5) and 3.3.2(1) through (3) inclusive)

(2) Test-case specifications in the unit test design specification or separate documents (from 3.4.2(3) and (4)

(3) Software data structure descriptions

(4) Test support resources

(5) Test items

(6) Test data from previous testing activities—if available

(7) Test tools from previous testing activities—if available

3.5.2 Implement Tasks
(1) *Obtain and Verify Test Data.* Obtain a copy of existing test data to be modified or used without modification. Generate any new data required. Include additional data necessary to ensure data consistency and integrity. Verify all data (including those to be used as is) against

the software data structure specifications. When the correlation between test cases and data sets is not readily apparent, develop a table to record this correlation and include it in the unit's test design specification.

(2) *Obtain Special Resources.* Obtain the test support resources specified in 3.3.2(2).

(3) *Obtain Test Items.* Collect test items including available manuals, operating system procedures, control data (for example, tables), and computer programs. Obtain software identified during test planning that directly interfaces with the test unit.

When testing a unit implemented with a procedural language, ensure that execution trace information will be available to evaluate satisfaction of the code-based completeness requirements.

Record the identifier of each item in the *Summary* section of the unit's test summary report.

3.5.3 Implement Outputs

(1) Verified test data (from 3.5.2(1))

(2) Test support resources (from 3.5.2(2))

(3) Configuration of test items (from 3.5.2(3))

(4) Initial summary information (from 3.5.2(3))

3.6 Execute the Test Procedures

3.6.1 Execute Inputs

(1) Verified test data (from 3.5.2(1))

(2) Test support resources (from 3.5.2(2))

(3) Configuration of test items (from 3.5.2(3))

(4) Test-case specifications (from 3.4.2(3) and (4))

(5) Test procedure specifications (from 3.4.2 (2))—if produced

(6) Failure analysis results (from debugging process)—if produced

3.6.2 Execute Tasks

(1) *Run Tests.* Set up the test environment. Run the test set. Record all test incidents in the *Summary of Results* section of the unit's test summary report.

(2) *Determine Results.* For each test case, determine if the unit passed or failed based on required result specifications in the case descriptions. Record pass or fail results in the *Summary of Results* section of the unit's test summary report. Record resource consumption data in the *Summary of Activities* section of the report. When testing a unit implemented with a procedural language, collect execution trace summary information and attach it to the report.

For each failure, have the failure analyzed and record the fault information in the *Summary of Results* section of the test summary report. Then select the applicable case and perform the associated actions.

Case 1: A Fault in a Test Specification or Test Data. Correct the fault, record the fault correction in the *Summary of Activities* section of the test summary report, and rerun the tests that failed.

Case 2: A Fault in Test Procedure Execution. Rerun the incorrectly executed procedures.

Case 3: A Fault in the Test Environment (for example, system software). Either have the environment corrected, record the fault correction in the *Summary of Activities* section of the test summary report, and rerun the tests that failed OR prepare for abnormal termination by documenting the reason for not correcting the environment in the *Summary of Activities* section of the test summary report and proceed to check for termination (that is, proceed to activity 3.7).

Case 4: A Fault in the Unit Implementation. Either have the unit corrected, record the fault correction in the *Summary of Activities* section of the test summary report, and rerun all tests OR prepare for abnormal termination by documenting the reason for not correcting the unit in the *Summary of Activities* section of the test summary report and proceed to check for termination (that is, proceed to activity 3.7).

Case 5: A Fault in the Unit Design. Either have the design and unit corrected, modify the test specification and data as appropriate, record the fault correction in the *Summary of Activities* section of the test summary report, and rerun all tests OR prepare for abnormal termination by documenting the reason for not correcting the design in the *Summary of Activities* section of the test summary report and proceed to check for termination (that is, proceed to activity 3.7).

NOTE: The cycle of Execute and Check Tasks must be repeated until a termination condition defined in 3.1.2(3) is satisfied (See Fig 3). Control flow within the Execute activity itself is pictured in Fig 2).

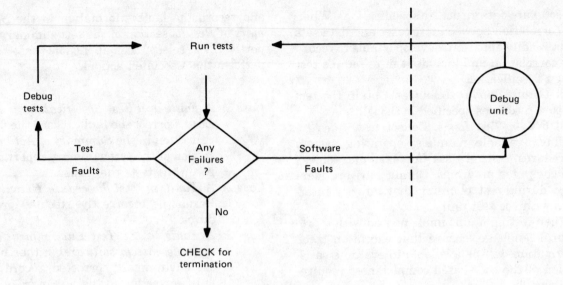

Fig 2
Control Flow Within the Execute Activity

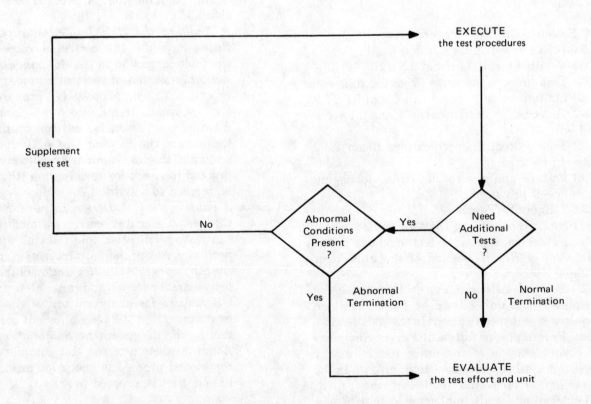

Fig 3
Control Flow Within the Check Activity

3.6.3 Execute Outputs

(1) Execution information logged in the test summary report including test outcomes, test incident descriptions, failure analysis results, fault correction activities, uncorrected fault reasons, resource consumption data and, for procedural language implementations, trace summary information (from 3.6.2(1) and (2))

(2) Revised test specifications—if produced from 3.6.2(2)

(3) Revised test data—if produced from 3.6.2(2)

3.7 Check for Termination

3.7.1 Check Inputs

(1) Completeness and termination requirements (from 3.1.2(2) and (3))

(2) Execution information (from 3.6.2(1) and (2))

(3) Test specifications (from 3.4.2(1) through (3) inclusive)—if required

(4) Software data structure descriptions—if required

3.7.2 Check Tasks

(1) *Check for Normal Termination of the Testing Process.* Determine the need for additional tests based on completeness requirements or concerns raised by the failure history. For procedural language implementations, analyze the execution trace summary information (for example, variable, flow).

If additional tests are *not* needed, then record normal termination in the *Summary of Activities* section of the test summary report and proceed to evaluate the test effort and unit (that is, proceed to activity 3.8).

(2) *Check for Abnormal Termination of the Testing Process.* If an abnormal termination condition is satisfied (for example, uncorrected major fault, out of time) then ensure that the specific situation causing termination is documented in the *Summary of Activities* section of the test summary report together with the unfinished testing and any uncorrected faults. Then proceed to evaluate the test effort and unit (that is, proceed to activity 3.8).

(3) *Supplement the Test Set.* When additional tests are needed and the abnormal termination conditions are not satisfied, supplement the test set by following steps (a) through (e).

(a) Update the test set architecture in accordance with 3.4.2(1) and obtain additional test-case specifications in accordance with 3.4.2(3).

(b) Modify the test procedure specifications in accordance with 3.4.2(2) as required.

(c) Obtain additional test data in accordance with 3.5.2(1).

(d) Record the addition in the *Summary of Activities* section of the test summary report.

(e) Execute the additional tests (that is, return to activity 3.6).

3.7.3 Check Outputs

(1) Check information logged in the test summary report including the termination conditions and any test case addition activities (from 3.7.2(1) through (3) inclusive)

(2) Additional or revised test specifications—if produced from 3.7.2(3)

(3) Additional test data—if produced from 3.7.2(3)

3.8 Evaluate the Test Effort and Unit

3.8.1 Evaluate Inputs

(1) Unit Test Design Specification (from 3.4.2(5)

(2) Execution information (from 3.6.2(1) and (2))

(3) Checking information (from 3.7.2(1) through (3) inclusive)

(4) Separate test-case specifications (from 3.4.2(3) and (4))—if produced

3.8.2 Evaluate Tasks

(1) *Describe Testing Status.* Record variances from test plans and test specifications in the *Variances* section of the test summary report. Specify the reason for each variance.

For abnormal termination, identify areas insufficiently covered by the testing and record reasons in the *Comprehensiveness Assessment* section of the test summary report.

Identify unresolved test incidents and the reasons for a lack of resolution in the *Summary of Results* section of the test summary report.

(2) *Describe Unit's Status.* Record differences revealed by testing between the unit and its requirements documentation in the *Variances* section of the test summary report.

Evaluate the unit design and implementation against requirements based on test results and detected fault information. Record evaluation information in the *Evaluation* section of the test summary report.

(3) *Complete the Test Summary Report.* Complete the test summary report for the unit in accordance with ANSI/IEEE Std 829-1983 [2].

(4) *Ensure Preservation of Testing Products.* Ensure that the testing products are collected,

organized, and stored for reference and reuse. These products include the test design specification, separate test-case specifications, separate test procedure specifications, test data, test data generation procedures, test drivers and stubs, and the test summary report.

3.8.3 Evaluate Outputs

(1) Complete test summary report (from 3.8.2(3))

(2) Complete, stored collection of testing products (from 3.8.2(4))

Appendixes

(These Appendixes are not a part of ANSI / IEEE Std 1008-1987, IEEE Standard for Software Unit Testing, but are included for information only.)

Appendix A

Implementation and Usage Guidelines

This section contains information intended to be of benefit when the standard is being considered for use. It is therefore recommended that this section be read in its entirety before any extensive planning is done.

A1. Use of the Standard

The standard can be used
(1) As a basis for comparison to confirm current practices
(2) As a source of ideas to modify current practices
(3) As a replacement for current practices

A2. Additional Testing Requirements

Requirements such as the amount of additional test documentation (for example, test logs), the level of detail to be included, and the number and types of approvals and reviews must be specified for each project. Factors, such as unit criticality, auditing needs, or contract specifications will often dictate these requirements. The standard leaves it to the user to specify these requirements either by individual project or as organizational standards. If the requirements are project specific, they should appear in the project plan, quality assurance plan, verification and validation plan, or overall test plan.

A3. Additional Test Documentation

The information contained in the test design specification and the test summary report is considered an absolute minimum for process visibility. In addition, it is assumed that any test information need can be satisfied by the set of test documents specified in ANSI / IEEE Std 829-

1983 [2], either by requiring additional content in a required document or by requiring additional documents.

A4. Approvals and Reviews

If more control is desired, the following additional tasks should be considered:
(1) Approval of general approach at the end of Plan
(2) Approval of identified requirements at the end of Determine
(3) Approval of specific plans at the end of Refine
(4) Approval of test specifications at the end of Design
(5) Review of test readiness at the end of Implement
(6) Review of test summary report at the end of Evaluate

A5. Audit Trails

It is assumed that auditing needs are taken into account when specifying control requirements. Therefore, the set of test documents generated together with the reports from test reviews should be sufficient to supply all required audit information.

A6. Configuration Management

Configuration management should be the source of the software requirements, software architectual design, software data structure, and unit requirements documentation. These inputs must be managed to ensure confidence that we have current information and will be notified of any changes.

The final unit testing products should be provided to configuration management. These outputs must be managed to permit thorough and economical regression testing. See ANSI/IEEE Std 828-1983, IEEE Standard for Software Configuration Management Plans, for details.

A7. Determination of Requirements-Based Characteristics

Psychological factors (for example, self-confidence, a detailed knowledge of the unit design) can make it very difficult for the unit developer to determine an effective set of requirements-based elements (for example, features, procedures, state transitions, data characteristics) to be included in the testing. Often, this determination should be made by someone else.

There are several ways to organize this separation.

(1) Developers determine these elements for each other.

(2) Developers fully test each other's code. This has the added advantage that at least two developers will have a detailed knowledge of every unit.

(3) A separate test group should be available The size of the project or the criticality of the software may determine whether a separate group can be justified.

If developers determine requirements-based elements for their own software, they should perform this determination *before* software design begins.

A8. User Involvement

If the unit to be tested interacts with users (for example, menu displays), it can be very effective to involve those users in determining the requirements-based elements to be included in the testing. Asking users about their use of the software may bring to light valuable information to be considered during test planning. For example, questioning may identify the relative criticality of the unit's functions and thus determine the testing emphasis.

A9. Stronger Code-Based Coverage Requirements

Based on the criticality of the unit or a shortage of unit requirement and design information (for example, during maintenance of older software), the code-based coverage requirement specified in 3.1.2(2) could be strengthened. One option is to strengthen the requirement from instruction coverage to branch coverage (that is, the execution of every branch in the unit).

A10. Code Coverage Tools

An automated means of recording the coverage of source code during unit test execution is highly recommended. Automation is usually necessary because manual coverage analysis is unreliable and uneconomical. One automated approach uses a code instrumentation and reporting tool. Such a tool places software probes in the source code and following execution of the test cases provides a report summarizing data and control-flow information. The report identifies unexecuted instructions. Some tools also identify unexecuted branches. This capability is a feature in some compilers.

A11. Process Improvement

To evaluate and improve the effectiveness of unit testing, it is recommended that failure data be gathered from those processes that follow unit testing, such as integration test, system test, and production use. This data should then be analyzed to determine the nature of those faults that should have been detected by unit testing but were not.

A12. Adopting the Standard

Implementing a new technical process is itself a process that requires planning, implementation, and evaluation effort. To successfully implement a testing process based on this standard, one must develop an implementation strategy and tailor the standard. Both activities must reflect the culture and current abilities of the organization. Long-term success will require management commitment, supporting policies, tools, training, and start-up consulting. Management can demonstrate commitment by incorporating the new process into project tracking systems and performance evaluation criteria.

A13. Practicality of the Standard

This standard represents consensus on the definition of good software engineering practice. Some organizations use practices similar to the process specified here while others organize this work quite differently. In any case, it will involve considerable change for many organizations that choose to adopt it. That change involves new policies, new standards and procedures, new tools, and new training programs. If the differences between the standard and current practice are too great, then the changes will need to be phased in. The answer to the question of practicality is basically one of desire. How badly does an organization want to gain control of its unit testing?

Appendix B

Concepts and Assumptions

B1. Software Engineering Concepts

The standard unit testing process specified in this standard is based on several fundamental software engineering concepts which are described in B1.1 through B1.8 inclusive.

B1.1 Relationship of Testing to Verification and Validation. Testing is just one of several complementary verification and validation activities. Other activities include technical reviews (for example, code inspections), static analysis, and proof of correctness. Specification of a comprehensive verification and validation process is outside the scope of this standard.

B1.2 Testing As Product Development. Testing includes a product development process. It results in a *test set* composed of data, test support software, and procedures for its use. This product is documented by test specifications and reports. As with any product development process, test set development requires planning, requirements (test objectives), design, implementation, and evaluation.

B1.3 Composition of Debugging. The debugging process is made up of two major activities. The objective of the first activity, *failure analysis,* is to locate and identify all faults responsible for a failure. The objective of the second, *fault correction,* is to remove all identified faults while avoiding the introduction of new ones. Specification of the process of either failure analysis or fault correction is outside the scope of this standard.

B1.4 Relationship of Testing to Debugging. Testing entails attempts to cause failures in order to detect faults, while debugging entails both failure analysis to locate and identify the associated faults and subsequent fault correction. Testing may need the results of debugging's failure analysis to decide on a course of action. Those actions may include the termination of testing or a request for requirements changes or fault correction.

B1.5 Relationship Between Types of Units. A one-to-one relationship between design units, implementation units, and test units is not necessary. Several design units may make up an implementation unit (for example, a program) and several implementation units may make up a test unit.

B1.6 Need for Design and Implementation Information. Often, requirements information is not enough for effective testing, even though, fundamentally, testing measures actual behavior against required behavior. This is because its usually not feasible to test all possible situations and requirements often do not provide sufficient guidance in identifying situations that have high failure potential. Design and implementation information often are needed, since some of these high-potential situations result from the design and implementation choices that have been made.

B1.7 Incremental Specification of Elements To Be Considered in Testing. Progressively more detailed information about the nature of a test unit is found in the unit requirements documentation, the unit design documentation, and finally in the unit's implementation. As a result, the elements to be considered in testing may be built up incrementally during different periods of test activity.

For procedural language (for example, COBOL) implementations, element specification occurs in three increments. The first group is specified during the Determine activity and is based on the unit requirements documentation. The second group is specified during the Design activity and is based on the unit design (that is, algorithms and data structures) as stated in a software design description. The third group is specified during the Check activity and is based on the unit's code.

For nonprocedural language (for example, report writer or sort specification languages) implementations, specification occurs in two increments. The first is during the Determine activity and is based on requirements and the second is during Design and is based on the nonprocedural specification.

An incremental approach permits unit testing to begin as soon as unit requirements are available and minimizes the bias introduced by detailed knowledge of the unit design and code.

B1.8 Incremental Creation of a Test Design Specification. Information recorded in the test design specification is generated during the Determine, Refine, and Design activities. As each of these test activities progress, information is recorded in appropriate sections of the specification. The whole document must be complete at the end of the final iteration of the Design activity.

B1.9 Incremental Creation of the Test Summary Report. Information recorded in the test summary report is generated during all unit testing activities expect Plan. The report is initiated during Implement, updated during Execute and Check, and completed during Evaluate.

B2. Testing Assumptions

The approach to unit testing specified in this standard is based on a variety of economic, psychological, and technical assumptions. The significant assumptions are given in B2.1 through B2.7 inclusive.

B2.1 The objective of unit testing is to attempt to determine the correctness and completeness of an implementation with respect to unit requirements and design documentation by attempting to uncover faults in:

(1) The unit's required features in combination with their associated states (for example, inactive, active awaiting a message, active processing a message)

(2) The unit's handling of invalid input

(3) Any usage or operating procedures associated only with the unit

(4) The unit's algorithms or internal data structures, or both

(5) The decision boundaries of the unit's control logic

B2.2 Testing entails the measurement of behavior against requirements. Although one speaks informally of *interface testing, state testing,* or even *requirement testing,* what is meant is measuring actual behavior associated with an interface, state, or requirement, against the corresponding required behavior. Any verifiable unit testing process must have documented requirements for the test unit. This standard assumes that the documentation of unit requirements exists before testing begins.

B2.3 Unit requirements documentation must be thoroughly reviewed for completeness, testability, and traceability. This standard assumes the requirements have been reviewed either as a normal part of the documentation review process or in a special unit requirements review.

B2.4 There are significant economic benefits in the early detection of faults. This implies that test set development should start as soon as practical following availability of the unit requirements documentation because of the resulting requirements verification and validation. It also implies that as much as practical should be tested at the unit level.

B2.5 The levels of project testing (for example, acceptance, system, integration, unit) are specified in project plans, verification and validation plans, or overall test plans. Also included is the unit test planning information that is applicable to all units being tested (for example, completeness requirements, termination requirements, general resource requirements). Subsequently, based on an analysis of the software design, the test units will be identified and an integration sequence will be selected.

B2.6 The availability of inputs and resources to do a task is the major constraint on the sequencing of activities and on the sequencing of tasks within an activity. If the necessary resources are available, some of the activities and some of the tasks within an activity may be performed concurrently.

B2.7 This standard assumes that it is usually most cost-effective to delay the design of test cases based on source-code characteristics until the set of test cases based on requirements and design characteristics has been executed. This approach minimizes the code-based design task. If code-based design is started before test execution data is available, it should not start until the test cases based on unit requirements and design characteristics have been specified.

Appendix C

Sources for Techniques and Tools

C1. General

Software tools are computer programs and software techniques are detailed methods that aid in the specification, construction, testing, analysis, management, documentation, and maintenance of other computer programs. Software techniques and tools can be used and reused in a variety of development environments. Their effective use increases engineering productivity and software quality.

The references given in C2 of this Appendix contain information on most of the testing techniques and tools in use today. The set of references is not exhaustive, but provides a comprehensive collection of source material. To keep up to date, the reader is encouraged to obtain information on recent IEEE tutorials and recent documents in the Special Publications series of the National Bureau of Standards.[5] Current information on test tools can be obtained from the Federal Software Testing Center[6] and software tool data bases are accessible through the Data & Analysis Center for Software.[7]

A set of general references on software testing is listed in Appendix D.

C2. References

BEIZER, BORIS. *Software Testing Techniques.* New York: Van Nostrand Reinhold, 1983. This book presents a collection of experience-based test techniques. It describes several test design techniques together with their mathematical foundations. The book describes various techniques (decision tables and formal grammars) that provide a precise specification of the input and software. It also discusses a data-base-driven testing technique. Many techniques are based on the author's first-hand experience as director of testing and quality assurance for a telecommunications software producer. The inclusion of experiences and anecdotes makes this book enjoyable and informative.

HOUGHTON, Jr, RAYMOND C. Software Development Tools: A Profile. *IEEE Computer* vol

---

[5] The NBS publications and software tools survey may be obtained from Superintendent of Documents, US Government Printing Office, Washington, DC 20402.

[6] Information regarding test tools may be obtained by contacting Federal Software Testing Center, Office of Software Development, General Services Administration, 5203 Leesburg Pike, Suite 1100, Falls Church, VA 22041.

[7] Information regarding the tools data base may be obtained from Data & Analysis Center for Software (DACS), RADC/ISISI, Griffiss AFB NY 13441.

16, no 5, May 1983.[8] The Institute of Computer Science and Technology of the National Bureau of Standards studied the software tools available in the early 1980's. This article reports the results of that study and analyzes the information obtained. Various categorizations of the tools are presented, with tools listed by their characteristics. The lists incorporate percentage summaries based on the total number of tools for which information was available.

OSD/DDT & E Software Test and Evaluation Project, Phases I and II, Final Report, vol 2, *Software Test and Evaluation: State-of-the-Art Overview*. School of Information and Computer Science, Georgia Institute of Technology, June 1983, 350 pp.[9] This report contains a concise overview of most current testing techniques and tools. A set of references is provided for each one. A set of test tool data sheets containing implementation details and information contacts is also provided.

POWELL, PATRICIA B. (ed). *Software Validation, Verification, and Testing Technique and Tool Reference Guide*. National Bureau of Standards Special Publication 500–93, 1982. Order from GPO SN-003-003-02422-8.[5] Thirty techniques and tools for validation, verification, and testing are described. Each description includes the basic features of the technique or tool, its input, its output, and an example. Each description also contains an assessment of effectiveness and usability, applicability, an estimate of the learning time and training, an estimate of needed resources, and associated references.

PRESSON, EDWARD. *Software Test Handbook: Software Test Guidebook*. Rome Air Develop-

ment Center RADC-TR-84-53, vol 2 (of two) March 1984. Order from NTIS A147-289. This guidebook contains guidelines and methodology for software testing including summary descriptions of testing techniques, typical paragraphs specifying testing techniques for a Statement of Work, a cross-reference to government and commercial catalogs listing automated test tools, and an extensive bibliography.

REIFER, DONALD J. *Software Quality Assurance Tools and Techniques*. John D. Cooper and Matthew J. Fisher (eds). Software Quality Management, New York: Petrocelli Books, 1979, pp. 209–234. This paper explains how modern tools and techniques support an assurance technology for computer programs. The author first develops categories for quality assurance tools and techniques (aids) and discusses example aids. Material on toolsmithing is presented next. Finally, an assessment is made of the state of the technology and recommendations for improving current practice are offered.

SOFTFAIR 83. *A Conference on Software Development Tools, Techniques, and Alternatives*. IEEE Computer Society Press, 1983.[8] This is the proceedings of the first of what is likely to be a series of conferences aimed at showing the most promising approaches within the field of software tools and environments. It is a collection of 42 papers covering a broad range of software engineering tools from research prototypes to commercial products.

Software Aids and Tools Survey. Federal Software Management Support Center, Office of Software Development, Report OIT/FSMC-86/002, 1985.[6] The purpose of this document is to support management in various government agencies in the identification and selection of software tools. The document identifies and categorizes tools available in the marketplace in mid 1985. Approximately 300 tools are presented with various data concerning each one's function, producer, source language, possible uses, cost, and product description. The survey is expected to be updated periodically.

---

[8] Information regarding IEEE Computer Society publications may be obtained from IEEE Computer Society Order Department, PO Box 80452, Worldway Postal Center, Los Angeles, CA 90080.

[9] The Georgia Technology report may be obtained from Documents Librarian, Software Test and Evaluation Project, School of Information and Computer Science, Georgia Institute of Technology, Atlanta, Georgia 30332.

Appendix D

General References

This section identifies a basic set of reference works on software testing. While the set is not exhaustive, it provides a comprehensive collection of source material. Additional references focusing specifically on testing techniques and tools are contained in Appendix C.

CHANDRASEKARAN, B. and RADICCHI, S., (ed) *Computer Program Testing*, North-Holland, 1981. The following description is from the editors Preface:

"The articles in this volume, taken as a whole, provide a comprehensive, tutorial discussion of the current state of the art as well as research directions in the area of testing computer programs. They cover the spectrum from basic theoretical notions through practical issues in testing programs and large software systems to integrated environments and tools for performing a variety of tests. They are all written by active researchers and practitioners in the field."

DEUTSCH, MICHAEL S. *Software Verification and Validation*. ENGLEWOOD CLIFFS: Prentice-Hall, 1982. The following description is taken from the Preface.

"The main thrust of this book is to describe verification and validation approaches that have been used successfully on contemporary large-scale software projects. Methodologies are explored that can be pragmatically applied to modern complex software developments and that take account of cost, schedule, and management realities in the actual production environment. This book is intended to be tutorial in nature with a 'This is how it's done in the real world' orientation. Contributing to this theme will be observations and recounts from actual software development project experiences in industry."

Guideline for Lifecycle Validation, Verification, and Testing of Computer Software. Federal Information Processing Standards (FIPS) Publication 101.[10] Order from NTIS FIPSPUB101 1983 (See Appendix C). This guideline presents an integrated approach to validation, verification, and testing that should be used throughout the software lifecycle. Also included is a glossary of technical terms and a list of supporting ICST publications. An Appendix provides an outline for formulating a VV & T plan.

HETZEL, WILLIAM, *The Complete Guide to Software Testing*. QED Information Sciences,

1984. This book covers many aspects of software verification and validation with a primary emphasis on testing. It contains an overview of test methods and tools including sample reports from several commercially available tools. The book is especially useful when used for viewing testing from a management perspective and discussing many of the associated management issues. An extensive bibliography is included.

McCABE, THOMAS J. (ed). *Structured Testing*. IEEE Computer Society Press, Cat no EHO 200–6, 1983.[8] This IEEE Tutorial is a collection of papers focusing on the relationship between testing and program complexity. The first two papers define cyclomatic complexity and describe an associated technique for developing program test cases. The third paper describes a systematic approach to the development of system test cases. The fourth paper provides general guidelines for program verification and testing. The balance of the papers deal with complexity and reliability.

MILLER, EDWARD and HOWDEN, WILLIAM E. (ed). Tutorial: *Software Testing & Validation Techniques* (2nd ed) IEEE Computer Society Press, Cat no EHO 180–0, 1981.[8] This IEEE Tutorial is a collection of some significant papers dealing with various aspects of software testing. These aspects include theoretical foundations, static analysis, dynamic analysis, effectiveness assessment, and software management. An extensive bibliography is included.

MYERS, GLENFORD J. *The Art of Software Testing*. New York: Wiley–Interscience, 1979. This book contains practical, *How To Do It* technical information on software testing. The main emphasis is on methodologies for the design of effective test cases. It also covers psychological and economic issues, managerial aspects of testing, test tools, debugging, and code inspections. Comprehensive examples and checklists support the presentation.

---

[10] The FIPS VV & T Guideline may be obtained from National Technical Information Service, 5285 Port Royal Road, Springfield, VA 22161.

POWELL, PATRICIA B. (ed). *Plan for Software Validation, Verification, and Testing.* National Bureau of Standards Special Publication 500–98, 1982.[5] Order from GPO SN-003-003-02449-0 (See Appendix C). This document is for those who direct and those who implement computer projects. It explains the selection and use of validation, verification, and testing (VV & T) tools and techniques. It explains how to develop a plan to meet specific software VV & T goals.

Acknowledgment

Appreciation is expressed to the following companies and organizations for contributing the time of their employees to make possible the development of this text:

Algoma Steel
Applied Information Development
AT & T Bell Labs
AT & T Information Systems
Automated Language Processing Systems
Bank of America
Bechtel Power
Bell Canada
Boeing Computer Services
Boston University
Burroughs, Scotland
CAP GEMINI DASD
Central Institute for Industrial Research, Norway
Communications Sciences
Conoco
Digital Equipment Corp
US Department of the Interior
US Department of Transportation
Data Systems Analysts
E-Systems
K.A. Foster, Inc
General Dynamics
Georgia Tech
General Services Administration
Honeywell
Hughes Aircraft
IBM
IBM Federal Systems Division
International Bureau of Software Test
Johns Hopkins University Applied Physics Laboratory
Lear Siegler
Logicon
Management and Computer Services
Martin Marietta Aerospace
McDonald-Douglas
Medtronic
Micom
Mitre
M. T. Scientific Consulting
NASA
National Bureau of Standards
NCR
Product Assurances Consulting
Professional Systems & Technology
Programming Environments
Quality Assurance Institute
RCA
Reynolds & Reynolds
Rolm Telecommunications
Rome Air Development Center
Sallie Mae
Seattle—First National Bank
SHAPE, BELGIUM
Software Engineering Service, Germany
Software Quality Engineering
Software Research Associates
Solo Systems
Sperry
SQS GmbH, Germany
Tandem Computers
Tektronix
Televideo
Tenn Valley Authority
Texas Instruments
Time
University of DC
University of Texas, Arlington
US Army Computer Systems Command
Warner Robins ALC
Westinghouse Hanford

ANSI/IEEE
Std 1012-1986

An American National Standard

IEEE Standard for Software Verification and Validation Plans

Sponsor

**Software Engineering Technical Committee
of the
IEEE Computer Society**

Approved September 18, 1986

IEEE Standards Board

Approved February 10, 1987

American National Standards Institute

1012

Foreword

(This Foreword is not a part of IEEE Std 1012-1986, IEEE Standard for Software Verification and Validation Plans.)

This standard provides uniform and minimum requirements for the format and content of Software Verification and Validation Plans (SVVPs). Performing software verification and validation (V&V) as defined in this standard provides for a comprehensive evaluation throughout each phase of the software project to help ensure that:

(1) Errors are detected and corrected as early as possible in the software life cycle

(2) Project risk, cost, and schedule effects are lessened

(3) Software quality and reliability are enhanced

(4) Management visibility into the software process is improved

(5) Proposed changes and their consequences can be quickly assessed

This standard applies to both critical and noncritical software.

(1) For critical software, this standard:

(a) Requires that minimum V&V tasks, inputs, and outputs specified in this standard be included in SVVPs

(b) Permits the SVVP to be extended by selecting additional V&V tasks from the optional tasks described in this standard or new tasks identified by the V&V planner

(2) For noncritical software, this standard:

(a) Recommends the use of minimum V&V tasks

(b) Permits the SVVP to be tailored to V&V efforts by selecting any of the V&V tasks (minimum, optional, new)

This standard applies to all phases of the software life cycle from the Concept Phase to the Operation and Maintenance Phase. Maximum benefits are derived when V&V is started early in the software life cycle, preferably at project initiation during the Concept Phase. Benefits can be derived for software already in development or in the Operation and Maintenance Phase if the V&V requirements from this standard are invoked consistent with cost and schedule constraints. When V&V is invoked for software in development or in operation and maintenance, required V&V inputs may not exist. Under these conditions, this standard permits the V&V tasks to be tailored to adjust for missing V&V inputs. In some instances, this may require the generation of appropriate software documentation.

V&V is performed in parallel with software development. Each V&V life-cycle phase ends when the V&V tasks of that phase are completed and the software development products are determined to be adequate. V&V life-cycle phases may overlap as activities of the new life-cycle phase are beginning and activities of the previous life-cycle phase are completing.

V&V tasks are iterative: as changes are made to the software product, selected V&V tasks from the previous life-cycle phases are reperformed, or additional V&V tasks are performed to address the changes. V&V tasks are reperformed if errors are discovered in the V&V inputs or outputs. The complexity and scope of changes determine the level of detail covered by the iteration. The SVVP identifies the criteria for performing the iterative V&V tasks.

This standard defines a V&V reporting structure by identifying format and content of the Software Verification and Validation Report (SVVR). The standard for Software Quality Assurance Plans (SQAP, ANSI/IEEE Std-730-1984) requires the SVVR to include both V&V and other quality assurance results. The SVVR defined here is flexible enough to include both types of results. The interim phase reports, final summary report, and optional SQAP-related activity reports defined by the SVVP provide visibility into the development and V&V processes.

This standard considers both the software and its system or operating environment. It can be used where software is the system or where software is part of a larger system. V&V should have a total system scope (that is, including interfaces between software, hardware, and operators) during the product life cycle. Embedded software is strongly coupled to hardware and other subsystems, and requires a system-level SVVP.

This standard was written to provide direction to organizations responsible for preparing or assessing a Software Verification and Validation Plan. This standard may be used by project management, software developers, quality assurance organizations, purchasers, end users, maintainers, and verification and validation organizations. If V&V is performed by an independent group, then the SVVP should specify the criteria for maintaining the independence of the V&V effort from the software development and maintenance efforts.

Suggestions for the improvement of this standard will be welcomed. They should be sent to

Secretary
IEEE Standards Board
Institute of Electrical and Electronics Engineers, Inc
345 East 47th Street
New York, New York 10017

The working group that developed this standard consisted of the following members:

Roger U. Fujii, *Chairman* **Doug McMann,** *Vice Chairman*
Dolores R. Wallace, *Secretary*

Stephen Benz	Ralph A. Kubek	David M. Siefert
Julian O. Blosiu	Joyce Lewis	Hugh Spillane
Martha Branstad	Roger J. Martin	George Tice
Fletcher J. Buckley	Jerome W. Mersky	Richard Thayer
François Coallier	Dennis E. Nickle	David Turner
James A. Darling	Larry E. Nitszche	William S. Turner
Taz Daughtrey	A.E. Nountor	Adam Valentine
David C. Doty	Jane W. Radatz	Robert A. Walker
Sam Dugdale	Don J. Robbins	Jay W. Wiley
William Dupras	J. A. Ronbeck	Andrea Williams
Michael Edwards	Hans Schaefer	Laurence Wilson
John Horch	David Schultz	Helen M. Wood

When the IEEE Standards Board approved this standard on September 18, 1986, it had the following membership:

John E. May, *Chairman* **Irving Kolodny,** *Vice Chairman*
Sava I. Sherr, *Secretary*

James H. Beall	Jack Kinn	Robert E. Rountree
Fletcher J. Buckley	Joseph L. Koepfinger*	Martha Sloan
Paul G. Cummings	Edward Lohse	Oley Wanaselja
Donald C. Fleckenstein	Lawrence V. McCall	J. Richard Weger
Jay Forster	Donald T. Michael*	William B. Wilkens
Daniel L. Goldberg	Marco W. Migliaro	Helen M. Wood
Kenneth D. Hendrix	Stanley Owens	Charles J. Wylie
Irvin N. Howell	John P. Riganati	Donald W. Zipse
	Frank L. Rose	

*Member emeritus

The standard was approved by the Software Engineering Standards Subcommittee of the IEEE Computer Society. At the time it approved this standard, the Ballot Group had the following membership:

John W. Horch, *Chairman*

A. Frank Ackerman
Jagdish Agrawal
Tom Armbruster
Richard L. Aurbach
James Baldo, Jr
Geoff Baldwin
H. Jack Barnard
Roy W. Bass
Leo Beltracchi
Yechiel Ben-Naftau
H.R. Berlack
Matt Biewer
J. Emmett Black
Michael A. Blackledge
Ronald M. Blair
Walter DuBlanica
Kevin W. Bowyer
Ingar Brauti
Michael F. Brennter
Kathleen L. Briggs
William L. Bryan
Fletcher J. Buckley
Douglas Burt
Homer C. Carney
C.L. Carpenter, Jr
Ronald R. Carter
R.L. Chilavsky
Tsun S. Chow
Jung K. Chung
Peter Coad, Jr
François Coallier
Sharon R. Cobb
William J. Cody
Christopher M. Cooke
Gail A. Cordes
A.J. Cote
Patricia W. Daggett
James A. Darling
George D. Darling
Taz Daughtrey
P.A. Denny
James H. Dobbins
David C. Doty
Einar Dragstedt
Robert Dunn
William P. Dupras
Robert E. Dwyer
Mary Eads
John D. Earls
Michael Edwards
L.G. Egan
Wolfgang Ehrenberger
Steven R. Eisen
Caroline L. Evans
David W. Favor
John Fendrich
Robert G. Ferreol
Glenn S. Fields
Wayne Fischer
Gordon Force
Julian Forster
C.R. Frederick
Carl Friedlander
Richard C. Fries
Ismael Fuentes
Roger U. Fujii
Michel Galinier
Leonard B. Gardner
David Gelperin
J. Kaye Grau
Andres Grebenc
Thomas Griest
James L. Gildersleeve
Shirley A. Gloss-Soler
Victor M. Guarnera
Lawrence M. Gunther

David A. Gustafson
Russell Gustin
Howard Hamer
Harry E. Hansen
Allen L. Hankinson
Robert M. Haralick
Hans Ludwig Hausen
Clark M. Hay
Herb Hecht
Terry L. Hengl
Charles P. Hollocker
John W. Horch
James W. Howatt
Cheng Hu
Peter L. Hung
Don L. Jackson
Shang-Sheng Jeng
Laurel Kaleda
Constantine Kaniklidis
Myron S. Karasik
Adi Kasad
Ron Kenett
R.A. Kessler
John M. Kinn
Shaye Koenig
Edward E. Kopicky
Joseph A. Krupinski
Joan Kundig
Tom Kurihara
Lak Ming Lam
John B. Lane
Robert A. Lane
William P. LaPlant
Greg Larsen
John A. Latimer
Paul Lebertz
J.A.N. Lee
Leon S. Levy
F.C. Lim
Bertil Lindberg
Gary Lindsay
David P. Linssen
Steven Litvintchouk
John M. Long
Donald C. Loughry
John K. Lowell
Bill Macre
Harold T. Maguire
Andy Mahindru
Kartik C. Majumdar
Henry A. Malec
Paulo C. Marcondes
Stuart Marcotte
Philip C. Marriott
Nicholas L. Marselos
Roger J. Martin
Paul Mauro
L.J. Mazlack
Ivano Mazza
J.A. McCall
Paul E. McKenney
Jack McKissick
Stanley E. McQueen
Glen A. Meldrum
Mordechai Ben Menachen
Belden Menkus
Jerome W. Mersky
W.F. Mitchell
Celia Modell
Charles S. Mooney
Gary Moorhead
Gene T. Morun
David G. Mullens
Myron L. Nack
Hironobu Nagano
Saied Najafi

G.R. Neidhart
Dennis E. Nickle
Perry R. Nuhn
J.H. Obbink
Deene Ogden
Wilma Osborne
D.J. Ostrom
Thomas D. Parrish
William E. Perry
Donald J. Pfeiffer
Harpal S. Phama
Robert M. Poston
Peter Prinzivalli
I.C. Pyle
Jane W. Radatz
Thomas S. Radi
Jock Rader
Wendy Rauch-Hindein
Meir Razy
John Reddan
Larry K. Reed
Matthias F. Reese
T.D. Regulinski
Paul Renaud
John P. Riganati
Gary S. Robinson
Hom Sack
J. Gonzales Sanz
Lawrence R. Satz
Franz P. Schauer
Peter E. Schilling
Max J. Schindler
Norman Schneidewind
Wolf A. Schnoege
Robert Schueppert
David J. Schultz
Gregory D. Schumacher
Leonard W. Seagren
Craig L. Shermer
Robert W. Shillato
Victor Shtern
David M. Siefert
David J. Simkins
Jacob Slonim
Jean-Christopher Slucki
Marion P. Smith
Harry M. Sneed
Al Sorkowitz
Hugh B. Spillane
Lee Sprague
G. Wayne Staley
Robert G. Stewart
Vegard Stuan
Alan N. Sukert
William G. Sutcliffe
Robert A. Symes
Richard H. Thayer
Paul U. Thompson
Michael H. Thursby
George Tice
R.L. Van Tilburg
Terrence L. Tillmanns
Lawrence F. Tracey
Henry J. Trochesset
Robert Troy
C.L. Troyanowski
Dana L. Ulery
David Usechak
P.M. Vater
Osmo Vikman
R. Wachter
Dolores R. Wallace
Thomas J. Walsh
William M. Walsh
Roger Warburton
Robert Werlwas

(Continued on next page)

(Continued from preceding page)

Charles J. Wertz
N.P. Wilburn
Andrew F. Wilson
Patrick J. Wilson
Paul A. Willis
Walter L. Whipple
Theodore J. Wojcik

Paul Wolfgang
Tom Worthington
W. Martin Wong
Dennis L. Wood
Helen M. Wood
Charles Wortz
A.W. Yonda

Natalie C. Yopconka
Michael E. York
Janusz Zalewski
Donald J. Zeleny
Marvin Zelkowitz
Hugh Zettel
Peter F. Zoll

Contents

An American National Standard

IEEE Standard for Software Verification and Validation Plans

1. Scope and References

1.1 Scope. This standard has a threefold purpose:

(1) To provide, for both critical and noncritical software, uniform and minimum requirements for the format and content of Software Verification and Validation Plans (SVVPs)

(2) To define, for critical software, specific minimum verification and validation (V&V) tasks and their required inputs and outputs that shall be included in SVVPs

(3) To suggest optional V&V tasks to be used to tailor SVVPs as appropriate for the particular V&V effort

This standard requires that an SVVP be written for both critical and noncritical software. Critical software is software in which a failure could have an impact on safety or could cause large financial or social losses.

This SVVP shall include V&V tasks to:

(1) Verify that the products of each software life-cycle phase:

    (a) Comply with previous life-cycle phase requirements and products (for example, for correctness, completeness, consistency, accuracy)

    (b) Satisfy the standards, practices, and conventions of the phase

    (c) Establish the proper basis for initiating the next life-cycle phase activities

(2) Validate that the completed end product complies with established software and system requirements.

For critical software, this standard requires that minimum V&V tasks and their inputs and outputs be included in all SVVPs. For noncritical software, this standard does not specify minimum required V&V tasks; however, all other requirements of this standard shall be satisfied. This standard does recommend that the minimum V&V tasks for critical software also be employed for noncritical software.

This standard defines optional V&V tasks that permit V&V planners to tailor an SVVP for a V&V effort. For critical software, the minimum tasks may be supplemented with tasks selected from the optional tasks. For noncritical software, tasks may be selected from the minimum and optional tasks. Additional tasks identified by the user of this standard may be included in the SVVP for critical and noncritical software.

The life cycle used in this standard serves as a model and consists of the following life-cycle phases:

(1) Concept
(2) Requirements
(3) Design
(4) Implementation
(5) Test
(6) Installation and checkout
(7) Operation and maintenance

Compliance with this standard does not require use of the life-cycle model presented here. If a different model is used, the SVVP shall include cross-references to this standard's life cycle and to the V&V tasks, inputs, and outputs specified here for each life-cycle phase.

9

This standard requires that the following be defined for each phase:

(1) Verification and validation tasks
(2) Methods and criteria
(3) Inputs and outputs
(4) Schedule
(5) Resources
(6) Risks and assumptions
(7) Roles and responsibilities

This standard requires a management effort that encompasses all life-cycle phases. The management section of the SVVP defines information necessary to manage and perform the V&V effort, and to coordinate V&V with other aspects of the project. The standard requires the SVVP to specify how the V&V results shall be documented in the Software Verification and Validation Report (SVVR).

When this standard is invoked for existing software, the SVVP shall describe how V&V will be performed when required inputs do not exist. The standard does not prohibit the incorporation of additional content into an SVVP.

The SVVP standard derives its scope from ANSI/IEEE Std 730-1984 [2].[1] The SVVP standard may be applied in conjunction with, or independent of, other IEEE software engineering standards. This standard uses the definitions of ANSI/IEEE Std 729-1983 [1]. This SVVP standard contains V&V configuration analysis tasks that, in part or in whole, are reflected in ANSI/IEEE Std 828-1983 [3]. Test documentation is compatible with that in ANSI/IEEE Std 829-1983 [4].

1.2 References. This standard shall be used in conjunction with the following publications:

[1] ANSI/IEEE Std 729-1983, IEEE Standard Glossary of Software Engineering Terminology.[2]

[2] ANSI/IEEE Std 730-1984, IEEE Standard for Software Quality Assurance Plans.

[3] ANSI/IEEE Std 828-1983, IEEE Standard for Software Configuration Management Plans.

[4] ANSI/IEEE Std 829-1983, IEEE Standard for Software Test Documentation.

---

[1] Numbers in brackets correspond to those of the references in 1.2 of this standard.

[2] ANSI documents are available from the Sales Department, American National Standards Institute, 1430 Broadway, New York, NY 10018.

2. Conventions, Definitions, and Acronyms

2.1 Conventions. The use of the term *documentation* rather than *document* indicates that the information may exist in several documents or may be embedded within a document addressing more than one subject.

2.2 Definitions. The following terms, including those defined in other standards, are used as indicated in this standard.

acceptance testing. Formal testing conducted to determine whether or not a system satisfies its acceptance criteria and to enable the customer to determine whether or not to accept the system. (See ANSI/IEEE Std 729-1983 [1].)

anomaly. Anything observed in the documentation or operation of software that deviates from expectations based on previously verified software products or reference documents. A critical anomaly is one that must be resolved before the V&V effort proceeds to the next life-cycle phase.

component testing. Testing conducted to verify the implementation of the design for one software element (for example, unit, module) or a collection of software elements.

concept phase. The initial phase of a software development project, in which user needs are described and evaluated through documentation (for example, statement of needs, advance planning report, project initiation memo, feasibility studies, system definition documentation, regulations, procedures, or policies relevant to the project).

critical software. Software whose failure could have an impact on safety, or could cause large financial or social loss.

design phase. The period of time in the software life cycle during which the designs for architecture, software components, interfaces, and data are created, documented, and verified to satisfy requirements. (See ANSI/IEEE Std 729-1983 [1].)

implementation phase. The period of time in the software life cycle during which a software product is created from design documentation and debugged. (See ANSI/IEEE Std 729-1983 [1].)

installation and checkout phase. The period of time in the software life cycle during which a software product is integrated into its operational environment and tested in this environment to ensure that it performs as required. (See ANSI/IEEE Std 729-1983 [1].)

integration testing. An orderly progression of testing in which software elements, hardware elements, or both are combined and tested until the entire system has been integrated. (See ANSI/IEEE Std 729-1983 [1].)

life-cycle phase. Any period of time during software development or operation that may be characterized by a primary type of activity (such as design or testing) that is being conducted. These phases may overlap one another; for V&V purposes, no phase is concluded until its development products are fully verified.

minimum tasks. Those V&V tasks applicable to all projects. V&V planning for critical software shall include all such tasks; these tasks are recommended for the V&V of noncritical software.

operation and maintenance phase. The period of time in the software life cycle during which a software product is employed in its operational environment, monitored for satisfactory performance, and modified as necessary to correct problems or to respond to changing requirements. (See ANSI/IEEE Std 729-1983 [1].)

optional tasks. Those V&V tasks that are applicable to some, but not all, software, or that may require the use of specific tools or techniques. These tasks should be performed when appropriate. The list of tasks provided in Table 2 is not exhaustive.

required inputs. The set of items necessary to perform the minimum V&V tasks mandated within any life-cycle phase.

required outputs. The set of items produced as a result of performing the minimum V&V tasks mandated within any life-cycle phase.

requirements phase. The period of time in the software life cycle during which the requirements, such as functional and performance capabilities for a software product, are defined and documented. (See ANSI/IEEE Std 729-1983 [1].)

software design description. A representation of software created to facilitate analysis, planning, implementation, and decision making. The software design description is used as a medium for communicating software design information, and may be thought of as a blueprint or model of the system.

software requirements specification. Documentation of the essential requirements (functions, performance, design constraints, and attributes) of the software and its external interfaces. (See ANSI/IEEE Std 730-1984 [2].)

software verification and validation plan. A plan for the conduct of software verification and validation.

software verification and validation report. Documentation of V&V results and appropriate software quality assurance results.

system testing. The process of testing an integrated hardware and software system to verify that the system meets its specified requirements. (See ANSI/IEEE Std 729-1983 [1].)

test case. Documentation specifying inputs, predicted results, and a set of execution conditions for a test item. (See ANSI/IEEE Std 829-1983 [4].)

test design. Documentation specifying the details of the test approach for a software feature or combination of software features and identifying the associated tests. (See ANSI/IEEE Std 829-1983 [4].)

test phase. The period of time in the software life cycle in which the components of a software product are evaluated and integrated, and the software product is evaluated to determine whether or not requirements have been satisfied. (See ANSI/IEEE Std 729-1983 [1].)

test plan. Documentation specifying the scope, approach, resources, and schedule of intended testing activities. (See ANSI/IEEE Std 829-1983 [4].)

test procedure. Documentation specifying a sequence of actions for the execution of a test. (See ANSI/IEEE Std 829-1983 [4].)

validation. The process of evaluating software at the end of the software development process to ensure compliance with software requirements. (See ANSI/IEEE Std 729-1983 [1].)

verification. The process of determining whether or not the products of a given phase of the software development cycle fulfill the requirements established during the previous phase. (See ANSI/IEEE Std 729-1983 [1].)

2.3 Acronyms. The following acronyms appear in this standard:

SDD	Software Design Description
SRS	Software Requirements Specification
SVVP	Software Verification and Validation Plan
SVVR	Software Verification and Validation Report
V&V	Verification and Validation

3. Software Verification and Validation Plan

The Software Verification and Validation Plan (also referred to as the Plan) shall include the sections shown below to be in compliance with this standard. If there is no information pertinent to a section or a required paragraph within a section, the following shall appear below the section or paragraph heading together with the appropriate reason for the exclusion: *This section/paragraph is not applicable to this plan.* Additional sections may be added at the end of the plan as required. Some of the material may appear in other documents. If so, reference to those documents shall be made in the body of the Plan.

Software Verification and Validation Plan Outline
  1. Purpose
  2. Referenced Documents
  3. Definitions
  4. Verification and Validation Overview
    4.1 Organization

    4.2 Master Schedule
    4.3 Resources Summary
    4.4 Responsibilities
    4.5 Tools, Techniques, and Methodologies
  5. Life-Cycle Verification and Validation
    5.1 Management of V&V
    5.2 Concept Phase V&V
    5.3 Requirements Phase V&V
    5.4 Design Phase V&V
    5.5 Implementation Phase V&V
    5.6 Test Phase V&V
    5.7 Installation and Checkout Phase V&V
    5.8 Operation and Maintenance Phase V&V
  6. Software Verification and Validation Reporting
  7. Verification and Validation Administrative Procedures
    7.1 Anomaly Reporting and Resolution
    7.2 Task Iteration Policy
    7.3 Deviation Policy
    7.4 Control Procedures
    7.5 Standards, Practices, and Conventions

3.1 Purpose. (Section 1 of the Plan.) This section shall delineate the specific purpose and scope of the Software Verification and Validation Plan, including waivers from this standard. The software project for which the Plan is being written and the specific software product items covered by the Plan shall be identified. The goals of the verification and validation efforts shall be specified.

3.2 Referenced Documents. (Section 2 of the Plan.) This section shall identify the binding compliance documents, documents referenced by this Plan, and any supporting documents required to supplement or implement this Plan.

3.3 Definitions. (Section 3 of the Plan.) This section shall define or provide a reference to the definitions of all terms required to properly interpret the Plan. This section shall describe the acronyms and notations used in the Plan.

3.4 Verification and Validation Overview. (Section 4 of the Plan.) This section shall describe the organization, schedule, resources, responsibilities, and tools, techniques, and methodologies necessary to perform the software verification and validation.

3.4.1 Organization. (Section 4.1 of the Plan.) This section shall describe the organization of the V&V effort. It shall define the relationship of V&V to other efforts such as development, project management, quality assurance, configuration or data management, or end user. It shall define the lines of communication within the V&V effort, the authority for resolving issues raised by V&V tasks, and the authority for approving V&V products.

3.4.2 Master Schedule. (Section 4.2 of the Plan.) This section shall describe the project life cycle and milestones, including completion dates. It shall summarize the scheduling of V&V tasks and shall describe how V&V results provide feedback to the development process to support project management functions (for example, comments on design review material).

If the life cycle used in the Plan differs from the life-cycle model in the standard, this section shall show how all requirements of the standard are satisfied (for example, cross-reference for life-cycle phases, tasks, inputs, and outputs). When planning V&V tasks, it should be recognized that the V&V process is iterative. The summary of tasks may be in narrative, tabular, or graphic form (for example, Fig 1). The life-cycle model in Fig 1 is a sample model used for this standard.

3.4.3 Resources Summary. (Section 4.3 of the Plan.) This section shall summarize the resources needed to perform the V&V tasks, including staffing, facilities, tools, finances, and special procedural requirements such as security, access rights, or documentation control.

3.4.4 Responsibilities. (Section 4.4 of the Plan.) This section shall identify the organizational element(s) responsible for performing each V&V tasks. It shall identify the specific responsibility of each element for tasks assigned to more than one element. This section may be a summary of the roles and responsibilities defined in each of the life-cycle phases (see 3.5 of this standard).

3.4.5 Tools, Techniques, and Methodologies. (Section 4.5 of the Plan.) This section shall identify the special software tools, techniques, and methodologies employed by the V&V effort. The purpose and use of each shall be described. Plans for the acquisition, training, support, and qualification for each shall be included. This section may reference a V&V Tool Plan.

3.5 Life-Cycle Verification and Validation. (Section 5 of the Plan.) This section of the Plan shall provide the detailed plan for the V&V

tasks throughout the life cycle. The detailed plan (Section 5.1—Management, and Sections 5.2 through 5.8—Life-Cycle Phases) shall address the following topics:

(1) Verification and Validation Tasks. Identify the V&V tasks for the phase. Describe how each task contributes to the accomplishment of the project V&V goals. For all critical software, the SVVP shall include all minimum V&V tasks for the management of V&V and for each life-cycle phase. Any or all of these minimum tasks may be used for noncritical software. These minimum V&V tasks are referenced in the management and life-cycle phases sections of the standard (3.5.1 through 3.5.8), and are described in Table 1. The minimum tasks are also consolidated in graphic form in Fig 1.

Optional V&V tasks may also be selected to tailor the V&V effort to project needs for critical or noncritical software. Optional V&V tasks are defined in the Appendix and a suggested application for the management of V&V and for each life-cycle phase is presented in Table 2. The optional V&V tasks identified in this standard may be applicable to some, but not all, critical software. These tasks may require the use of specific tools or techniques. The list in Table 2 is illustrative and not exhaustive. The standard allows for the optional V&V tasks and any others identified by the planner to be used as appropriate.

Testing requires advance planning that spans several life-cycle phases. Test documentation and its occurrence in specific life-cycle phases are shown in Fig 2 as a recommended approach. To be in compliance with this standard, the test documentation and test execution specified in Fig 2 shall be required. If the V&V planner uses different test documentation or test types (for example, component, integration, system, acceptance) from those in this standard, the SVVP shall contain a mapping of the proposed test documentation and execution to the items shown in Fig 2. Test planning criteria defined in Table 1 (Tasks 5.3 (4a), 5.3 (4b), 5.4 (4a), 5.4 (4b)) shall be implemented in the test plan, test design(s), test case(s), and test procedure(s) documentation, and shall be validated by test execution.

(2) Methods and Criteria. Identify the methods and criteria used in performing the V&V tasks. Describe the specific methods and procedures for each task. Define the detailed criteria for evaluating the task results.

(3) Inputs/Outputs. Identify the inputs re-

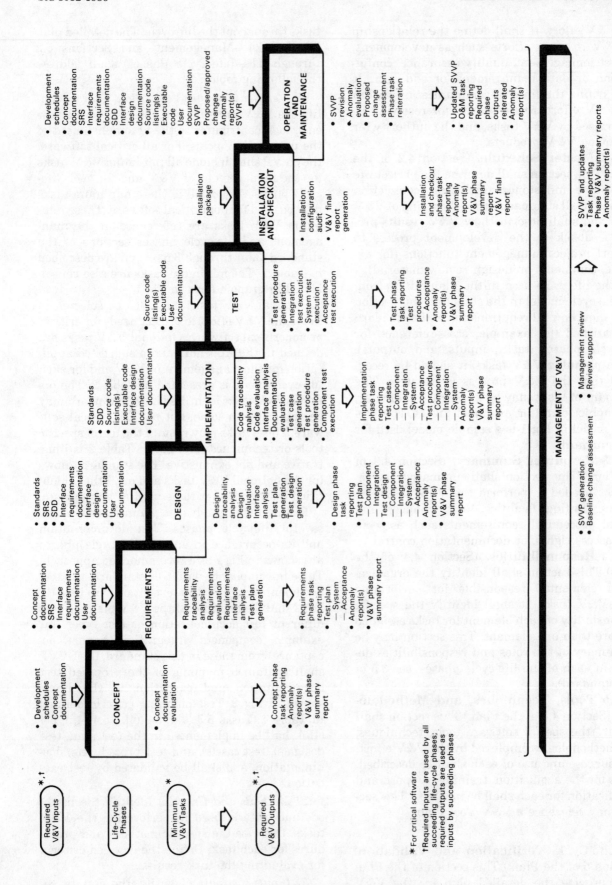

Fig 1

Software Verification and Validation Plan Overview

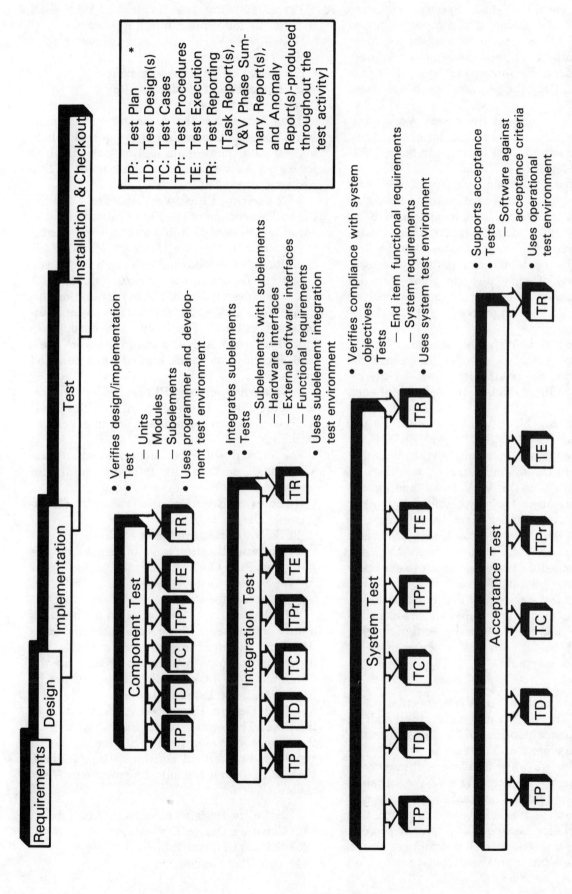

Fig 2
V&V Test Tasks and Documentation

* This test planning documentation need not be individual documents. The placement of test outputs in specific life-cycle phases indicates a recommended approach.

quired for each V&V task. Specify the source and format of each input. The inputs required for each of the minimum V&V tasks are identified in Table 1. The required inputs are used, as appropriate, by subsequent life-cycle phase V&V tasks. Only the primary inputs are listed in Table 1.

Identify the outputs from each V&V task. Specify the purpose and format for each output. The outputs from each of the minimum V&V tasks are identified in Table 1.

The outputs of the management of V&V and of the life-cycle phases shall become inputs to subsequent life-cycle phases, as appropriate.

Anomaly report(s), task report(s), and phase summary report(s) provide feedback to the software development process regarding the technical quality of each life-cycle phase software product. Each critical anomaly shall be resolved before the V&V effort proceeds to the next life-cycle phase.

(4) Schedule. Identify the schedule for the V&V tasks. Establish specific milestones for initiating and completing each task, for the receipt of each input, and for the delivery of each output.

(5) Resources. Identify the resources for the performance of the V&V tasks. Specify resources by category (for example, staffing, equipment, facilities, schedule, travel, training). If tools are used in the V&V tasks, specify the source of the tools, their availability, and other usage requirements (for example, training).

(6) Risks and Assumptions. Identify the risks and assumptions associated with the V&V tasks, including schedule, resources, or approach. Specify a contingency plan for each risk.

(7) Roles and Responsibilities. Identify the organizational elements or individuals responsible for performing the V&V tasks. Assign specific responsibilities for each task to one or more organizational element.

3.5.1 Management of V&V. (Section 5.1 of the Plan.) This section of the Plan shall address the seven topics identified in 3.5 of this standard. The management of V&V spans all life-cycle phases. The software development may be a cyclic or iterative process. The V&V effort shall reperform previous V&V tasks or initiate new V&V tasks to address software changes created by the cyclic or iterative development process. V&V tasks are reperformed if errors are discovered in the V&V inputs or outputs.

For all software, management of V&V shall include the following minimum tasks:

(1) Software Verification and Validation Plan (SVVP) Generation

(2) Baseline Change Assessment

(3) Management Review of V&V

(4) Review Support

Table 1 describes the minimum management V&V tasks and identifies the required inputs and outputs. The inputs and outputs required for each V&V task shall include, but not be limited to, those listed in Table 1.

3.5.2 Concept Phase V&V. (Section 5.2 of the Plan.) This section of the Plan shall address the seven topics identified in 3.5 of this standard.

For critical software, Concept Phase V&V shall include the following minimum V&V task:

Concept Documentation Evaluation. Table 1 contains a description of the minimum Concept Phase V&V task and identifies the required inputs and outputs. The inputs and outputs required to accomplish the minimum V&V task shall include, but not be limited to, those listed in Table 1.

3.5.3 Requirements Phase V&V. (Section 5.3 of the Plan.) This section of the Plan shall address the seven topics identified in 3.5 of this standard.

For critical software, Requirements Phase V&V shall include the following minimum tasks:

(1) Software Requirements Traceability Analysis

(2) Software Requirements Evaluation

(3) Software Requirements Interface Analysis

(4) Test Plan Generation

  (a) System Test

  (b) Acceptance Test

Table 1 contains a description of the minimum Requirements Phase V&V tasks and identifies the required inputs and outputs. The inputs and outputs required to accomplish the minimum V&V tasks shall include, but not be limited to, those listed in Table 1.

3.5.4 Design Phase V&V. (Section 5.4 of the Plan.) This section of the Plan shall address the seven topics identified in Section 3.5 of this standard. For critical software, Design Phase V&V shall include the following minimum V&V tasks:

(1) Software Design Traceability Analysis

(2) Software Design Evaluation

(3) Software Design Interface Analysis

(4) Test Plan Generation

(a) Component Test
(b) Integration Test
(5) Test Design Generation
(a) Component Test
(b) Integration Test
(c) System Test
(d) Acceptance Test

Table 1 contains a description of the minimum Design Phase V&V tasks and identifies the required inputs and outputs. The inputs and outputs required to accomplish the minimum V&V tasks shall include, but not be limited to, those listed in Table 1.

3.5.5 Implementation Phase V&V. (Section 5.5 of the Plan.) This section of the Plan shall address the seven topics identified in 3.5 of this standard.

For critical software, Implementation Phase V&V shall include the following minimum V&V tasks:

(1) Source Code Traceability Analysis
(2) Source Code Evaluation
(3) Source Code Interface Analysis
(4) Source Code Documentation Evaluation
(5) Test Case Generation
(a) Component Test
(b) Integration Test
(c) System Test
(d) Acceptance Test
(6) Test Procedure Generation
(a) Component Test
(b) Integration Test
(c) System Test
(7) Component Test Execution

Table 1 contains a description of the minimum Implementation Phase V&V tasks and identifies the required inputs and outputs. The inputs and outputs required to accomplish the minimum V&V tasks shall include, but not be limited to, those listed in Table 1.

3.5.6 Test Phase V&V. (Section 5.6 of the Plan.) This section of the Plan shall address the seven topics identified in 3.5 of this standard.

Testing activities and their interrelationships with previous V&V phases are shown in Fig 2.

For critical software, Test Phase V&V shall include the following minimum V&V tasks:

(1) Acceptance Test Procedure Generation
(2) Test Execution
(a) Integration Test
(b) System Test
(c) Acceptance Test

Table 1 contains a description of the minimum Test Phase V&V tasks and identifies the re-

quired inputs and outputs. The inputs and outputs required to accomplish the minimum V&V tasks shall include, but not be limited to, those listed in Table 1.

3.5.7 Installation and Checkout Phase V&V. (Section 5.7 of the Plan.) This section of the Plan shall address the seven topics identified in Section 3.5 of this standard.

For critical software, Installation and Checkout Phase V&V shall include the following minimum V&V tasks:

(1) Installation Configuration Audit
(2) Final V&V Report Generation

Table 1 contains a description of the minimum Installation and Checkout Phase V&V tasks and identifies the required inputs and outputs. The inputs and outputs required to accomplish the minimum V&V tasks shall include, but not be limited to, those listed in Table 1.

3.5.8 Operation and Maintenance Phase V&V. (Section 5.8 of the Plan.) This section of the Plan shall address the seven topics identified in Section 3.5 of this standard.

Any modifications, enhancements, or additions to software during this phase shall be treated as development activities and shall be verified and validated as described in 3.5.1 through 3.5.7. These modifications may derive from requirements specified to correct software errors (that is, corrective), to adapt to a changed operating environment (that is, adaptive), or to respond to additional user requests (that is, perfective).

If the software was verified under this standard, the standard shall continue to be followed in the Operation and Maintenance Phase. If the software was not verified under this standard, the V&V effort may require documentation that is not available or adequate. If appropriate documentation is not available or adequate, the SVVP shall comply with this standard within cost and schedule constraints. The V&V effort may generate the missing documentation.

For critical software, Operation and Maintenance Phase V&V tasks shall include the following minimum V&V tasks:

(1) Software Verification and Validation Plan Revision
(2) Anomaly Evaluation
(3) Proposed Change Assessment
(4) Phase Task Iteration

Table 1 contains a description of the minimum Operation and Maintenance Phase V&V tasks. The inputs and outputs required to accomplish the minimum V&V tasks shall include, but not be limited to, those listed in Table 1.

3.6 Software Verification and Validation Reporting.
(Section 6 of the Plan.) This section shall describe how the results of implementing the Plan will be documented. V&V reporting shall occur throughout the software life cycle. This section of the Plan shall specify the content, format, and timing of all V&V reports. These V&V reports shall constitute the Software Verification and Validation Report (SVVR).

3.6.1 Required Reports. The following reports shall be generated for each software V&V effort.

(1) Task Reporting. These shall report on the individual V&V phase tasks and shall be issued as necessary. They may document interim results and status. They may be in a format appropriate for technical disclosure (for example, technical reports or memos).

(2) V&V Phase Summary Report. A Phase Summary Report shall summarize the results of V&V tasks performed in each of the following life-cycle phases: Concept, Requirements, Design, Implementation, Test, and Installation and Checkout. For the Operation and Maintenance Phase, V&V phase summary reports may be either updates to previous V&V phase summary reports or separate documents. Each V&V Phase Summary Report shall contain the following:

(a) Description of V&V tasks performed
(b) Summary of task results
(c) Summary of anomalies and resolution
(d) Assessment of software quality
(e) Recommendations

(3) Anomaly Report. An Anomaly Report shall document each anomaly detected by the V&V effort. Each Anomaly Report shall contain the following:

(a) Description and location
(b) Impact
(c) Cause
(d) Criticality
(e) Recommendations

(4) V&V Final Report. The Verification and Validation Final Report shall be issued at the end of the Installation and Checkout phase or at the conclusion of the V&V effort. The Final Report shall include the following information:

(a) Summary of all life-cycle V&V tasks
(b) Summary of task results
(c) Summary of anomalies and resolutions

(d) Assessment of overall software quality
(e) Recommendations

3.6.2 Optional Reports
The following reports are optional.

(1) Special Studies Report. This report shall describe any special studies conducted during any life-cycle phase. The report shall document technical results and shall include, at a minimum, the following information:

(a) Purpose and objectives
(b) Approach
(c) Summary of results

(2) Other Reports. These reports shall describe the results of tasks not defined in the SVVP. These other activities and results may include quality assurance results, end user testing results, or configuration and data management status results.

3.7 Verification and Validation Administrative Procedures.
(Section 7 of the Plan). This section of the Plan shall describe, at a minimum, the V&V administrative procedures described in 3.7.1 through 3.7.5.

3.7.1 Anomaly Reporting and Resolution. (Section 7.1 of the Plan.) This section shall describe the method of reporting and resolving anomalies, including the criteria for reporting an anomaly, the anomaly report distribution list, and the authority and time lines for resolving anomalies. The section shall define the anomaly criticality levels. Each critical anomaly shall be resolved satisfactorily before the V&V effort can formally proceed to the next life-cycle phase.

3.7.2 Task Iteration Policy. (Section 7.2 of the Plan.) This section shall describe the criteria used to determine the extent to which a V&V task shall be reperformed when its input is changed. These criteria may include assessments of change, criticality, and cost, schedule, or quality effects.

3.7.3 Deviation Policy. (Section 7.3 of the Plan.) This section shall describe the procedures and forms used to deviate from the Plan. The information required for deviations shall include task identification, deviation rationale, and effect on software quality. The section shall define the authorities responsible for approving deviations.

3.7.4 Control Procedures. (Section 7.4 of the Plan.) This section shall identify control procedures applied to the V&V effort. These procedures shall describe how software products and results of software V&V shall be configured, protected, and stored.

These procedures may describe quality assurance, configuration management, data management, or other activities if they are not addressed by other efforts. At a minimum, this section shall describe how SVVP materials shall comply with existing security provisions and how the validity of V&V results shall be protected from accidental or deliberate alteration.

3.7.5 Standards, Practices, and Conventions. (Section 7.5 of the Plan.) This section shall identify the standards, practices, and conventions that govern the performance of V&V tasks, including internal organizational standards, practices, and policies.

Table 1
Required V&V Tasks, Inputs, and Outputs for Life-Cycle Phases[3]

Minimum V&V Tasks	Required Inputs	Required Outputs*
5.1 MANAGEMENT OF V&V		
(1) Software Verification and Validation Plan (SVVP) Generation. Generate SVVP (during Concept Phase) for all life-cycle phases in accordance with this standard based upon available documentation. Include estimate of anticipated V&V activities for Operation and Maintenance Phase. Update SVVP for each life-cycle phase, particularly prior to Operation and Maintenance. Consider SVVP to be a *living document,* and make changes as necessary. A baseline SVVP should be established prior to the Requirements Phase.	Development Schedules Concept Documentation SRS Interface Requirements Documentation SDD Interface Design Documentation Source Code Listing(s) Executable Code User Documentation Proposed Changes	SVVP and Updates
(2) Baseline Change Assessment. Evaluate proposed software changes (for example, anomaly corrections, performance enhancements, requirement changes, clarifications) for effects on previously completed V&V tasks. When changes are made, plan iteration of affected tasks which includes reperforming previous V&V tasks or initiating new V&V tasks to address the software changes created by the cyclic or iterative development process.	Proposed Changes	Updated SVVP
(3) Management Review. Conduct periodic reviews of V&V effort, technical accomplishments, resource utilization, future planning, risk management. Support daily management of V&V phase activities, including technical quality of final and interim V&V reports and results. Review the task and V&V phase summary reports of each life-cycle phase. Evaluate V&V results and anomaly resolution to determine when to proceed to next life-cycle phase and to define changes to V&V tasks to improve the V&V effort.	Development Schedules V&V Outputs	Task Reporting V&V Phase Summary Reports
(4) Review Support. Correlate V&V task results to support management and technical reviews (for example, Software Requirements Review, Preliminary Design Review, Critical Design Review). Identify key review support milestones in SVVP. Schedule V&V tasks to meet milestones. Establish methods to exchange V&V data and results with development effort.	V&V Outputs	Task Reporting Anomaly Report(s)
5.2 CONCEPT PHASE V&V		
(1) Concept Documentation Evaluation. Evaluate concept documentation to determine if proposed concept satisfies user needs and project objectives (for example, performance goals). Identify major constraints of interfacing systems and constraints or limitations of proposed approach. Assess allocation of functions to hardware and software items, where appropriate. Assess criticality of each software item.	Concept Documentation (for example, Statement of Need, Advance Planning Report, Project Initiation Memo, Feasibility Studies, System Definition Documentation, Governing Regulations, Procedures, Policies, and customer acceptance criteria/requirements)	Task Reporting Anomaly Report(s)
5.3 REQUIREMENTS PHASE V&V		
(1) Software Requirements Traceability Analysis. Trace SRS requirements to system requirements in concept documentation. Analyze identified relationships for correctness, consistency, completeness, accuracy.	Concept Documentation SRS Interface Requirements Documents	Task Reporting Anomaly Report(s)
(2) Software Requirements Evaluation. Evaluate SRS requirements for correctness, consistency, completeness, accuracy, readability, and testability. Assess how well SRS satisfies software system objectives. Assess the criticality of requirements to identify key performance or critical areas of software.	Concept Documentation SRS Interface Requirements Documentation	Task Reporting Anomaly Report(s)

* Outputs from phase tasks are used to develop corresponding V&V phase summary reports and are ongoing inputs to the SVVR. Outputs of V&V tasks become inputs to subsequent life-cycle V&V tasks.

[3] The section numbers referred to in this Table refer to Section 5 of the Plan.

Table 1 (Continued)

Minimum V&V Tasks	Required Inputs	Required Outputs*
5.3 REQUIREMENTS PHASE V&V (Continued)		
(3) Software Requirements Interface Analysis. Evaluate SRS with hardware, user, operator, and software interface requirements documentation for correctness, consistency, completeness, accuracy, and readability.	SRS Interface Requirements Documentation	Task Reporting Anomaly Report(s)
(4a) System Test Plan Generation. Plan system testing to determine if software satisfies system objectives. Criteria for this determination are, at a minimum: (a) compliance with all functional requirements as complete software end item in system environment (b) performance at hardware, software, user, and operator interfaces (c) adequacy of user documentation (d) performance at boundaries (for example, data, interface) and under stress conditions. Plan tracing of system end-item requirements to test design, cases, procedures, and execution results. Plan documentation of test tasks and results.	Concept Documentation SRS Interface Requirements Documentation User Documentation	System Test Plan Anomaly Report(s)
(4b) Acceptance Test Plan Generation. Plan acceptance testing to determine if software correctly implements system and software requirements in an operational environment. Criteria for this determination are, at a minimum: (a) compliance with acceptance requirements in operational environment (b) adequacy of user documentation. Plan tracing of acceptance test requirements to test design, cases, procedures, and execution results. Plan documentation of test tasks and results.	Concept Documentation SRS Interface Requirements Documentation User Documentation	Acceptance Test Plan Anomaly Report(s)
5.4 DESIGN PHASE V&V		
(1) Design Traceability Analysis. Trace SDD to SRS and SRS to SDD. Analyze identified relationships for correctness, consistency, completeness, and accuracy.	SRS SDD Interface Requirements Documentation Interface Design Documentation	Task Reporting Anomaly Report(s)
(2) Design Evaluation. Evaluate SDD for correctness, consistency, completeness, accuracy, and testability. Evaluate design for compliance with established standards, practices, and conventions. Assess design quality.	SDD Interface Design Documentation Standards (standards, practices, conventions)	Task Reporting Anomaly Report(s)
(3) Design Interface Analysis. Evaluate SDD with hardware, operator, and software interface requirements for correctness, consistency, completeness, and accuracy. At a minimum, analyze data items at each interface.	SDD Interface Design Documentation	Task Reporting Anomaly Report(s)
(4a) Component Test Plan Generation. Plan component testing to determine if software elements (for example, units, modules) correctly implement component requirements. Criteria for this determination are, at a minimum: (a) compliance with design requirements (b) assessment of timing, sizing, and accuracy (c) performance at boundaries and interfaces and under stress and error conditions (d) measures of test coverage and software reliability and maintainability. Plan tracing of design requirements to test design, cases, procedures, and execution results. Plan documentation of test tasks and results.	SRS SDD Interface Requirements Documentation Interface Design Documentation	Component Test Plan Anomaly Report(s)
(4b) Integration Test Plan Generation. Plan integration testing to determine if software (for example, subelements, interfaces) correctly implements the software requirements and design. Criteria for this determination are, at a minimum: (a) compliance with increasingly larger set of functional requirements at each stage of integration (b) assessment of timing, sizing, and accuracy (c) performance at boundaries and under stress conditions (d) measures of functional test coverage and software reliability. Plan tracing of requirements to test design, cases, procedures, and execution results. Plan documentation of test tasks and results.	SRS SDD Interface Requirements Documentation Interface Design Documentation	Integration Test Plan Anomaly Report(s)

* Outputs from phase tasks are used to develop corresponding V&V phase summary reports and are ongoing inputs to the SVVR. Outputs of V&V tasks become inputs to subsequent life-cycle V&V tasks.

Table 1 *(Continued)*

Minimum V&V Tasks	Required Inputs	Required Outputs*
5.4 DESIGN PHASE V&V *(Continued)*		
(5) Test Design Generation. Design tests for: (a) component testing (b) integration testing (c) system testing (d) acceptance testing. Continue tracing required by the Test Plan.	SDD Interface Design Documentation User Documentation	Component Test Design(s) Integration Test Design(s) System Test Design(s) Acceptance Test Design(s) Anomaly Report(s)
5.5 IMPLEMENTATION PHASE V&V		
(1) Source Code Traceability Analysis. Trace source code to corresponding design specification(s) and design specification(s) to source code. Analyze identified relationships for correctness, consistency, completeness, and accuracy.	SDD Interface Design Documentation Source Code Listing(s)	Task Reporting Anomaly Report(s)
(2) Source Code Evaluation. Evaluate source code for correctness, consistency, completeness, accuracy, and testability. Evaluate source code for compliance with established standards, practices, and conventions. Assess source code quality.	Source Code Listing(s) Standards (standards, practices, conventions) SDD Interface Design Documentation User Documentation	Task Reporting Anomaly Report(s)
(3) Source Code Interface Analysis. Evaluate source code with hardware, operator, and software interface design documentation for correctness, consistency, completeness, and accuracy. At a minimum, analyze data items at each interface.	Source Code Listing(s) User Documentation	Task Reporting Anomaly Report(s)
(4) Source Code Documentation Evaluation. Evaluate draft code-related documents with source code to ensure completeness, correctness, and consistency.	Source Code Listing(s) User Documentation	Task Reporting Anomaly Report(s)
(5) Test Case Generation. Develop test cases for: (a) component testing (b) integration testing (c) system testing (d) acceptance testing. Continue tracing required by the Test Plan.	SDD Interface Design Documentation Source Code Listing(s)	Component Test Cases Integration Test Cases System Test Cases Acceptance Test Cases Anomaly Report(s)
(6) Test Procedure Generation. Develop test procedures for: (a) component testing (b) integration testing (c) system testing. Continue tracing required by the Test Plan.	SDD Interface Design Documentation Source Code Listing(s) User Documentation	Component Test Procedures Integration Test Procedures System Test Procedures Anomaly Report(s)
(7) Component Test Execution. Perform component testing as required by component test procedures. Analyze results to determine that software correctly implements design. Document and trace results as required by the Test Plan.	Source Code Listing(s) Executable Code SDD Interface Design Documentation	Task Reporting Anomaly Report(s)
5.6 TEST PHASE V&V		
(1) Test Procedure Generation. Develop test procedures for acceptance test. Continue tracing required by the Test Plan.	SDD Interface Design Documentation Source Code Listing(s) User Documentation	Acceptance Test Procedures Anomaly Report(s)

* Outputs from phase tasks are used to develop corresponding V&V phase summary reports and are ongoing inputs to the SVVR. Outputs of V&V tasks become inputs to subsequent life-cycle V&V tasks.

Table 1 *(Continued)*

Minimum V&V Tasks	Required Inputs	Required Outputs*
5.6 TEST PHASE V&V *(Continued)*		
(2a) Integration Test Execution. Perform integration testing in accordance with test procedures. Analyze results to determine if software implements software requirements and design and that software components function correctly together. Document and trace results as required by the Test Plan.	Source Code Listing(s) Executable Code	Task Reporting Anomaly Report(s)
(2b) System Test Execution. Perform system testing in accordance with test procedures. Analyze results to determine if software satisfies system objectives. Document and trace all testing results as required by the Test Plan.	Source Code Listing(s) Executable Code User Documentation	Task Reporting Anomaly Report(s)
(2c) Acceptance Test Execution. Perform acceptance testing in accordance with test procedures under formal configuration control. Analyze results to determine if software satisfies acceptance criteria. Document and trace all testing results as required by the Test Plan.	Source Code Listing(s) Executable Code User Documentation	Task Reporting Anomaly Report(s)
5.7 INSTALLATION AND CHECKOUT PHASE V&V		
(1) Installation Configuration Audit. Audit installation package to determine that all software products required to correctly install and operate the software are present, including operations documentation. Analyze all site-dependent parameters or conditions to determine that supplied values are correct. Conduct analyses or tests to demonstrate that installed software corresponds to software subjected to V&V.	Installation Package (for example, Source Code Listing(s), Executable Code, User Documentation, SDD, Interface Design Documentation, SRS, Concept Documentation, Installation Procedures, and Installation Tests)	Task Reporting Anomaly Report(s)
(2) V&V Final Report Generation. Summarize all V&V activities and results, including status and disposition of anomalies in the V&V final report (see 3.6.1 of this standard).	All V&V Phase Summary Report(s)	V&V Final Report
5.8 OPERATION AND MAINTENANCE PHASE V&V		
(1) Software V&V Plan Revision. For software verified and validated under this standard, revise SVVP to comply with new constraints based upon available documentation. For software not verified and validated under this standard, write new SVVP.	Development Schedules Concept Documentation SRS Interface Requirements Documentation SDD Interface Design Documentation Source Code Listing(s) User Documentation Installation Package Proposed Changes	Updated SVVP
(2) Anomaly Evaluation. Evaluate severity of anomalies in software operation. Analyze effect of anomalies on system.	Anomaly Report(s)	Task Reporting
(3) Proposed Change Assessment. Assess all proposed modifications, enhancements, or additions to determine effect each change would have on system. Determine extent to which V&V tasks would be iterated.	Proposed Changes	Task Reporting
(4) Phase Task Iteration. For approved software changes, perform V&V tasks necessary to ensure that: planned changes are implemented correctly; all documentation is complete and up to date; and no unacceptable changes have occurred in software performance.	Approved Changes	Task Reporting from Iterated Tasks Anomaly Report(s) Required Phases Outputs of Iterated Tasks

* Outputs from phase tasks are used to develop corresponding V&V phase summary reports and are ongoing inputs to the SVVR. Outputs of V&V tasks become inputs to subsequent life-cycle V&V tasks.

Table 2
Optional V&V Tasks and Suggested Applications

Optional V&V Tasks	Life-Cycle Phases							
	Management	Concept	Requirements	Design	Implementation	Test	Installation and Checkout	Operation and Maintenance
Algorithm Analysis			●	●	●	●		●
Audit Performance								
Configuration Control					●	●	●	●
Functional					●	●	●	●
In-Process			●	●	●	●	●	●
Physical						●	●	●
Audit Support								
Configuration Control					●	●	●	●
Functional					●	●	●	●
In-Process			●	●	●	●	●	●
Physical						●	●	●
Configuration Management	●	●	●	●	●	●	●	●
Control Flow Analysis			●	●	●			
Database Analysis			●	●	●			●
Data Flow Analysis			●	●	●			●
Feasibility Study Evaluation		●						●
Installation and Checkout Testing*					●	●	●	●
Performance Monitoring								●
Qualification Testing*					●	●	●	●
Regression Analysis and Testing			●	●	●	●	●	●
Reviews Support								
Operational Readiness							●	●
Test Readiness					●	●	●	●
Simulation Analysis			●	●	●			●
Sizing and Timing Analysis				●	●	●		●
Test Certification						●	●	●
Test Evaluation			●	●	●	●	●	●
Test Witnessing						●	●	●
User Documentation Evaluation		●	●	●	●	●	●	●
V&V Tool Plan Generation	●							●
Walkthroughs								
Design				●				●
Requirements			●					●
Source Code					●			●
Test					●	●	●	●

* Test plan, test design, test cases, test procedures, and test execution.

Appendix

(This Appendix is not a part of IEEE Std 1012-1986, IEEE Standard for Software Verification and Validation Plans, but is included for information only.)

Description of Optional V&V Tasks

The descriptions of optional V&V tasks listed in Table 2 of this standard are defined in this Appendix. These V&V tasks are not mandatory for all V&V projects because they may apply to only selected software applications or may force the use of specific tools or techniques. These optional V&V tasks are appropriate for critical and noncritical software. By selecting V&V tasks from these optional V&V tasks, one can tailor the V&V effort to project needs and also achieve a more effective V&V effort.

algorithm analysis. Ensure that the algorithms selected are correct, appropriate, and stable, and meet all accuracy, timing, and sizing requirements.

audit performance. Conduct independent compliance assessment as detailed for configuration control audit, functional audit, in-process audit, or physical audit.

audit support. Provide documentation for, or participate in, any audits performed on the software development (for example, configuration control, functional, in-process, physical).

configuration control audit. Assess the configuration control procedures and the enforcement of these procedures.

configuration management. Control, document, and authenticate the status of items needed for, or produced by, activities throughout the software life cycle.

control flow analysis. Ensure that the proposed control flow is free of problems, such as design or code elements that are unreachable or incorrect.

database analysis. Ensure that the database structure and access methods are compatible with the logical design.

data flow analysis. Ensure that the input and output data and their formats are properly defined, and that the data flows are correct.

design walkthrough. Participate in walkthroughs of the preliminary design and updates of the design to ensure technical integrity and validity.

feasibility study evaluation. Evaluate any feasibility study performed during the concept phase for correctness, completeness, consistency, and accuracy. Trace back to the statement of need for the user requirements. Where appropriate, conduct an independent feasibility study as part of the V&V task.

functional audit. Prior to delivery, assess how well the software satisfies the requirements specified in the Software Requirements Specifications.

in-process audit. Assess consistency of the design by sampling the software development process (for example, audit source code for conformance to coding standards and conventions and for implementation of the design documentation).

installation and checkout testing. Generate the test plan, test design, test cases, and test procedures in preparation for software installation and checkout. Place the completed software product into its operational environment, and test it for adequate performance in that environment.

operational readiness review. Examine the installed software, its installation documentation, and results of acceptance testing to determine that the software is properly installed and ready to be placed in operation.

performance monitoring. Collect information on the performance of the software under operational conditions. Determine whether system and software performance requirements are satisfied.

physical audit. Assess the internal consistency of the software, its documentation, and its readiness for delivery.

qualification testing. Generate the test plan, test design, test cases, and test procedures in preparation for qualification testing. Perform formal testing to demonstrate to the customer that the software meets its specified requirements.

regression analysis and testing. Determine the extent of V&V analysis and testing that must be repeated when changes are made to any software products previously examined.

requirements walkthrough. Ensure that the software requirements are correct, consistent, complete, unambiguous, and testable by participating in a walkthrough of the requirements specification.

review support. Provide the results of applicable V&V tasks to support any formal reviews. The results may be provided in written form or in a presentation at the formal review meeting (for example, operational readiness, test readiness).

simulation analysis. Simulate critical aspects of the software or system environment to analyze logical or performance characteristics that would not be practical to analyze manually.

sizing and timing analysis. Obtain program sizing and execution timing information to determine if the program will satisfy processor size and performance requirements allocated to software.

source code walkthrough. Ensure that the code is free from logic errors and complies with coding standards and conventions by participating in a walkthrough of the source code.

test certification. Ensure that reported test results are the actual findings of the tests. Test-related tools, media, and documentation shall be certified to ensure maintainability and repeatability of tests.

test evaluation. Confirm the technical adequacy of test plans, test design, test cases, test procedures, and test results.

test readiness review. Evaluate the code, software documentation, test procedures, test reporting, error detection, and correction procedures to determine that formal testing may begin.

test walkthrough. Ensure that the planned testing is correct and complete and that the test results are properly interpreted by participating in walkthroughs of test documentation.

test witnessing. Observe testing to confirm that the tests are conducted in accordance with approved test plans and procedures.

user documentation evaluation. Examine draft documents during the development process to ensure correctness, understandability, and completeness. Documentation may include user manuals or guides, as appropriate for the project.

V&V tool plan generation. Produce plans for the acquisition, development, training, and quality assurance activities related to tools identified for support of V&V tasks (for example, test bed software used in validation).

walkthrough. Participate in the evaluation processes in which development personnel lead others through a structured examination of a product. See specific descriptions of requirements walkthrough, design walkthrough, source code walkthrough, and test walkthrough.

Acknowledgements

The following organizations supported employee participation in the development of this standard:

ACEx Technology
Army Computer Systems Command
AT&T Technologies
Babcock & Wilcox
Bechtel Power Corporation
Bell Canada
The Boeing Company
Booz Allen Hamilton
Central Institute For Industrial Research
Computer Science Corporation
Data Logic
E-Systems
Gemini
Hewlett Packard
Jet Propulsion Laboratory

Johns Hopkins University Applied Physics Laboratory
Logicon, Inc
Lucas Micro, Ltd
National Bureau of Standards
NCR Corporation
RCA
STC - Standard Telecommunications
Teledyne Brown Engineering
Televideo Systems
TRW
U.S. Department of Agriculture
U.S. Department of Transportation
Veatch, Rich, & Nadler
Walt Disney World
Worldwide Service Technologies, Ltd

IEEE Recommended Practice for
Software Design Descriptions

Sponsor

**Software Engineering Subcommittee
of the
Technical Committee on Software Engineering of the
IEEE Computer Society**

1016

© Copyright 1987 by

**The Institute of Electrical and Electronics Engineers, Inc
345 East 47th Street, New York, NY 10017, USA**

Foreword

(This Foreword is not a part of IEEE Std 1016-1987, IEEE Recommended Practice for Software Design Descriptions.)

Purpose

This recommended practice specifies the necessary information content and recommends an organization for software design descriptions. This document does not explicitly support, nor is it limited to, any particular software design methodology or descriptive technology. It will guide the production of anything from paper design documents to an automated database of design information. For an organization in the process of developing a design description standard, use of this document will help the new standard meet the needs of all of its users. For an organization with a mature design description standard, it should prove useful in evaluating and modifying that standard in light of the informational and organizational needs of the design description user community.

This practice can be applied to commercial, scientific, and military software. Applicability is not restricted by size, complexity, or criticality of the software. This practice considers both the software and its system operational environment. It can be used where software is the system or where software is part of a larger system that is characterized by hardware and software components and their interfaces.

Overview

This document consists of six sections. Section 1 defines the scope of the recommended practice and Section 2 references other ANSI/IEEE standards that should be followed when applying this practice. Section 3 provides definitions of terms within the context of the practice. Section 4 places the Software Design Description into the framework of the software development life cycle. Section 5 describes the minimum information that shall be included in a software design description and Section 6 gives a recommended organization for software design descriptions. The Appendix shows a sample table of contents for a software design description.

Audience

This document is intended for those in technical and managerial positions who prepare and use software design descriptions. It will guide a designer in the selection, organization, and presentation of design information. It will help standards developers ensure that a design description is complete, concise, and well organized.

Software design descriptions play a pivotal role in the development and maintenance of software systems. During its lifetime, a given design description is used by project managers, quality assurance staff, configuration managers, software designers, programmers, testers, and maintainers. Each of these users has unique needs, both in terms of required design information and optimal organization of that information. Hence, a design description must contain all the design information needed by those users.

Terminology

This recommended practice follows the IEEE Guide to Standards Development. In particular, the word *shall* and the imperative form identify mandatory material within the recommended practice. The words *should*, *might*, and *may* identify advisory material.

History

The project authorization request for development of this recommended practice was approved by the IEEE Standards Board on September 22, 1983. Modification of the authorization request to change the title and scope was approved on March 13, 1986. A series of 10 meetings were held within the United States and internationally between March, 1983 and March, 1986. These meetings produced the draft submitted for balloting in April, 1986.

Suggestions for the improvement of this practice will be welcome. They should be sent to

Secretary
IEEE Standards Board
Institute of Electrical and Electronics Engineers, Inc
345 East 47th Street
New York, NY 10017

Contributors

This document was developed by the Software Design Description Working Group of the Software Engineering Standards Subcommittee of the IEEE Computer Society. The Software Design Description Working Group Steering Committee had the following members:

H. Jack Barnard, *Chairman*   **James A. Darling,** *Vice Chairman*

Robert F. Metz, *Secretary*

Chris Beall	H. Gregory Frank	John McArdle
Patricia Cox	Manoochehr Ghiassi	Arthur L. Price
Leo Endres	Daniel E. Klingler	Basil Sherlund

The Software Design Description Working Group had the following members:

A. Frank Ackerman	Yair Gershkovitch	Walter Merenda
Jim Anderson	Tom Gilb	Randy Peterson
Sandro Bologna	Shirley A. Gloss-Soler	Robert Poston
Fletcher Buckley	Larry J. Hardouin	Ian C. Pyle
Lori J. Call	Fredrick Ho	Ann S. Ping
Wan P. Chiang	David M. Home	Hans Schaefer
Francois Coallier	William S. Junk	David Schultz
Cliff Cockerham	Laurel Kaleda	David Siefert
Patricia W. Daggett	Tom Kurihara	Peter Smith
Jim DeLeo	Jim Lemmon	Richard H. Thayer
Cammie Donaldson	F. C. Lim	T. H. Tse
Euiar Dragstedt	Oyvind Lorentzen	David Weiss
Laurence E. Fishtahler	Bert Martin	Charles J. Wertz
David Gelperin	Lindsay McDermid	G. Robert Zambs
	Glen Meldrum	

The following persons were on the balloting committee that approved this document for submission to the IEEE Standards Board:

A. Frank Ackerman	William P. Dupres	Harry E. Hansen, Jr
Jagdish Agrawal	Michael Dutton	Robert M. Haralick
Richard L. Aurbach	Robert E. Dwyer	Haus-Ludis Hauser
James Baldo, Jr	Mary L. Eads	Clark M. Hay
H. Jack Barnard	John D. Earls	H. Hect
Leo Beltracchi	Mike Edwards	Terry L. Hengl
Yechiel Ben-Naftali	L. G. Egan	Maretta T. Holden
H. R. Berlack	W. D. Ehrenberger	Charles P. Hollocker
Michael A. Blackledge	Steven R. Eisen	Mark Holthouse
Ron Blair	Caroline L. Evans	John Horch
Kevin W. Bowyer	John W. Fendrich	Cheng Hu
Kathleen L. Briggs	Robert G. Ferreol	Peter L. Hung
A. Winsor Brown	Glenn S. Fields	Sheng-Sheng Jeng
F. Buckley	Gordon Force	Laurel Kaleda
Homer C. Carney	Julian Forster	Charles F. Kaminski
Ronald G. Carter	Deborah L. Franke	Constantine Kaniklidis
Richard L. Chilausky	C. R. Frederick	Myron S. Karasik
Robert N. Chorette	Carl Friedlander	Adi N. Kasad
T. S. Chow	Richard Fries	Ron Kenett
Slucki Jean Christophe	Michael Galinier	R. A. Kessler
Jung K. Chung	Leonard B. Gardner	Shaye Koenig
Peter Coad, Jr	David Gelperin	Edward E. Kopicky
François Coallier	Tom Gilb	Joseph A. Krupinski
Sharon R. Cobb-Pierson	James L. Gildersleeve	H. M. Kudyan
Christopher M. Cooke	Shirley Gloss-Soler	Joan Kundig
A. J. Cote, Jr	Ole Golubjatnikov	Lak-Ming Lam
Ismael Fuentes Crespo	J. Kaye Grau	John B. Lane
Patricia W. Daggett	Andrej Grebenc	Robert Lane
George D. Darling	Thomas Griest	William P. LaPlant
Taz Daughtry	Robert S. Grossman	Greg Larsen
Peter A. Denny	Victor M. Guarnera	John A. Latimer
Harpal S. Dhama	Lawrence M. Gunther	John A. N. Lee
Mike Dotson	David A. Gustafson	Leon S. Levy
David C. Doty	Russell Gustin	Paul Liebertz
Einar Dragstedt	Michael Haggerty	F. C. Lim
W. DuBlanica	Howard Hamer	Bertil Lindberg

When the IEEE Standards Board approved this standard on March 12, 1987, it had the following membership:

Contents

IEEE Recommended Practice for Software Design Descriptions

1. Scope

This is a recommended practice for describing software designs. It specifies the necessary information content, and recommended organization for a software design description. A software design description is a representation of a software system that is used as a medium for communicating software design information.

The practice may be applied to commercial, scientific, or military software that runs on any digital computer. Applicability is not restricted by the size, complexity, or criticality of the software.

This practice is not limited to specific methodologies for design, configuration management, or quality assurance. It is assumed that the quality design information and changes to the design of description will be managed by other project activities. Finally, this document does not support nor is it limited to any particular descriptive technique. It may be applied to paper documents, automated databases, design description languages, or other means of description.

2. References

This standard shall be used in conjunction with the following publications:

[1] ANSI/IEEE Std 729-1983, IEEE Standard Glossary of Software Engineering Terminology.[1]

[2] ANSI/IEEE Std 730-1984, IEEE Standard for Software Quality Assurance Plans.

[3] ANSI/IEEE Std 828-1983, IEEE Standard for Software Configuration Management Plans.

[4] ANSI/IEEE Std 830-1984, IEEE Guide to Software Requirements Specifications

[5] Freeman, P. and A. I. Wasserman. *Tutorial on Software Design Techniques*. 4th Edition, IEEE Computer Society Press, Annotated Bibliography, pp 715–718, 1983.

3. Definitions

The definitions listed here establish meaning in the context of this recommended practice. Definitions of other terms used in this document can be found in ANSI/IEEE Std 729-1983 [1].[2]

design entity. An element (component) of a design that is structurally and functionally distinct from other elements and that is separately named and referenced.

design view. A subset of design entity attribute information that is specifically suited to the needs of a software project activity.

entity attribute. A named characteristic or property of a design entity. It provides a statement of fact about the entity.

software design description (SDD). A representation of a software system created to facilitate analysis, planning, implementation, and decision making. A blueprint or model of the software system. The SDD is used as the primary medium for communicating software design information.

4. Considerations for Producing a Software Design Description (SDD)

This section provides information to be considered before producing an SDD. How the SDD fits

---

[1] ANSI/IEEE publications can be obtained from the Sales Department, American National Standards Institute, 1430 Broadway, New York, NY 10018, or from the Service Center, The Institute of Electrical and Electronics Engineers, 445 Hoes Lane, Piscataway, NJ 08855-1331.

[2] Numbers in brackets correspond to those of the references in Section 2 of this standard.

into the software life cycle, where it fits, and why it is used are discussed.

4.1 Software Life Cycle. The life cycle of a software system is normally defined as the period of time that starts when a software product is conceived and ends when the product is no longer available for use. The life cycle approach is an effective engineering management tool and provides a model for a context within which to discuss the preparation and use of the SDD. While it is beyond the scope of this document to prescribe a particular standard life cycle, a typical cycle will be used to define such a context for the SDD. This cycle is based on ANSI/IEEE Std 729-1983 [1] and consists of a concept phase, requirements phase, design phase, implementation phase, test phase, installation and checkout phase, operation and maintenance phase, and retirement phase.

4.2 Software Design Description (SDD) within the Life Cycle. For both new software systems and existing systems under maintenance, it is important to ensure that the design and implementation used for a software system satisfy the requirements driving that system. The minimum documentation required to do this is defined in ANSI/IEEE Std 730-1984 [2]. The SDD is one of these required products. It records the result of the design processes that are carried out during the design phase.

4.3 Purpose of a Software Design Description (SDD). The SDD shows how the software system will be structured to satisfy the requirements identified in the software requirements specification ANSI/IEEE Std 830-1984 [4]. It is a translation of requirements into a description of the software structure, software components, interfaces, and data necessary for the implementation phase. In essence, the SDD becomes a detailed blueprint for the implementation activity. In a complete SDD, each requirement must be traceable to one or more design entities.

5. Design Description Information Content

5.1 Introduction. A software design description is a representation or model of the software system to be created. The model should provide the precise design information needed for planning, analysis, and implementation of the software system. It should represent a partitioning of the system into design entities and describe the important properties and relationships among those entities.

The design description model used to represent a software system can be expressed as a collection of design entities, each possessing properties and relationships.[3] To simplify the model, the properties and relationships of each design entity are described by a standard set of attributes. The design information needs of project members are satisfied through identification of the entities and their associated attributes. A design description is complete when the attributes have been specified for all the entities.

5.2 Design Entities. A *design entity* is an element (component) of a design that is structurally and functionally distinct from other elements and that is separately named and referenced.

Design entities result from a decomposition of the software system requirements. The objective is to divide the system into separate components that can be considered, implemented, changed, and tested with minimal effect on other entities.

Entities can exist as a system, subsystems, data stores, modules, programs, and processes; see ANSI/IEEE Std 729-1983 [1]. The number and type of entities required to partition a design are dependent on a number of factors, such as the complexity of the system, the design technique used, and the programming environment.

Although entities are different in nature, they possess common characteristics. Each design entity will have a name, purpose, and function. There are common relationships among entities such as interfaces or shared data. The common characteristics of entities are described by design entity attributes.

5.3 Design Entity Attributes. A *design entity attribute* is a named characteristic or property of a design entity. It provides a statement of fact about the entity.

Design entity attributes can be thought of as questions about design entities. The answers to those questions are the values of the attributes. All the questions can be answered, but the content of the answer will depend upon the nature of the entity. The collection of answers provides a complete description of an entity.

---

[3] The design description model is similar to an entity-relationship model, a common approach to information modeling.

The list of design entity attributes presented in this section is the minimum set required for all software design descriptions. The selection of these attributes is based on three criteria:

(1) The attribute is necessary for all software projects

(2) An incorrect specification of the attribute value could result in a fault in the software system to be developed

(3) The attribute describes intrinsic design information and not information related to the design process. Examples of attributes that do not meet the second and third criteria are designer names, design status, and revision history. This important process information is maintained by other software project activities as described in ANSI/IEEE Std 730-1984 [2] and ANSI/IEEE Std 828-1983 [3].

All attributes shall be specified for each entity. Attribute descriptions should include references and design considerations such as tradeoffs and assumptions when appropriate. In some cases, attribute descriptions may have the value *none*. When additional attributes are identified for a specific software project, they should be included in the design description. The attributes and associated information items are defined in 5.3.1 through 5.3.10.

5.3.1 Identification. *The name of the entity.* Two entities shall not have the same name. The names for the entities may be selected to characterize their nature. This will simplify referencing and tracking in addition to providing identification.

5.3.2 Type. *A description of the kind of entity.* The type attribute shall describe the nature of the entity. It may simply name the kind of entity, such as subprogram, module, procedure, process, or data store. Alternatively, design entities may be grouped into major classes to assist in locating an entity dealing with a particular type of information. For a given design description, the chosen entity types shall be applied consistently.

5.3.3 Purpose. *A description of why the entity exists.* The purpose attribute shall provide the rationale for the creation of the entity. Therefore, it shall designate the specific functional and performance requirements for which this entity was created; see ANSI/IEEE Std 830-1984 [4]. The purpose attribute shall also describe special requirements that must be met by the entity that are not included in the software requirements specification.

5.3.4 Function. *A statement of what the entity does.* The function attribute shall state the transformation applied by the entity to inputs to produce the desired output. In the case of a data entity, this attribute shall state the type of information stored or transmitted by the entity.

5.3.5 Subordinates. *The identification of all entities composing this entity.* The subordinates attribute shall identify the *composed of* relationship for an entity. This information is used to trace requirements to design entities and to identify parent/child structural relationships through a software system decomposition.

5.3.6 Dependencies. *A description of the relationships of this entity with other entities.* The dependencies attribute shall identify the *uses* or *requires the presence of* relationship for an entity. These relationships are often graphically depicted by structure charts, data flow diagrams, and transaction diagrams.

This attribute shall describe the nature of each interaction including such characteristics as timing and conditions for interaction. The interactions may involve the initiation, order of execution, data sharing, creation, duplicating, usage, storage, or destruction of entities.

5.3.7 Interface. *A description of how other entities interact with this entity.* The interface attribute shall describe the *methods* of interaction and the *rules* governing those interactions. The methods of interaction include the mechanisms for invoking or interrupting the entity, for communicating through parameters, common data areas or messages, and for direct access to internal data. The rules governing the interaction include the communications protocol, data format, acceptable values, and the meaning of each value.

This attribute shall provide a description of the input ranges, the meaning of inputs and outputs, the type and format of each input or output, and output error codes. For information systems, it should include inputs, screen formats, and a complete description of the interactive language.

5.3.8 Resources. *A description of the elements used by the entity that are external to the design.* The resources attribute shall identify and describe all of the resources *external* to the design that are needed by this entity to perform its function. The interaction rules and methods for using the resource shall be specified by this attribute.

This attribute provides information about items such as physical devices (printers, disc-partitions, memory banks), software services (math libraries, operating system services), and processing resources (CPU cycles, memory allocation, buffers).

The resources attribute shall describe usage characteristics such as the process time at which resources are to be acquired and sizing to include quantity, and physical sizes of buffer usage. It should also include the identification of potential race and deadlock conditions as well as resource management facilities.

5.3.9 Processing. *A description of the rules used by the entity to achieve its function.* The processing attribute shall describe the algorithm used by the entity to perform a specific task and shall include contingencies. This description is a refinement of the function attribute. It is the most detailed level of refinement for this entity.

This description should include timing, sequencing of events or processes, prerequisites for process initiation, priority of events, processing level, actual process steps, path conditions, and loop back or loop termination criteria. The handling of contingencies should describe the action to be taken in the case of overflow conditions or in the case of a validation check failure.

5.3.10 Data. *A description of data elements internal to the entity.* The data attribute shall describe the method of representation, initial values, use, semantics, format, and acceptable values of internal data.

The description of data may be in the form of a data dictionary that describes the content, structure, and use of all data elements. Data information shall describe everything pertaining to the use of data or internal data structures by this entity. It shall include data specifications such as formats, number of elements, and initial values. It shall also include the structures to be used for representing data such as file structures, arrays, stacks, queues, and memory partitions.

The meaning and use of data elements shall be specified. This description includes such things as static versus dynamic, whether it is to be shared by transactions, used as a control parameter, or used as a value, loop iteration count, pointer, or link field. In addition, data information shall include a description of data validation needed for the process.

6. Design Description Organization

6.1 Introduction. Each design description user may have a different view of what is considered the essential aspects of a software design. All other information is extraneous to that user. The proportion of useful information for a specific user will decrease with the size and complexity of a software project. The needed information then becomes difficult or impractical to extract from the description and impossible to assimilate. Hence, a practical organization of the necessary design information is essential to its use.

This section introduces the notion of *design views* to aid in organizing the design attribute information defined in Section 5. It does not supplement Section 5 by providing additional design information nor does it prescribe the format or documentation practice for design views.

A recommended organization of design entities and their associated attributes are presented in this section to facilitate the access of design information from various technical viewpoints. This recommended organization is flexible and can be implemented through different media such as paper documentation, design languages, or database management systems with automated report generation, and query language access. Since paper documentation is currently the primary design description medium, a sample table of contents is given in the Appendix.

6.2 Design Views. Entity attribute information can be organized in several ways to reveal all of the essential aspects of a design. In so doing, the user is able to focus on design details from a different perspective or viewpoint. A *design view* is a subset of design entity attribute information that is specifically suited to the needs of a software project activity.

Each design view represents a separate concern about a software system. Together, these views provide a comprehensive description of the design in a concise and usable form that simplifies information access and assimilation.

A recommended organization of the SDD into separate design views to facilitate information access and assimilation is given in Table 1. Each of these views, their use, and representation are discussed in detail.

6.2.1 Decomposition Description

6.2.1.1 Scope. The decomposition description records the division of the software system into design entities. It describes the way the system has been structured and the purpose and function of each entity. For each entity, it provides a reference to the detailed description via the identification attribute.

Table 1
Recommended Design Views

Design View	Scope	Entity Attributes	Example Representations
Decomposition Description	Partition of the system into design entities	Identification, type, purpose, function, subordinates	Hierarchical decomposition diagram, natural language
Dependency Description	Description of the relationships among entities and system resources	Identification, type, purpose, dependencies, resources	Structure charts, data flow diagrams, transaction diagrams
Interface Description	List of everything a designer, programmer, or tester needs to know to use the design entities that make up the system	Identification, function, interfaces	Interface files, parameter tables
Detail Description	Description of the internal design details of an entity	Identification, processing, data	Flowcharts, N-S charts, PDL

The attribute descriptions for identification, type, purpose, function, and subordinates should be included in this design view. This attribute information should be provided for all design entities.

6.2.1.2 Use. The decomposition description can be used by designers and maintainers to identify the major design entities of the system for purposes such as determining which entity is responsible for performing specific functions and tracing requirements to design entities. Design entities can be grouped into major classes to assist in locating a particular type of information and to assist in reviewing the decomposition for completeness. For example, a module decomposition may exist separately from a data decomposition.

The information in the decomposition description can be used by project management for planning, monitoring, and control of a software project. They can identify each software component, its purpose, and basic functionality. This design information together with other project information can be used in estimating cost, staff, and schedule for the development effort.

Configuration management may use the information to establish the organization, tracking, and change management of emerging work products; see ANSI/IEEE Std 828-1983 [3]. Metrics developers may also use this information for initial complexity, sizing, staffing, and development time parameters. The software quality assurance staff can use the decomposition description to construct a requirements traceability matrix.

6.2.1.3 Representation. The literature on software engineering describes a number of methods that provide consistent criteria for entity decomposition [5]. These methods provide for designing simple, independent entities and are based on such principles as structured design and information hiding. The primary graphical technique used to describe system decomposition is a hierarchical decomposition diagram. This diagram can be used together with natural language descriptions of purpose and function for each entity.

6.2.2 Dependency Description

6.2.2.1 Scope. The dependency description specifies the relationships among entities. It identifies the dependent entities, describes their coupling, and identifies the required resources.

This design view defines the strategies for interactions among design entities and provides the information needed to easily perceive how, why, where, and at what level system actions occur. It specifies the type of relationships that exist among the entities such as shared information, prescribed order of execution, or well defined parameter interfaces.

The attribute descriptions for identification, type, purpose, dependencies, and resources should be included in this design view. This attribute information should be provided for all design entities.

6.2.2.2 Use. The dependency description provides an overall picture of how the system works in order to assess the impact of requirements and design changes. It can help maintainers to isolate entities causing system failures or resource bottlenecks. It can aid in producing the system integration plan by identifying the entities that are needed by other entities and that must be developed first. This description can also be used by integration testing to aid in the production of integration test cases.

6.2.2.3 Representation. There are a number of methods that help minimize the relationships among entities by maximizing the relationship among elements in the same entity. These methods emphasize low module coupling and high module cohesion [5].

Formal specification languages provide for the specification of system functions and data, their interrelationships, the inputs and outputs, and other system aspects in a well-defined language. The relationship among design entities is also represented by data flow diagrams, structure charts, or transaction diagrams.

6.2.3 Interface Description

6.2.3.1 Scope. The entity interface description provides everything designers, programmers, and testers need to know to correctly use the functions provided by an entity. This description includes the details of external and internal interfaces not provided in the software requirements specification.

This design view consists of a set of interface specifications for each entity. The attribute descriptions for identification, function, and interfaces should be included in this design view. This attribute information should be provided for all design entities.

6.2.3.2 Use. The interface description serves as a binding contract among designers, programmers, customers, and testers. It provides them with an agreement needed before proceeding with the detailed design of entities. In addition, the interface description may be used by technical writers to produce customer documentation or may be used directly by customers. In the later

case, the interface description could result in the production of a human interface view.

Designers, programmers, and testers may need to use design entities that they did not develop. These entities may be reused from earlier projects, contracted from an external source, or produced by other developers. The interface description settles the agreement among designers, programmers, and testers about how cooperating entities will interact. Each entity interface description should contain everything another designer or programmer needs to know to develop software that interacts with that entity. A clear description of entity interfaces is essential on a multiperson development for smooth integration and ease of maintenance.

6.2.3.3 Representation. The interface description should provide the language for communicating with each entity to include screen formats, valid inputs, and resulting outputs. For those entities that are data driven, a data dictionary should be used to describe the data characteristics. Those entities that are highly visible to a user and involve the details of how the customer should perceive the system should include a functional model, scenarios for use, detailed feature sets, and the interaction language.

6.2.4 Detailed Design Description

6.2.4.1 Scope. The detailed design description contains the internal details of each design entity. These details include the attribute descriptions for identification, processing, and data. This attribute information should be provided for all design entities.

6.2.4.2 Use. This description contains the details needed by programmers prior to implementation. The detailed design description can also be used to aid in producing unit test plans.

6.2.4.3 Representation. There are many tools used to describe the details of design entities. Program design languages can be used to describe inputs, outputs, local data and the algorithm for an entity. Other common techniques for describing design entity logic include using metacode or structured English, or graphical methods such as Nassi-Schneidermann charts or flowcharts.

Appendix

(This Appendix is not a part of IEEE Std 1016-1987, IEEE Recommended Practice for Software Design Descriptions, but is included for information only.)

The following example of a table of contents shows only one of many possible ways to organize and format the design views and associated information presented in Section 6 of this standard.

Table of Contents for an SDD

The following organizations supported working group members in the development of this recommended practice:

AT&T Bell Laboratories
AT&T Information Systems
Atkinson System Technologies Co
Bell Canada
Bendix Field Engineering Corp
California State University, Sacramento
Center for Industrial Research (Norway)
Computer Sciences Corp
Computer Systems & Sciences
Douglas Aircraft Co
Digital Equipment Corp
Erisoft AB, Sweden
GEAC Computers International, Inc
General Electric Co
Grumman-CTEC, Inc
Harris Corp
Hewlett Packard
Hughes Aircraft
ITT-Chernow Communications, Inc

Jet Propulsion Laboratory
John Fluke Mfg Co
London School of Economics
McDonald Dettwiler & Associates
National Semiconductor
NCR
Northern Telecom
Ortho Pharmaceutical Corp
Programming Environments, Inc
Raytheon
RCA
Santa Clara University
Storage Technology Corp
Systems Designers
Unisyn Inc
University of Hong Kong
University of Idaho
U.S. Dept of Transportation
Zilog Corp